HENRY HOLT EDITIONS IN PSYCHOLOGY

BEHAVIOR
An Introduction to Comparative Psychology

By JOHN B. WATSON

WITH AN INTRODUCTION BY

R. J. Herrnstein
HARVARD UNIVERSITY

A HENRY HOLT EDITION IN PSYCHOLOGY

1866

HOLT, RINEHART AND WINSTON, INC.
NEW YORK · CHICAGO · SAN FRANCISCO · TORONTO · LONDON

Contents

Unsatisfactory nature of present psychological premises.—The nature of the behaviorist's program.—The image as a form of implicit behavior.—Affection as a form of instinctive behavior.—Summary.

No lack of unity in behavior problems.—Field *versus* laboratory studies.—Grouping of problems. I. Sense organ processes.—Introduction.—1. Vision.—Necessity for considering anatomical structure.—Reflex responses to light.—General division of problems in vision.—(*a*) White light vision.—(*b*) Response to monochromatic light.—2. Audition.—Grouping of problems.—(1) Response to pendular vibrations.—(*a*) Range of sensitivity.—(*b*) Localization—(*c*)Response to clangs.—(2) Response to a-periodic vibrations.—(*a*) Stimulus threshold.—(*b*) Difference threshold.—(3) Response to ordinary sounds in the environment. —(*a*) Instinctive repertoire of sounds.—(*b*) Modification of vocal sounds through social influences.—(*c*) Influence of such sounds upon mates.—3. Olfaction and gustation.—Lack of definite knowledge about smell functions.—Problems in olfaction.—Function of olfaction in habit formation.—Problems in gustation.—4. Cutaneous, proprio- and entero-ceptive systems.—Difficulties in the way of making satisfactory tests.—Proprio-ceptive system.—Cutaneous system as a distance receptor. II. Instinctive functions.—Introduction.—Some types of instinctive response.—The animal's instinctive mode of attack on problems.—Instinct and habit. III. Learning.—Introduction.—Grouping of problems.—(1) Perse-

III. APPARATUS AND METHODS

IV. OBSERVATIONAL AND EXPERIMENTAL STUDIES UPON INSTINCT

ticulate sounds.—Tests upon mice and rats.—Incidental tests upon
other mammals: (*a*) Monkeys. (*b*) Horses. (*c*) Bats.—Auditory
response in birds.—In pigeons and parrots.—Auditory response
in amphibia.—Frogs.—Auditory response in fishes.—Some investigators who report lack of auditory sensitivity in fishes.—Investigators reporting sensitivity to auditory stimuli.—Intensity of
sound stimuli in water.—Summary.—The lateral line organs.

I. Smell.—Olfactory reactions in mammals.—Romanes' test of
the hunting dog.—Difficulties in the way of explaining the hunting
behavior of dogs.—Experiments on the olfactory sensitivity of
birds.—The sense of smell in fishes.—Experiments by Parker and
Sheldon. II. Taste.—Location of gustatory organs.—Herrick's experiments upon the functional significance of the taste buds.—
Parker's experiments upon the gustatory responses of fishes. III.
The "common chemical sense."—Introduction.—Sheldon's experiments upon the smooth dogfish.—The "common chemical sense"
in amphibia. —Summary.

I. Cutaneous.—Cutaneous sensitivity in mammals.—Hahn's experiments upon the bat.—The "sense of support" in mammals.—
Yoakum's experiments upon the temperature sense in mammals.
—Contact sensitivity in fish.—Contact and temperature sensitivity
in amphibia. II. The organic system. III. The kinæsthetic system.

Introduction

BEHAVIOR
An Introduction
to Comparative Psychology
JOHN B. WATSON

R. J. HERRNSTEIN, HARVARD UNIVERSITY

To find out what behaviorism was, consult this book, for without a doubt John B. Watson defined it, shaped it, promoted it, and coined its terminology. To find out what it is now is a harder task, perhaps even a futile one. Today psychologists cannot even agree that the field is still alive; the earliest obituaries started appearing in the 1920s and have not stopped yet. Nor can they agree if the field was ever verdant, or barren from the beginning, as it was according to the traditionalists who were called to arms by Watson's attacks in this book.

Let us hold aside for a few pages the pristine clarity of Watson's behaviorism, and consider the contemporary scene, of which any view is bound to be idiosyncratic. The view to be depicted, it should be noted, is a favorable one, arising in a conviction that the behavioristic revolution in psychology is but one aspect of the evolution of scientific psychology out of philosophical speculation.

After Watson, behaviorism trifurcated, yielding three important and distinct roads, disregarding the numerous false starts and minor pathways that a thorough portrayal would require. The main roads are known by the names of the men who took the first steps down them. There is Edward Chace Tolman (1886–1959), the Berkeley professor whose systematic work, *Purposive Behavior in Animals and Men,* was published in 1932. There is Clark L. Hull (1884–1952), the Yale professor whose first systematic work, *Principles of Behavior,* was published in 1943, but only after a series of theoretical articles during the 1930s had adumbrated the larger work, and who is therefore in effect Tolman's contemporary. And there is B. F. Skinner (1904–   ), the still active Harvard professor whose first book, *The Behavior of Organ-*

isms, was published in 1938, but whose influence has grown only in the last decade or so. It is surprising how much of a story is told by the titles of these three books to one who is already familiar with the story. All three display the word "behavior," and do so meaningfully, for each man was reacting against an older view of psychology as the study of mind. Behavior is the word that identifies them with Watson's revolution, but each man was trying to modify behaviorism, as succinctly revealed in the other words of the titles.

All three of the new behaviorisms were disputing the central feature of Watson's scheme, the characterization of behavior itself. For Watson, behavior was movement, actual physical movement of the body, the activity of muscles and glands, whether on a large scale, as in locomotion, or so small as to be hidden from casual observation, as in the case of the hypothesized movements of the larynx in Watson's theory of thought. For none of his followers, was Watson's simple definition of behavior acceptable. For all of them, behavior was a more abstract entity, more closely allied to what a layman might call an "act," rather than to what he might call a "movement." In the vocabulary of psychology, the new behaviorists were "molar" in their approach to behavior instead of "molecular," as Watson was.

It was E. C. Tolman who applied the words "molar" and "molecular" in this sense, even though he was using a terminology he had found in the writings of C. D. Broad. In Broad's book *The Mind and Its Place in Nature* (1925), there was a contrast between molar behaviorism and molecular behaviorism, with the former referring to the idea that every psychological process can be identified with a bit of behavior and the latter referring to the idea that every psychological process has a physiological basis. Although this was a significant issue in itself, Tolman's usage pre-empted Broad's, at least in the American psychological literature. Tolman was concerned with a different problem, one that had already been the source of some discussion even before Watson might have stimulated it. For example, in 1915—published too soon after the present book to have been a reaction to it—E. B. Holt discussed in *The Freudian Wish* the profound contrast between a creature moved by isolated reflexes and one moved by reflexes acting in some sort of mutual coordination or integration. The first kind of creature, of whose existence Holt was skeptical, is a mechanical system triggered into action from moment to moment by the stimuli impinging on it. The second kind of creature, by virtue of the integration of its reflexes, is behaving with respect to some stable aspect of its environment, notwithstanding the momentary variations in stimuli. Consider, said Holt, the example of the bee foraging for nectar. Viewed as the first kind of creature, a description of its activity would consist of a recital of minute movements touched off by the momentary pattern of visual, olfactory, and tactual stimulation. Viewed as the second kind, the description would also reveal that these movements are coordinated to equip the bee to forage for nectar. The fact of its foraging—probably the most reliable fact of all—would never emerge in the first account, which is an inadequacy great enough to invalidate it as psychological description, said Holt. Behavior, innate or learned, argued Holt, is organized so as to be linked to its objective context, rather than to be elicited by whatever representation of the context happens to be adventitiously portrayed in the momentary stimuli.

Holt was arguing against neither the reality of reflexes nor the adequacy of a scientific account of behavior; he was fully in favor of both. Rather, he was arguing for a description of behavior in terms of the objects in the creature's environment around which behavior was so self-evidently organized. In other words, purposiveness was a property of behavior that Holt was unwilling to forego in his account. The other anticipators of molar behaviorism, like the psychologist, William McDougall, or the philosopher, Ralph Barton Perry, similarly believed that a proper description of behavior must encompass the terminal events for a sequence of acts, as well as the initiating ones; the goals, that is, in addition to the stimuli.

Watson's behaviorism, when it came along, left out these goals. He was opposed to the idea of purpose because a purpose cannot be a cause of behavior in the sense that a stimulus is, and, with his deterministic faith, he was persuaded that a stimulus would eventually be found for every bit of behavior. Moreover, purpose is not directly observable; it arises only in introspection, of which more than anything else, Watson wanted to rid psychology. And so, his behaviorism was molecular, restricted to isolated movements triggered by momentary stimulation, that is, the very approach that Holt, along with others, had condemned. The new behaviorists did not, however, follow Watson's line. Each tried to create an objective, deterministic psychology, as scientific as Watson's was supposed to be, but molar, dealing with the fact that behavior had objective reference, that it was goal directed. The three new behaviorisms can, then, be seen as three distinct attempts to reconcile empirical science with purpose.

It may seem strange that behaviorism was confronted with the problem of purpose. After all, had not some eminent prebehaviorists—William James, for example—focused their attention on purpose as the key to the mind? The answer, of course, is yes, but the prebehaviorists were content to deal with purpose introspectively, and if there is one thing uniting all species of behaviorists, it has been a distrust of introspection. Purpose, then, became behaviorism's special problem.

Tolman's behaviorism was a frontal assault on the problem of purpose, as evidenced by the title of his systematic book, *Purposive Behavior. . . .* He tried to find an objective criterion of purposiveness to replace the subjectivity of the earlier psychologists and settled on "docility," in the sense of teachability. Thus, a rat learning to thread its way through a maze—for many years Tolman's favorite experimental situation—gains its reward progressively more efficiently, which Tolman took as the proof of purpose and cognition in the rat. His revision of behaviorism did more than restore the importance of purpose. The criterion of purpose as docility, given the importance of purpose in his definition of behavior, made Tolman's behaviorism, unlike Watson's, little more than the study of learning itself. Of course, what was really involved was a matter of emphasis, rather than of total exclusion or inclusion. Tolman's book, as well as Watson's, discussed both learning and instinct, but there was a clear shift in primary concern.

The coalescence of behaviorism and learning theory that distinguishes Watson from Tolman also distinguishes Watson from both Hull and Skinner, each of whom, by similar, but distinct, chains of argument, redefined behavior so as to make crucial the capacity to learn. For Hull, as for Tolman, behavior is molar rather than molecular. The essence of molarity is again the goal-directedness of global acts, although Hull did not make his criterion of molarity as explicit as Tolman had. Hull was committed to a more mechanistic view of psychology than was Tolman, and so strove for a formula that would at once capture the adaptiveness of behavior as well as the simple reflexive analysis that Watson had favored. Hull's solution, again betrayed by the title of the systematic work, *Principles of Behavior,* was a quasi-axiomatic structure of first principles, patterned after Newtonian mechanics, from which theorems presumably followed with geometrical precision to predict what animals actually do. Among these first principles was the concept of reinforcement, the technical term for the idea that organisms tend to repeat rewarded acts, which was supposed to account for adaptiveness and purpose by the selective effects of past success on subsequent behavior. Whereas Tolman wanted to make purpose scientifically respectable by identifying it with the capacity to learn, Hull wanted to explain it away altogether. His stratagem was to propose a theory of learning that made no reference to purpose, but did not suffer the implausibilty of denying adaptiveness. In fact, the index of Hull's book contains no references either to purpose or cognition. The frontal assault on the problem of purpose was distinctively Tolman's; Hull (and Skinner, as will be shown later) preferred a more indirect approach. But from a far-removed vantage point, one can see that Hull, like Tolman, was creating a behaviorism of adaptive behavior. And in so doing, Hull, like Tolman, became a learning theorist.

Skinner, too, sought to deal with behavior at the adaptive level and also formulated a learning theory that distinguishes his variety of behaviorism. And once again, the distinctive feature of the approach is captured in the title of his systematic book, *The Behavior of Organisms,* for Skinner wanted a rigorous commitment to the study of behavior itself, not inferred entities like purpose (Tolman) or first principles from which behavior could be deduced (Hull). Skinner's behaviorism has therefore been properly called a "descriptive" behaviorism, one presumably stating all its laws and predictions in terms of behavior itself. But for all of its stark empiricism, Skinner defined behavior not as Watson did, in terms of actual movements, but in terms of the effects of movement on the environment. Skinnerian research typically uses animals working in confined chambers and getting food or water for their labors. For example, a rat may be rewarded by a small pellet of food for depressing a lever protruding into a chamber. For Skinner, all the different ways of pressing the lever are grouped together into a single class of behavior, a single response-class identified by the property of operating the lever and without regard to anatomical configuration. In Skinner's analysis, the behavior is "lever-pressing," a characterization that the true Watsonian could have forgiven only on the grounds of expedience; each of the many ways a rat can press a lever is a different response in the Watsonian scheme of things. Like Hull, Skinner leaves the "purpose" out of his system in any explicit form, but it is there nevertheless, since each class of behavior is defined by its consequences.

The excuse for this excursion into modern behaviorism is simply that there seems to be no better way to judge the impact of Watson on psychology than to consult the judgment of time itself as made known in the contributions of his intellectual heirs, of whom Tolman, Hull, and Skinner are both primary and representative. The judgment of time is clear, or at least as clear as it can become in just fifty years. Watson's behaviorism has been judged to have been too intimately linked to an analysis of behavior in terms of muscle twitches and gland secretions. It failed to solve the uniquely psychological problem of purpose. It failed to take into account the transcendent importance of learning in the dynamics of behavior, and, also, to recognize the difficulties in creating a satisfactory theory of learning. But if all this seems like a harsh judgment, it is not really. For Watson's goal was as much to see psychology become a natural science—predictive, experimental, and useful—as it was to advance the substantive particulars of his theory of behavior. And in that, his heirs support him entirely, and have made their modifications in the hopes of furthering the very same goal.

Watson's behaviorism was a reaction against the psychology of the time, primarily against the introspective German structuralists searching for the contents of the mind, but also against those American psychologists who, although themselves opposed to structuralism, had not fully abandoned the introspective method. His alternative to introspection was the direct observation of behavior, in the laboratory and in natural situations, with the goal of finding the connections between behavior and its underlying physiology. At the time this book was written, Watson was clearly in the Darwinian tradition, trusting in the continuity of species to provide clues in animal behavior for an understanding of behavior in general. Watson's psychology was reflexological; behavior was to be analyzed into the quasi-mechanical connections between stimuli and responses. In some instances, he could point to relatively well isolated simple reflexes, in the higher organisms as well as in the lower. In other instances, when discussing instinct, he argued that reflexes may become concatenated in long sequences to produce complex adjustments. And, finally, when discussing habit—which was the current term for the study of learning—Watson further argued that these, too, are but networks of concatenated reflexes, differing from instinct only in the genesis of the pattern and order of the individual movements, and not in the movements themselves.

A large part of the book is an attempt to substantiate the reflexological approach to behavior, and thereby to all of psychology. The flavor of Watson's dialectical method is best obtained from a concrete instance, for example, the treatment of learning (pp. 256–269). Watson recognized that the capacity to learn poses several problems for a reflexological theory. There is the problem that learning is often, indeed usually, an adaptive change in behavior. An animal gains skills not for their own sake, but for the benefits they bring—food, shelter, and so on. In fact, the course of learning is little else than a growing facility in gaining these benefits. For the reflexologist, who may not ascribe the growing facility to a conscious mental process, the adaptiveness of learning is a challenge, if not a refutation. Watson's answer was Darwinian. He pointed out that because of its long evolutionary history, the animal is likely to have adaptive reflexes, disposing it to approach the things it needs and to shun the things that might damage it. The creatures that were remiss about approaching food or potential mates were at so serious a disadvantage in the race for survival that their descendents are not around to testify to the essentially mechanistic control of behavior. What we see around us instead, said Watson, are the descendents of the animals with the right reflexes, misleading us to see adaptiveness as the cause, instead of the effect, of the psychological mechanism.

But inherited reflexes, whether adaptive or not, do not explain how behavior changes at all, which is an even more fundamental property of learning, and a reflexological theory seems to imply that new behavior cannot be produced during the lifetime of any given creature. Watson made this implication explicit by saying that the only changes in behavior are in the pattern of movements, never in the movements themselves.

Suppose, said Watson, a rat is confronted with a box which it is motivated to open. (Watson did not specify the motive, but since the example is hypothetical, we may assume that the rat is after food.) We observe the rat and find that most of its movements are irrelevant to the task at hand, but a few, such as approaching the box, digging away at the sawdust that obscures the latch, and so on, are essential. Eventually, in this hit or miss way, the rat gets the box open and is fed. On subsequent occasions, the rat's behavior becomes progressively more focused on getting the box open, until at last the rat approaches the job in full command of the necessary skills. To all appearances, granted Watson, it is as if the rat had acquired new behavior, not readily attributable to inherited reflexes, for the required skills depend on wholly arbitrary features of the situation. Watson's answer here was statistical. Suppose, he said, that we put ten slips of paper, numbered 1 to 10, in a container and draw then out randomly one at a time until a certain numeral, let us say 5, is drawn. Then we return all the slips drawn, after tallying them, and repeat the game. It can be shown, said Watson, that the number 5 would, in the limit, turn up twice as often as any other number, let us say 9, that one might compare it with. It is, in principle, equally likely that 9 come before 5 or afterwards, but since drawing is terminated at 5, half of the occurrences of 9, on the average, are prevented. This, said Watson, is similar to what is happening with the rat's movements. The sequence of movements is reflexive and random, but the "drawings" are artificially terminated at the occurrence of the critical movements, and, therefore, the critical movements will occur more often than any others.

At this point, Watson affirmed that the sheer practice of a movement increases its frequency. Given the law of practice, it follows that the animal's behavior will evolve toward the minimal configuration of effective and necessary movements, with the superfluous ones tending to vanish. By chance, it is possible that some superfluous ones will also get practiced and therefore strengthened, but that, said Watson, is why the world is not populated by virtuosos, and not a problem with his theory.

As a theory of learning, Watson's was far from original. The idea of learning by practice is undoubtedly ancient and had already been incorporated into experimental psychology by Hermann Ebbinghaus, the German psychologist who invented the nonsense syllable and the procedures for studying rote memorization. And Watson also discussed the importance of "recency," another favorite of the rote-memorization psychologists, which held simply that, all other things being equal, a more recent response is more likely to be repeated than a less recent one. But there was very little in Watson, taken item by item, that was original. The novelty of the approach was its comprehensiveness. Neither Ebbinghaus, nor any of his followers, was willing or disposed to use the principle of frequency as an argument against the importance of adaptiveness, as Watson was. Nor had it been used before as part of an argument for a reflexological approach to all of psychology.

Watson's example of the rat and the box would have served well as the paradigm for a different sort of learning theory. In 1898, a young American psychologist named Edward L. Thorndike published a monograph describing the learning of chickens and cats in an apparatus similar to Watson's hypothetical device, but destined to make Thorndike famous as the inventor of the "puzzle box." The animal was placed inside the box, from which it could escape and be fed by tripping a latch mechanism. Thorndike collected curves of the time taken to escape on successive trials, which, as would be expected, revealed a fairly orderly decrease to a minimum value. These were "learning curves," among the earliest in the literature of psychology and therefore of historical importance in their own right. From these data and from other observations of the animals, Thorndike formulated his laws of learning, of which the most important was the law of "effect." An animal, this law says, repeats actions that have gained it satisfaction and avoids actions that have cost it discomfort; in other words, an animal is influenced by the "effects" of its actions. Here is not the proper place to discuss the history of this hedonistic principle, except to note that in Thorndike's time, it was already a widely held, if loosely stated, theory of learning among psychologists in the Darwinian tradition. It was a theory that neatly guaranteed the adaptiveness of behavior, a requirement that Darwinians were naturally sensitive to, given their concern with adaptiveness on the broader scale of evolution. Thorndike, too, was a Darwinian and so his adherence to a hedonistic account is compatible with his general convictions. Curiously, Watson was also a Darwinian, as numerous passages in this book demonstrate, and yet he chose a non-hedonistic theory as his own.

Thorndike has not been remembered as a behaviorist, although his contribution resembles Watson's, with its insistence on objective data, on experimental, rather than anecdotal or introspective, observation, on the suitability of animal subjects in the psychological laboratory, on the usefulness of science instead of its more abstract justifications, on an interest in action at the expense of a concern with cognition. In many ways, as a matter of fact, the modern behaviorists owe more to, or at least are more like, Thorndike than like Watson. Like them, Thorndike was caught up most directly in the question of the learning process, and was content to deal with behavior at the level of act, rather than of movement. His law of effect has continued to be a vital issue in psychology.

Why, then, do we call Watson a behaviorist, and not Thorndike? The answer is partly chronological. Watson coined the vocabulary of behaviorism, and he did so after Thorndike had already reached a level of eminence that virtually prohibited him from changing his affiliations. But part of the answer is also substantive, dealing with learning theory itself. Watson felt that the law of effect, along with all the other versions of the hedonistic principle, is untenable because it seems to speak of the animal's state of mind. For Watson, and thus for the early behaviorists, the state of pleasure or otherwise in the mind of a chicken is unknown and unknowable, and hence could not possibly enter into a behavioristic account. Judging from what has happened since, Watson was wrong about what could be incorporated into behaviorism and what could not, for most of the modern versions still retain the law of effect in some form or other.

The contrast between Thorndike and Watson need not be mere speculation, for Thorndike wrote one of the few reviews of this book. In general, the review is favorable. Thorndike commended Watson for his devotion to experimentation, for his contribution to animal psychology, for his distrust of introspection, for his detailed and scholarly accounts of particular pieces of experimental apparatus and instructions as to their use, for his criterion of prediction as the measure of scientific truth, and for almost everything else we have come to think of as behaviorism. But he disagreed with a theory of learning based exclusively on frequency and recency, and took pains to refute in Watson's own terms the statistical argument outlined earlier. For, as Thorndike pointed out, the theory works only if the various responses constituting the animal's behavior are equi-probable, as the example with numbered slips of paper tacitly assumes. If, on the other hand, the correct response happens to be very much less probable than some other response, the practice will selectively strengthen the other response. Thorndike thought something more was needed to focus on the correct response, presumably his own law of effect.

It is not only in Thorndike's work that one encounters significant similarities to Watsonian behaviorism. Watson was writing in a period of rapid change in psychology, and many of the landmarks that are sometimes credited to Watson were, in fact, only signs of the times. The Watsonian predilection for neurological theorizing was too widespread to be documented here, but a few examples are William James's *Principles of Psychology* (1890), W. B. Pillsbury's *Essentials of Psychology* (1911), and Knight Dunlap's *An Outline of Psychobiology* (1914). The interest in animal psychology was, of course, an offshoot of Darwinian theory, already formulated in such books as G. J. Romanes' *Animal Intelligence* (1882), C. Lloyd Morgan's *Introduction to Comparative Psychology* (1894), and H. S. Jennings' *Behavior of the Lower Organisms* (1906). The idea that nineteenth-century psychology had been neglecting the study of behavior was stated in many places, many of them seemingly unlikely, such as William James's *Talks to Teachers* (1898) and William McDougall's *Physiological Psychology* (1905). By 1914, there were already self-conscious schools of psychology with systematic positions not very different from Watson's. There were the Russian reflexologists, of whom Pavlov was the outstanding figure, and about whom there will be more later. There were also the German biologists, typified by Jacques Loeb, who subscribed to a mechanistic account of behavior in terms of tropisms and other forced movements.

It should not be surprising, then, that Watson's book was not ushered into the intellectual community to the blare of trumpets. Thorndike thought it was a good book, useful in the classroom for bringing together the growing body of fact and method in the field of animal psychology. And Harvey Carr, Watson's successor at the University of

Chicago six years before, also wrote a favorable review emphasizing the value of the books as text, but criticizing Watson's tendency to become overly polemical and his failure to recognize the importance of the learning process in the description of behavior. The experts were, of course, right in one sense. Watson's behaviorism was not all that new. The traditional introspective psychology against which he was railing was already mortally weakened, particularly in the hostile environment of American pragmatism. But the experts were wrong in another sense, for in this reaction against the old psychology, Watson was to be the most potent catalyst. Young students, coming into psychology innocently unaware of the ferment therein, gravitated to Watson's brand of objective psychology and, in so doing, made an important figure of him.

Because this book was so much a part of what was happening in psychology, it was not immediately seen as the beginning of a revolution. But within a very few years, there were behaviorists, self-conscious about their membership in a new school. Watson's writings took on the quality of a new orthodoxy, which is not to suggest that obedience was required, for the behaviorists fell into factional dispute virtually immediately. Nor is it to suggest that Watson's views became static, for in his later books his theory changed, mainly in highlighting its more radical aspects and in diminishing its dependence on the experimental findings of behavioral research, the very feature that both Thorndike and Carr had praised. As Watson's ideas became more clearly distinguishable from the historical stream from which they emerged, they became less defensible.

Most of the radical ideas were already in this book, but often not fully elaborated. There is the attack on the idea of images. Watson wrote (p. 18), "there are no centrally initiated processes." What seems to go on in the mind, said Watson, is either not going on at all in any scientifically demonstrable way, or else is going on as small-scale behavior, too small to be grossly detected, but potentially measurable by a sufficiently sensitive instrument applied to the right muscles. There is Watson's distinction between man and beast (Chapter X), which reduces to the existence of language in the one and not in the other. There is the identification of language with habit, differing in no fundamental way from any other kind of habit. There is the relegation of thought to small-scale habits, many of them language habits and thus to be detected at some future time as movements of the larynx. There is the identification of emotion with stimuli arising in the erogenous zones of the body. What is missing from this book and what later became one of the most potent, and therefore most outrageous, aspects of Watson's behaviorism is the almost unrestrained environmentalism, and the concomitant claim that by proper training virtually anyone can do anything. Within ten years, when he wrote *Behaviorism* (1924), Watson had come to recognize the importance of learning so well that he felt justified in saying:

Give me a dozen healthy infants, well-formed, and my own specified world to bring them up in and I'll guarantee to take any one at random and train him to become any type of specialist I might select—doctor, lawyer, artist, merchant-chief and, yes, even beggar-man and thief, regardless of his talents, penchants, tendencies, abilities, vocations, and race of his ancestors. I am going beyond my facts and I admit it, but so have the advocates of the contrary and they have been doing it for many thousands of years.

Behaviorism was reviewed in the book review section of Sunday's *New York Times,* a distinction reserved for few books by experimental psychologists and for which Watson's book qualified by virtue of its radical thesis and, of course, its author's eminence. The reviewer, Evans Clark, said, "These lectures show that he has hardly yet made a beginning [in his program to create a science of behavior]—some experiment[s] on infants, some investigation of the relation of the muscles and glands to conduct, and a few other scattered tests—but that he should have done even that marks a new epoch in the intellectual history of man." The concern for instinct that marks the book reprinted here had so far faded that Watson had begun to doubt if there were any human instincts at all. And if Watson was only doubting, some other behaviorists, such as the Chinese psychologist, Z. Y. Kuo, and the American sociologist, L. L. Bernard, felt they had grounds for the positive denial of all instincts.

Watson's involvement with learning was not like that of Tolman, Hull, or Skinner. For these modern behaviorists, the importance of learning emerged from an attempt to redefine behavior itself in a psychologically valid way; but for Watson, the definition of behavior seems to have come easily, and he seems to have had no inclination to question it. Behavior was reflexive first and always. Instead, the change seems to have come about when he recognized the importance of the work on conditioned reflexes by I. P. Pavlov, the Nobel Prize winning Russian physiologist. It was a recognition that must have come after the present book was written, judging from the critical tone and the brevity with which he disposes of Pavlov in the chapter on apparatus and methods (pp. 65 ff).

Starting in the first years after the turn of the century, Pavlov began publishing brief reports of his studies of salivary conditioning, studies that soon began to attract interest in the western world. What became clear only later was that Pavlov was part of a movement in Russia towards objective psychology, similar to the one that Watson promoted in America, but considerably ahead of it chronologically and technically. In 1863, I. M. Sechenov, a leading figure in physiological circles in Russia, published a monograph entitled *Reflexes of the Brain*. Unlike most of Sechenov's publications, which concerned conventional neurophysiology and neuroanatomy, this one was a wholly speculative treatise on the idea, first, that all behavior is composed of reflexes, and, second, that all of psychology can be reduced to the study of behavior. Sechenov argued that only complexity distinguishes these "reflexes of the brain" from the spinal reflexes that physiologists usually study, and hence there is no basic distinction between the mental life of an organism and its simple bodily functions. He argued further that the ancient distinction between voluntary and involuntary behavior vanishes in the light of reflex integration and reflex inhibition—already well-established physiological phenomena in the 1860s—so that all activity, mental or otherwise, is equally involuntary.

Sechenov's radical thesis attracted attention among Russian intellectuals. He had adoring disciples and bitter opponents. He was seen as the pioneer for a positive and useful science; and as an unholy heretic who threatened the best values in life. He won eminence among a circle of young and fervent scientists, but he got into trouble with the authorities over his monograph, which for a time was banned. A few years later, he resigned his professorship at the Medico-Surgical Academy in St. Petersburg, and then later returned to his alma mater, Moscow University. These personal notes about Watson's Russian predecessor may seem pertinent later, when the details of Watson's personal and professional life are briefly noted.

Among the young men stimulated by the daring of Sechenov's mechanistic view of psychology was Ivan Petrovitch Pavlov, as he said in 1923 in the preface to the book, *Lectures on Conditioned Reflexes*. By 1923, Pavlov had achieved great scientific eminence in two fields, enough in either one to earn him a place in the history of the biological sciences. In 1904, he had been awarded the Nobel Prize for his experiments on the reflexes of the alimentary canal, but his Nobel Prize lecture, entitled "The First Sure Steps Along the Path of a New Investigation," outlined research in a new field, that of conditioned reflexes.

The experimental methods that assured his eminence in the study of digestive reflexes proved to be the source of his diversion to the study of behavior. Instead of the usual acute experimentation of the physiological laboratory, in which the experimental animal is sacrificed for the sake of a few brief observations, Pavlov invented chronic methods, restoring the animal as nearly as possible postoperatively to normal function, while still allowing observations to be made of the parts of the digestive system. In particular, Pavlov measured the secretions from the glands of the gastrointestinal system by diverting the appropriate duct away from its usual pathway and having it empty into a vial on the outside of the animal. Years of his life were spent devising ways to keep his subjects, usually dogs, as healthy and comfortable as possible under the circumstances, not only for humane reasons, but also because the delicate adjustments of the gastrointestinal system were so easily thrown awry by the smallest disturbance.

Although his caution was rewarded by a rich harvest of discovery about the operation of the digestive system, it also led to his encounter with "psychic secretion," his term for glandular activity produced mentally, rather than physiologically. Pavlov found that the gastrointestinal glands are primarily reflexive, which is to say that they are triggered into appropriate action by various definite and specifiable stimuli arising from particular substances in the canal itself. All of this was in accord with the physiological knowledge of the time, and with the Darwinian argument for adaptive reflexes. However, because his experiments were chronic and because dogs learned the daily routine, the glands were often thrown into action by remote stimuli, such as the approach of the experimenter or the sight of a particular substance. These secretions could hardly have been inherited reflexes, for such details of a laboratory's operation could have no representation in the hereditary endowment of the animal.

For a time, Pavlov was content to distinguish between the physiological secretions, produced by natural agents, and the psychic secretions, produced by expectations of the dog based upon its experience in the laboratory, and he disregarded the latter except in his efforts to minimize them. But at some point, the kernel sown by having read Sechenov as a young man developed into an eagerness to study these "higher" reflexes—reflexes of the brain, as Sechenov called them. Pavlov said more than once in his writings that the point at which he decided to investigate the psychic secretions was precisely the point at which he decided to call them psychic secretions no longer. The significant insight was that these "unnatural" secretions are, in fact, just as physiological, just as orderly, just as amenable to scientific scrutiny, and, finally, just as natural as are the reflexes whose study had won him the Nobel Prize. They differed only in being acquired, instead of inherited, and in revealing the operation of the nervous system at a higher level than the inherited digestive reflexes. The inherited reflexes are designed, in the biological scheme of things, to enable the animal to manage its internal environment, whereas the acquired reflexes enable the animal to cope with its surroundings. Pavlov devised a terminology for his new insights. The acquired reflexes were called "conditioned reflexes"; the inherited ones, "unconditioned reflexes," as a means of capturing the distinction between reflexes that are contingent upon other circumstances and reflexes that are not. From about 1902 until his death in 1936, Pavlov worked exclusively and productively on the properties of conditioned reflexes, creating a new field of inquiry that has ultimately become international, after several decades during which it was largely Russian.

Curiously, this story of Pavlov, Sechenov, and the discovery of a way of investigating the process of learning by objective methods could be virtually retold by substituting V. M. Bekhterev for Pavlov, for Bekhterev was another young Russian physiologist who transformed Sechenov's speculations into a program of research. Bekhterev's terminology was different from that of Pavlov. He spoke of association reflexes instead of conditioned reflexes. He studied motor responses, such as leg flexion, instead of the secretion of the salivary gland. And in certain technical ways, the type of learning he examined differs from Pavlovian conditioning. But the two men share an objective approach to traditionally subjective psychological issues, and share also in having been ahead of Watson in method, if not in conception. Pavlov, writing in 1923, acknowledged the contribution of Bekhterev and Watson, among others, to the growth of objective psychology, but granted priority to only one man as regards experimental work, and that was Thorndike and the puzzle box.

Pavlov, ordinarily the epitome of the cautious scientist, content to let his data do most of the speaking for him, could not restrain his enthusiasm for the vista that opened up when he contemplated a science of behavior based on conditioned reflexes. In 1923 he wrote:

About myself I shall add the following. At the beginning of our work and for a long time afterwards we felt the compulsion of habit in explaining our subject by psychological [i.e., subjective] interpretations. Every time the

objective investigation met an obstacle, or when it was halted by the complexity of the problem, there arose quite naturally misgivings as to the
correctness of our new method. Gradually with the progress of our research
these doubts appeared more rarely, and now I am deeply and irrevocably
convinced that along this path will be found the final triumph of the human
mind over its uttermost and supreme problem—the knowledge of the mechanism and laws of human nature. Only thus may come a full, true and
permanent happiness. Let the mind rise from victory to victory over surrounding nature, let it command for its service prodigious energy to flow
from one part of the universe to the other, let it annihilate space for the
transference of its thoughts—yet the same human creature, led by dark
powers to wars and revolutions and their horrors, produces for itself in-
calculable material losses and inexpressible pain and reverts to bestial conditions. Only science, exact science about human nature itself, and the most
sincere approach to it by the aid of the omnipotent scientific method, will
deliver man from his present gloom, and will purge him from his contemporary shame in the sphere of interhuman relations.

If the potentialities of this approach to behavior could raise a man
of Pavlov's sobriety to such heights of excitement, could it long leave
Watson unmoved, as he was in 1914 when he wrote the present book?
Clearly, the answer is no, for in his later works the importance of conditioned reflexes gradually dominated all of the other features of Watson's behaviorism. The process had already begun by 1915 when Watson's presidential address to the American Psychological Association
("The Place of the Conditioned Reflex in Psychology") argued that introspective accounts are properly replaced by conditioned responses in
a behavioristic psychology. Not only was Pavlovian conditioning a
practical, objective, and deterministic framework in which to cast as
much of psychology as one's imagination encompassed, but it was
built upon the reflex itself, Watson's first love in psychological analysis.
The marriage was a natural, and there were no impediments to it. It is
not surprising that in the everyday psychology of popular literature,
and in too many psychology texts as well, Watson's behaviorism is
equated with Pavlovian theory.

Watson's conversion to the conditioned reflex went hand in hand with
a change in the scope of his behaviorism. Instead of a mere faction
within an academic discipline, it became a program for social control
and improvement. During the 1920s Watson's books became more and
more concerned with practical questions in human affairs and more and
more devoid of scholarly contact with the rest of psychology. The books
themselves were usually compilations either of articles that had appeared
in various popular magazines or of popular lecture series. Here is a

sampling of some of the titles that appeared over his name: "The Behaviorist Looks at Instincts" (*Harper's,* 1927); "Feed Me on Facts" (*Saturday Review of Literature,* 1928); "The Weakness of Women" (*The Nation,* 1928); "Can We Make Our Children Behave?" (*Forum,* 1929); "It's Your Own Fault" (*Collier's,* 1928); "The Heart or the Intellect?" (*Harper's,* 1928); "Are Parents Necessary?" (*New York Times,* 1930). The articles are interesting, forceful, and assertive, but they are also propagandistic, sometimes simplistic, and occasionally un-scholarly. They seem to betray a mischievous pleasure in shocking their audience—the educated, conventional American middle class—by questioning cherished beliefs regarding child-rearing, marriage, religion, and so on. Watson was attacking certain aspects of morality in the name of behaviorism and the main weapon for his assault was Pavlovian conditioning. This may explain why even today Watson, behaviorism, and Pavlov are held in contempt by many non-psychologists who are, of course, unable to see how much this later stage in his career was the result of his personal experience and how little it had to do with the scientific movement of which he had been a part.

The rebellious streak in Watson's character is frankly revealed in an autobiographical sketch he wrote for Carl Murchison's *History of Psychology in Autobiography* (Vol. III, 1936). John Broadus Watson was born near Greenville, South Carolina, in 1878, the son of a prosperous farmer, and was educated in district schools in the countryside and in the public school of the town of Greenville. Of himself as a pupil he said, "I was lazy, somewhat insubordinate, and, so far as I know, I never made above a passing grade." His childhood interests seem to have tended toward the violent, having been arrested on two occasions for sheer hell raising. Yet even as a young boy, he had an aptitude and fondness for the chores around a farm, including carpentry. In his later life, the manual skills showed up as an interest in the technical aspects of psychological research, an interest that is unmistakable in the book here reprinted.

At the age of sixteen he entered Furman University, a Baptist school in Greenville, where he stayed for five years to earn an A.M. Although he appears to have found college neither interesting nor worthwhile, he decided after graduation to seek further study, choosing the then new University of Chicago, apparently because one of his teachers at Furman had studied there and because he had heard of John Dewey, who was then teaching the gospel of Pragmatism at Chicago. Watson went to Chicago to study philosophy, but was diverted into psychology, perhaps influenced by Dewey's strong interest in psychological matters at that time. There were exceptional men at Chicago, in and around the periphery of psychology. Watson acknowledged a profound debt of gratitude to James R. Angell who was then in psychology, and who later became president of Yale, for his "erudition, quickness of thought, and facility with words." Angell was in those years the leader of American functional psychology, a school that insisted upon a concern with the dynamic aspects of an organism's adjustments to its environment, as well as with the static properties of consciousness. It is easy to see Watson's behaviorism as a radical extension of Angell's functionalism. Watson studied also under H. H. Donaldson, the eminent neurologist and Jacques Loeb, the transported German biologist who had by this time his own version of objective psychology based, in a metaphoric way, on the botanical concept of tropisms. Watson was apparently tempted to write his dissertation under Loeb, but was advised against it by Angell and Donaldson because, according to Watson, Loeb was not considered a "very 'safe' man for a green Ph.D. candidate," presumably because of the heterodoxy of his views. Instead, Watson took his degree under Angell and Donaldson, working on the behavior of the white rat in relation to the growth of medullation in its central nervous system.

Philosophy, his original interest, seems to have gotten away from him. Watson said he studied it and took a good many courses, but gained so little understanding from them that he gradually lost his interest. He studied with G. H. Mead and Dewey, important names of the times, but it made little impression. About Dewey, Watson said, "I never knew what he was talking about then, and, unfortunately for me, I still don't know." But the break with philosophy was not a rancorous one; Watson's fondness for Mead was still evident in 1936 in his autobiography.

Watson flourished at Chicago. When he earned his doctorate in 1903, both Donaldson and Angell offered him positions, the one in neurology and the other in psychology. Watson chose psychology, staying on first as Assistant and then as Instructor until he was offered a job at Johns Hopkins University in 1907. The offer from Hopkins came from James Mark Baldwin, another of the leaders of American functionalism and was originally for an Associate Professorship, but, while Watson hesitated in his reluctance to leave Chicago, it was raised to a full Professorship. This, Watson could not refuse and so moved into a major university with a major position in 1908 at the age of 29. At Hopkins, Watson was fortunate to encounter yet another group of outstanding men. In addition to Baldwin, there was Knight Dunlap, a psychologist who was himself already tending toward behaviorism; H. S. Jennings, a zoologist who had written one of the earliest major books on comparative psychology and who had a keen sense of the demands of objectivism on psychology; A. O. Lovejoy, the prominent neo-realist philosopher, and, after a few years, the brilliant K. S. Lashley, a biologist who came to Watson from Jennings' laboratory and who went on to become the most outstanding physiological psychologist America has yet produced.

The book reprinted here was the product of this period in Watson's life, easily the best with regard to scholarly and scientific activity. Watson was active in his laboratory, working on sensory processes in animals, and in professional psychology at large. He was elected president of the American Psychological Association in 1915, just one year after this book was published. The book was itself an expansion upon a series of lectures that Watson had given at Columbia University in 1913. Its first chapter is almost identical to an article entitled "Psychology as the Behaviorist Views It," published in 1913 in the *Psychological Review* and usually taken as the founding manifesto of Watsonian behaviorism.

The disruption of this productive existence was augured by Watson's experience in the world war. He tried to enlist as a line officer, but was found unfit because of poor eyesight. Instead he was called to aid in the problems of personnel selection for the army. Being an officer was a nightmare for Watson. His stubborn independence guaranteed that he would clash with the military hierarchy in general and with a few officers in particular. About one of them he said in his autobiography, "His egotism and self-seeking soon made every one in the personnel section of aviation understand why it is that some officers fail to return from expeditions even when not engaged by enemy troops." About officers in general he said (excepting West Point and Naval Academy graduates), "Never have I seen such incompetence, such extravagance, such a group of overbearing, inferior men."

After the Armistice, Watson returned as promptly as possible to Hopkins, eager to resume his scientific life. He started work on the conditioning of infants, and began to assemble the material for his book, *Psychology from the Standpoint of a Behaviorist,* which was published in 1919, and which is a far more doctrinaire argument for behaviorism than the present one. But he had barely settled back into his old routine when he was asked to resign his professorship. The incident is still too obscured by unsubstantiated rumor to be fully recounted, but it was undoubtedly related to his divorce, after sixteen years of marriage, from Mary Ickes, a sister of the Harold Ickes who was to become Roosevelt's Secretary of the Interior, and his almost immediate remarriage to Rosalie Raynor, who was Watson's student, as well as collaborator in a famous experiment on the Pavlovian conditioning of a fear reaction in a child. Today, the scandal of Watson's resignation and the furor it provoked in the Baltimore newspapers seem very much out of proportion to the incident itself. Mores have changed greatly in forty-five years; nevertheless one might wonder if Watson was not in some measure paying for the novelty of his psychological theories and the radical tone in which he was disposed to pitch them.

Unlike his Russian predecessor Sechenov, Watson was not temperamentally disposed to wait for the storm to abate and then return to the sort of academic position his eminence and abilities fully justified. Instead, he chose to turn his back on the intellectual community that had so abruptly turned against him. He went to work for the J. Walter Thompson Co., the advertising firm, and rapidly brought his great talents to bear on the world of commerce. Four years after his resignation from Hopkins in 1920, Watson became a vice-president of the company. In 1936, he moved to another firm, William Esty and Co., also as vice-president, where he remained until his retirement in 1946. Life as a businessman seems to have satisfied him, for he wrote with enthusiasm of the challenges of his new life. But he retained an understandable hostility towards the academic community, one which often appeared in his later writings as a conviction that universities fail to equip students with the knowledge and skills that they will eventually need.

For about a dozen years after his resignation from Hopkins, Watson continued to develop the behavioristic credo, in lectures, popular articles, and books. In addition to *Psychology from the Standpoint of a Behaviorist,* which came out shortly before the scandal broke, he wrote *Behaviorism* (1924), *Psychological Care of Infant and Child* (1928), and *The Ways of Behaviorism* (1928). As the years passed, the discipline of scholarship became progressively less evident in his writings, while the skills of persuasion, perhaps sharpened by his job, became progressively more so. Then, in the middle 1930s, Watson finally reached the end of his psychological career, too occupied, as he said, with "business, my family and my farm." In 1958, at the age of eighty, Watson died, an event not unnoticed in academic circles, for the conservative *American Journal of Psychology* published an obituary with a photograph, a distinction reserved for only the very important members of the profession.

And very important he had been, notwithstanding the flaws that may be found in his contribution to psychology. The reflex, Watson's analytic unit, has not become the basis of scientific psychology nor even of modern behaviorism. Pavlovian conditioning is generally regarded as but one kind of learning among several, and probably not even the most important in complex human behavior. Radical environmentalism has given way to a more plausible synthesis of nature and nurture. Even introspection has persisted as a method in psychology, albeit with far less status than before Watson's attack. The higher mental processes, like language and thought, are viewed by virtually no one as mere habits localized in the peripheral musculature. The list of Watson's mistakes could be multiplied, but to do so is to distort what actually happened, for Watson's importance was more sociological than substantive. It was not his theories that changed psychology, except insofar as they were the medium by which he argued for psychology to be a natural science, more closely allied to biology than to philosophy, empirical instead of polemical. His insistence on the importance of experimentation was far more significant than the fact that his own experiments yielded little of permanent value. And his optimistic enthusiasm for a predictive science of behavior was to have far more impact than the fact that his enthusiasm was often unfounded. Of course, Watson was but part of the growth of objective psychology, in clear continuity with his precursors, but circumstances and his talents singled him out for special influence. In America at least, Watson is the link between the dawning objectivism of nineteenth-century psychology and the almost unquestioned empiricism around us today.

CAMBRIDGE, MASS.   *R. J. H.*
JANUARY 1967

BEHAVIOR

An Introduction to Comparative
Psychology

BY

JOHN B. WATSON

Professor of Psychology in The Johns Hopkins University

NEW YORK

HENRY HOLT AND COMPANY

To my Friends and Teachers
JAMES R. ANGELL ᴀɴᴅ HENRY H. DONALDSON
this Book is Gratefully
Dedicated.

PREFACE

This volume on behavior is an elaboration of the eight lectures given at Columbia University during the winter of 1913. It has been written with the hope that it may be found serviceable in classroom work in psychology and biology. Needless technicalities and detailed references have been omitted. For this reason the general reader may find something of interest in its pages. The book must not be looked upon as a reference book or treatise. The treatment of the research material has not been exhaustive. For the most part no attempt has been made to give investigators detailed credit for their work. I have not, however, been able to carry out consistently the plan of omitting references. In most sciences which have existed for any length of time a general body of data becomes common property, and it is unnecessary to mention the original discoverers of the universally accepted facts. Some parts of the study of behavior are so involved in controversy that no results can be said as yet to be universally accepted by specialists in the subject. In dealing with these facts, especially in the chapters on the sense organs, it has been necessary to enter with some detail into the discussion of the investigations and theories of individual writers. It is hoped that the volume will contribute something towards the introduction of more careful methods in the study of behavior, and serve to mark off the study from the other sciences.

An endeavor has been made to adapt the book to the needs of various classes of readers. Where only a short time can be devoted to a classroom course in behavior, I suggest that chapters I, II, III, V, VII, and IX be omitted.

In the preparation of the manuscript my heaviest obligation is to Dr. K. S. Lashley, Bruce Fellow in Biology, the Johns Hopkins University. He has given unsparingly of his time in helping in the actual preparation of the chapters on the origin of instincts and the fixation of arcs in habits. Dr. H. M. Johnson has assisted me greatly by furnishing the drawing and description of the Helmholtz method of tandem-driven forks.

I owe a heavy debt of gratitude to my colleagues Professors Arthur O. Lovejoy and Knight Dunlap for kindly criticisms and helpful suggestions during the preparation both of the Columbia lectures and of the manuscript of the book. My long and intimate association with Robert M. Yerkes and with Harvey Carr has been of great benefit to me. I owe them much more than can be gathered from a mere reading of the following pages.

Finally I wish to express my indebtedness to my secretary, Miss Clarice Shoemaker, who has been untiring in her work upon the manuscript.

J. B. W.

THE JOHNS HOPKINS UNIVERSITY,
    May, 1914.

BEHAVIOR

An Introduction to Comparative Psychology

BEHAVIOR

CHAPTER I

PSYCHOLOGY AND BEHAVIOR [1]

Unsatisfactory nature of present psychological premises.—The nature of the behaviorist's program.—The image as a form of implicit behavior.—Affection as a form of instinctive behavior.—Summary.

Unsatisfactory nature of present psychological premises.—Psychology as the behaviorist views it is a purely objective experimental branch of natural science. Its theoretical goal is the prediction and control of behavior. Introspection forms no essential part of its methods, nor is the scientific value of its data dependent upon the readiness with which they lend themselves to interpretation in terms of consciousness. The behaviorist attempts to get a unitary scheme of animal response. He recognizes no dividing line between man and brute. The behavior of man, with all of its refinement and complexity, forms only a part of his total field of investigation.

It has been maintained by its followers generally that psychology is a study of the science of the phenomena of consciousness. It has taken as its problem, on the one hand, the analysis of complex mental states (or processes) into simple elementary constituents, and on the other the construction of complex states when the elementary constituents are given. The world of physical objects (stimuli, including here anything which may excite activity in a receptor), which forms the total phenomenon of the natural scientist, is looked upon merely as means to an end. The

---

[1] A few new terms have been used in this discussion of behavior—such as *behaviorist, behavioristic, behaviorism.* While it is admitted that these words sound somewhat barbaric on a first hearing, they at least have the merit of being expressive and natural. Indulgence is also asked for the use of "*perseverance method*" in place of "trial and error" method in the description of the experiments on learning.

end is the production of mental states that may be " inspected " or " observed." The psychological object of observation in the case of an emotion, e.g., is the mental state itself. The problem in emotion is the determination of the number and kind of elementary constituents present, their loci, intensity, order of appearance, etc. It is agreed that introspection is the method *par excellence* by means of which mental states may be manipulated for purposes of psychology. On this assumption, behavior data (including under this term everything which goes under the name of comparative psychology) have no value *per se.* They possess significance only in so far as they may throw light upon conscious states.[2] Such data must have at least an analogical or indirect reference to belong to the realm of psychology.

Indeed, one finds at times psychologists who are skeptical of even this analogical reference. Such skepticism is often shown by the question which is put to the student of behavior, " what is the bearing of animal work upon human psychology? " With psychology based upon its present premises such a question is necessarily embarrassing for the reason that no answer is open to the man who uses animals for subjects. The behaviorist has found it convenient in the past to cultivate a repressed attitude when talking of his work before orthodox psychologists. He is interested in this work and believes firmly in its intrinsic value, albeit he is unable to trace its bearing upon psychological theory. Such a confession it is hoped will clear the atmosphere to such an extent that the behaviorist will no longer have to work under false pretenses. We in turn must frankly admit that the facts which we have been able to glean from extended work upon the senses of animals by behavior methods have contributed only in a fragmentary way to the general theory of human sense organ processes: and that they have not even suggested new ways of making experimental attacks upon the problems of human psychology. The enormous number of experiments

[2] I.e., either directly upon the conscious state of the observer or indirectly upon the conscious state of the experimenter.

which we have carried out upon learning has likewise contributed little to human psychology. It seems reasonably clear that some kind of compromise must be effected; either psychology must change its viewpoint so as to take in facts of behavior, whether or not they have bearing upon the problems of " consciousness; " or else behavior must stand alone as a wholly separate and independent science. Should human psychologists fail to look with favor upon our overtures and refuse to modify their position, the behaviorists will be driven to use human beings as subjects and to employ methods of investigation which are exactly comparable to those now employed in the animal work. Any other hypothesis than that which admits the independent value of the behavior material will inevitably force us to the absurd position of attempting to *construct* the conscious content of the animal whose behavior we have been studying. On this theory, after having determined our animal's ability to learn, the simplicity or complexity of its methods of learning, the effect of past habit upon present response, the range of stimuli to which it ordinarily responds, the widened range to which it can respond under experimental conditions,—in more general terms, its various problems and its various ways of solving them,—we should still feel that the task is unfinished and that the results are worthless, until we can interpret them by analogy in the light of consciousness. Although we have solved our problem we feel uneasy and unrestful because of our definition of psychology: we feel forced to say something about the possible mental processes of our animal. We say that, having no eyes, its stream of consciousness cannot contain brightness and color sensations as we know them,—having no taste buds this stream cannot contain sensations of sweet, sour, salt, and bitter. But on the other hand, since it does respond to thermal, tactual, and organic stimuli, its conscious content must be made up largely of these sensations; and we usually add, to protect ourselves against the reproach of being anthropomorphic, " If it has any consciousness." Surely this doctrine which calls for an analogical interpretation of all

behavior data must be shown to be false: the position that
the value of an observation upon behavior is determined
by its fruitfulness in yielding results which are interpret-
able only under the concept of consciousness.

This emphasis upon analogy in psychology has led the
behaviorist somewhat afield. Not being willing to throw
off the yoke of consciousness he feels impelled to make a
place in the scheme of behavior where the rise of consciousness can be determined. This point has been a shifting one.
A few years ago certain animals were supposed to possess
" associative memory," while certain others were supposed
to lack it. One meets this search for the origin of consciousness under a good many disguises. Some of our
texts state that consciousness arises at the moment when
reflex and instinctive activities fail properly to conserve the
organism. A perfectly adjusted organism would be lacking in consciousness. On the other hand, whenever we find
the presence of diffuse activity which results in habit
formation, we are justified in assuming consciousness.
Such arguments have weight with the neophyte, but as
time goes on and the horizon of animal work broadens, he
becomes less and less convinced of their weight. Many of
us are still viewing behavior problems with something like
this in mind, as is evidenced by the fact that more than one
student of behavior has attempted to frame criteria of the
psychic—to devise a set of objective, structural, and functional criteria which, when applied to the particular
instance, will enable him to decide whether such and such
responses are positively conscious, merely indicative of
consciousness, or whether they are purely " physiological."
Such problems as these can no longer satisfy behavior men.
It would be better to give up the province altogether and
admit frankly that the study of the behavior of animals
has no justification, than to admit that the search is of
such a " will o' the wisp " character. One can assume
either the presence or the absence of consciousness anywhere in the phylogenetic scale without affecting the
problems of behavior by one jot or one tittle; and without
influencing in any way the mode of experimental attack

upon them. On the other hand, one cannot for a moment assume that the Paramecium responds to light; that the rat learns a problem more quickly by working at the task five times a day than once a day, or that the human child exhibits plateaux in his learning curves. These are questions which vitally concern behavior and which must be decided by direct observation under experimental conditions.

This attempt to reason by analogy from human conscious processes to the conscious processes in animals, and *vice versa*, to make consciousness, as the human being knows it, the center of reference of all behavior, forces us into a position similar to that which existed in biology in Darwin's time. The whole Darwinian movement was judged by the bearing it had upon the origin and development of the human race. Expeditions were undertaken to collect material which would establish the position that the rise of the human race was a perfectly natural phenomenon and not an act of special creation. Variations were carefully noted and along with them the evidence that they might be heaped up along lines which would be of service to the animal; for in this and the other Darwinian mechanisms were to be found factors sufficiently complex to account for the origin and race differentiation of man. The wealth of material collected at this time was considered valuable largely in so far as it tended to develop the concept of evolution in man. It is strange that this situation should have remained the dominant one in biology for so many years. The moment zoölogy undertook the experimental study of evolution and descent, the situation immediately changed. Man ceased to be the center of reference. It is doubtful if any experimental biologist today, unless actually engaged in the problem of heredity in man, tries to interpret his findings in terms of human evolution, or ever refers to it in his thinking. He gathers his data from the study of many species of plants and animals and tries to work out the laws of inheritance in the particular type upon which he is conducting experiments. Naturally he follows the progress of the work upon race differentiation in man and the descent of man, but he looks upon these as special topics, equal in importance with his own yet ones in which his interests will never be vitally engaged. It is not fair to say that all of his work is directed toward human evolution or that it must be interpreted in terms of human evolution. He does not have to dismiss certain of his facts on the inheritance of coat color in mice because, forsooth, they have little bearing upon the differentiation of the *genus Homo* into separate races, or upon the descent of the *genus Homo* from some more primitive stock.

In psychology we are still in that stage of development where we feel that we must select our material. We have a general place of discard for processes, which we anathematize so far as their value for psychology is concerned by saying, " this is a reflex;" " that is a purely physiological fact which has nothing to do with psychology." We are not interested (as psychologists) in studying all of the processes of adjustment which the animal as a whole employs, and in finding how these various responses are connected, and how they fall apart, thus working out a systematic scheme for the prediction and control of response in general. Unless our observed facts are indicative of consciousness, we have no use for them, and unless our apparatus and method are designed to throw such facts into relief, they are thought of in just as disparaging a way.

Psychology has failed signally during the fifty odd years of its existence as an experimental discipline to make its place in the world as an undisputed natural science. Psychology, as it is generally thought of, has something esoteric in its methods. If you fail to reproduce my findings it is not due to some fault in your apparatus or the control of your stimuli, but it is due to the fact that your introspection is untrained.[3] The attack is made upon the

[3] In this connection attention is called to the controversy now on between the adherents and the opposers of imageless thought. The " types of reactors " (sensory and motor) was also a matter of bitter dispute. The complication experiment was likewise the source of a war of words concerning the accuracy of the opponent's introspection.

observer and not upon the experimental setting. In physics and in chemistry the attack is made upon the experimental conditions. The apparatus was not sensitive enough, impure chemicals were used, etc. In these sciences a better technique will give reproducible results. Psychology is otherwise. If you can't observe 3—9 states of clearness in attention, your introspection is poor. If, on the other hand, a feeling seems reasonably clear to you, your introspection is again faulty. You are experiencing too much.

The time seems to have come when psychology must discard all reference to consciousness; when it need no longer delude itself into thinking that it is making mental states the object of observation. We have become so enmeshed in speculative questions concerning the elements of mind, the nature of conscious content (e.g., imageless thought, attitudes, and Bewusstseinslage, etc.), that experimental students are beginning to feel that something is wrong with the premises and the types of problem which develop from them. There is no longer any guarantee that all mean the same thing when the terms now current in psychology are used. Take the case of sensation. A sensation is defined in terms of its attributes. One psychologist will state with readiness that the attributes of a visual sensation are *quality, extension, duration,* and *intensity.* Another will add *clearness.* Still another that of *order.* It is questionable whether any one psychologist can draw up a set of statements describing what he means by sensation which will be agreed to by three other psychologists of different training. Turn for a moment to the question relating to the number of isolable sensations. Is there an extremely large number of color sensations,— or only four, red, green, yellow, and blue? Again, yellow, while psychologically simple, can be obtained by superimposing red and green spectral rays upon the same diffusing surface! If, on the other hand, we say that every just noticeable difference in the spectrum is a simple sensation, and that every just noticeable increase in the white value of a given color gives simple sensations, we are forced to admit that the number is so large and the conditions for obtaining them so complex that the concept of sensation is unusable, either for the purpose of analysis or that of synthesis. Titchener, who has fought the most valiant fight in this country for a psychology based upon introspection, feels that these differences of opinion as to the number of sensations and their attributes; as to whether there are relations (in the sense of elements) and on the many others which seem to be fundamental in every attempt at analysis, are perfectly natural in the present undeveloped state of psychology. While it is admitted that every growing science is full of unanswered questions, surely only those who are wedded to the system as we now have it, who have fought and suffered for it, can confidently believe that there will ever be any greater uniformity than there is now in the answers we have to such questions. One must believe that two hundred years from now, unless the introspection method is discarded, psychology will still be divided on the question as to whether auditory sensations have the quality of " extension," whether intensity is an attribute which can be applied to color, whether there is a difference in " texture " between image and sensation; and upon many hundreds of others of like character.

Our psychological quarrel is not with the systematic and structural psychologist alone. The last fifteen years have seen the growth of what is called functional psychology. This type of psychology decries the use of elements in the static sense of the structuralists. It is stated in words which seem to throw emphasis upon the biological significance of conscious processes rather than upon the analysis of conscious states into introspectively isolable elements. The difference between functional psychology and structural psychology, as the functionalists have so far stated the case, is unintelligible. The terms sensation, perception, affection, emotion, volition are used as much by the functionalist as by the structuralist. The addition of the word " process " (" mental act as a whole " and like terms are frequently met) after each serves in some way to remove the corpse of " content " and to leave " function " in its stead. Surely if these concepts are elusive when looked at from a content standpoint, they are still more deceptive when viewed from the angle of function, and especially so when function is obtained by the introspective method.

One of the difficulties in the way of a consistent functional psychology is the parallelistic hypothesis. If the functionalist attempts to express his formulation in terms which make mental states really appear to function, to play some active rôle in the world of adjustment, he almost inevitably lapses into terms which are connotative of interaction. When taxed with this he replies that it is more convenient to do so and that he does it to avoid the circumlocutions and the clumsiness of statement which are inherent in any thoroughgoing parallelism. As a matter of fact the functionalist probably thinks in terms of interaction and resorts to parallelism only when forced to give expression to his views. We advance the view that *behaviorism* is the only consistent and logical functionalism. In it one avoids both the Scylla of parallelism and the Charybdis of interaction. Those time-honored relics of philosophical speculation need trouble the student of behavior as little as they trouble the student of physics. The consideration of the mind-body problem affects neither the type of problem selected nor the formulation of the solution of that problem.

The nature of the behaviorist's program.—This leads us to the point where argument should be made constructive. It is possible to write a psychology, to define it as Pillsbury does (as the " science of behavior "), and never go back upon the definition: never to use the terms consciousness, mental states, mind, content, will, imagery, and the like. It can be done naturally and conveniently in a few years from now without running into the absurd terminology of Beer, Bethe, Von Uexküll, Nuel, and that of the so-called objective school generally. It can be done in terms of stimulus and response, in terms of habit formation, habit integration, and the like. Furthermore it is worth while to make this attempt so far as animal psychology is concerned at the present time.

A psychology of interest to all scientific men would take as its starting point, first, the observable fact that organisms, man and animal alike, do adjust themselves to their environment by means of hereditary and habit equipments. These adjustments may be very adequate or they may be so inadequate that the organism barely maintains its existence; secondly, certain stimuli lead the organisms to make the responses. In a system of psychology completely worked out, given the responses the stimuli can be predicted; given the stimuli the responses can be predicted. Such a set of statements is crass and raw in the extreme, as all such generalizations must be. Yet they are hardly more raw and less realizable than the ones which appear in the psychology texts of the day. The point might better be illustrated by choosing an everyday problem which any one is likely to meet in the course of his work. Some time ago the author was called upon to make a study of certain species of birds. Until he went to Tortugas he had never seen these birds alive. On reaching this island he found the animals doing certain things: some of the acts seemed to work peculiarly well in such an environment, while others seemed to be unsuited to their type of life. The responses of the group as a whole were first studied and later those of individuals. In order to understand more thoroughly the relation between what was habit and what was hereditary in these responses, the young birds were captured and reared. In this way it was possible to study the order of appearance of hereditary adjustments and their complexity, and later the beginnings of habit formation. The attempts to determine the stimuli which called forth such adjustments were crude indeed. Consequently the attempts to control behavior and to produce responses at will did not meet with much success: food and water, sex and other social relations, light and temperature conditions were all beyond control in a field study. It was found possible to control their reactions in a measure by using the nest and egg (or young) as stimuli.

It is not necessary here to develop further how such a study should be carried out and how work of this kind needs to be supplemented by carefully controlled laboratory experiments. Were the task to examine the behavior of some of the Australian tribes the method adopted would have been much the same, but the problem would have been more difficult: the types of responses called forth by physical stimuli would have been more varied, and the number of effective stimuli larger. The social setting of their lives would have had to be examined in a far more careful way. These savages would naturally be far more influenced by the responses of each other than was the case with the birds. Furthermore, habits would have been more complex and the influence of past habits upon present responses would have appeared more clearly. Similar but more complex problems would arise in working out the psychology of a cosmopolitan race, but the method of attacking them would be the same. In the main, the desire in all such work is to gain an accurate knowledge of adjustments and the stimuli calling them forth. The reason for this is to learn general and particular methods by which behavior may be controlled. The goal is not " the description and explanation of states of consciousness as such," nor that of obtaining such proficiency in mental gymnastics that one can immediately lay hold of a state of consciousness and say, " this, as a whole, consists of gray sensation number 350, of such and such extent, occurring in conjunction with the sensation of cold of a certain intensity; one of pressure of a certain intensity and extent," and so on *ad infinitum*. If psychology would follow the plan suggested, the educator, the physician, the jurist, and the business man could utilize the data in a practical way, as soon as it could be experimentally obtained. Those who have occasion to apply psychological principles practically would find no need to complain as they do at the present time. Ask any physician or jurist today whether scientific psychology plays a practical part in his daily routine and you will hear him deny that the psychology of the laboratories finds a place in his scheme of work.

The criticism is extremely just. One of the principal reasons which makes psychology an unattractive subject is the fact that there is no realm of application for the principles which are being worked out in content terms.

What makes us hopeful that the behaviorist's position is a defensible one is the fact that those branches of psychology which have already partially withdrawn from the parent, experimental psychology, and which are consequently less dependent upon introspection, are today in a most flourishing condition. Experimental pedagogy, the psychology of drugs, the psychology of advertising, legal psychology, the psychology of tests, and psychopathology are all vigorous growths. These are sometimes wrongly called " practical " or " applied " psychology. Surely there was never a worse misnomer. In the future there may grow up vocational bureaus which really apply psychology. At present these fields are truly scientific and are in search of broad generalizations which will lead to the control of human behavior. E.g., we find out by experimentation whether a series of stanzas may be acquired more readily if the whole is learned at once, or whether it is more advantageous to learn each stanza separately and then pass to the succeeding. We do not attempt to apply our findings. The application of this principle is purely voluntary on the part of the teacher. In the psychology of drugs we may show the effect on behavior of certain doses of caffeine. We may reach the conclusion that caffeine has a good effect upon the speed and accuracy of work. But these are general principles. We leave it to the individual as to whether the results of our tests shall be applied or not. Again, in legal testimony, we test the effects of recency upon the reliability of a witness's report. We test the accuracy of the report with respect to moving objects, stationary objects, color, etc. It depends upon the judicial machinery of the country whether these facts are ever to be applied. For a " pure " psychologist to say that he is not interested in the questions raised in these divisions of the science because they relate indirectly to the application of psychology shows, in the first place, that he fails to understand the scientific aim in such problems, and secondly, that he is not interested in a psychology which concerns itself with human life. The only fault to be found with these disciplines is that much of their material is now stated in terms of introspection, whereas a statement in terms of objective results would be far more valuable. There is no reason why appeal should ever be made to consciousness in any of them. Or why introspective data should ever be sought during the experimentation, or published in the results. In experimental pedagogy especially we can see the desirability of keeping all of the results on a purely objective plane. If this is done, work there on the human being will be comparable directly with the work on animals.

We are more interested at the present moment in trying to show the necessity for maintaining uniformity in experimental procedure and in the method of stating results in both human and animal work than in enlarging upon the changes which are certain to come in the scope of human psychology. We shall examine for a moment the subject of the range of stimuli to which animals respond. Let us first consider the work upon vision in animals. We put our animal in a situation where he will respond (or learn to respond) positively to one of two monochromatic lights. We feed him at the one (positive) and punish him at the other (negative). In a short time the animal learns to go to the light at which he is fed. At this point questions arise which may be phrased in two ways: one may choose the psychological way and say, '' does the animal see these two lights as the human being does, i.e., as two distinct colors, or does it see them as two grays differing in brightness, as do the totally color blind? '' Phrased by the behaviorist it would read as follows: '' Is my animal responding upon the basis of the difference in intensity between the two stimuli, or upon the difference in wave-lengths? '' He nowhere thinks of the animal's response in terms of his own experiences of colors and grays. He wishes to establish the fact whether *wave-length* is a factor in that animal's adjustment.[4] If so, what wavelengths are effective and what differences in wave-length must be maintained in the different spectral regions in order to afford bases for differential responses? If wavelength is not a factor in adjustment he wishes to know what difference in *intensity* will serve as a basis for response, and whether the difference obtained at any one point in the spectrum will suffice throughout the spectrum. Furthermore, he wishes to test whether the animal can respond to wave-lengths which do not affect the human eye. He is as much interested in comparing the rat's spectral sensibility curve with that of the chick as in comparing it with man's. The point of view when the various sets of comparisons are made does not change in the slightest.

However we phrase the question to ourselves, we take our animal after the association has been formed and introduce certain control experiments which enable us to return answers to the questions just raised. But there is just as keen a desire on our part to test man under the same conditions, and to state the results in both cases in common terms.

The man and the animal should be placed as nearly as possible under the same experimental conditions. Instead of feeding or punishing the human subject, we should ask him to respond by setting a second apparatus until standard and control offered no basis for a differential response. Do we lay ourselves open to the charge here that we are using introspection? The reply is, Not at all; while we might very well feed the human subject for a right choice and punish him for a wrong one, and thus produce the response if the subject could give it, there is no need of going to extremes even on the platform we suggest. But it should be understood that we are merely using this second method as an abridged behavior method.[5] We can go just as far

[4] He would have exactly the same attitude if he were conducting an experiment to show whether an ant would crawl over a pencil laid across the trail or go around it.

[5] We should prefer to look upon this abbreviated method, where the human subject is told in words, e.g., to equate two stimuli; or to state in words whether a given stimulus is present or absent, etc., as

and reach just as dependable results by the longer method as by the abridged. In many cases the direct and typically human method cannot be safely used. Suppose that we doubt the accuracy of the setting of the control instrument, in the above experiment, as we very likely do if a defect in vision is suspected. It is hopeless for us to get his introspective report. He will say: " There is no difference in sensation, both are reds, identical in quality." But suppose we confront him with the standard and the control and so arrange the conditions that he is punished if he responds to the control but not if to the standard. We then interchange the positions of the standard and the control at will and force him to attempt to respond to the one and not to the other. If he can learn to make the adjustment even after a large number of trials it is evident that the two stimuli do afford the basis for a differential response. Such a method may sound nonsensical, but it is believed that we shall have to resort increasingly to just such methods where we have reason to distrust the language method.

There is hardly a problem in human vision which is not also a problem in animal vision: mention may be made of the limits of the spectrum, threshold values, absolute and relative, flicker, Talbot's law, Weber's law, field of vision, the Purkinje phenomenon, etc. Every one can be worked out by behavior methods. Many of them are being worked out at the present time.

All of the work upon the senses can be consistently carried forward along the lines we have suggested for vision. Our results will, in the end, give an excellent picture of what each organ stands for in the way of function. The

the *language method* in behavior. It in no way changes the status of experimentation. The method becomes possible merely by virtue of the fact that in the particular case the experimenter and his animal have systems of abbreviated or shorthand behavior signs (language), any one of which may stand for a habit belonging to the repertoire both of the experimenter and his subject. To make the data obtained by the language method virtually the whole of behavior —or to attempt to mold all of the data obtained by other methods in terms of the one which has by all odds the most limited range— is putting the cart before the horse with a vengeance.

anatomist and the physiologist may take our data and show, on the one hand, the structures which are responsible for these responses, and, on the other, the physico-chemical relations which are necessarily involved (physiological chemistry of nerve and muscle) in these and other reactions.

To the behaviorist's position thus briefly outlined some serious objections are sure to be raised. It may be argued that one might, if he were sufficiently foolhardy, hold such a view if the study of sensory responses were all that is demanded of the psychologist. But, alas, since imagery and affection are also fundamental elements (or processes?) of consciousness, the behaviorist, it is to be regretted, must be handed his passports. Before accepting them let us examine the nature of the supposed mental existences which refuse to listen to the siren voices of the behaviorists.

The image as a form of implicit behavior.—The most serious obstacle in the way of a free passage from structuralism to behaviorism is the " centrally aroused sensation " or " image." If thoughts go on in terms of centrally aroused sensations, as is maintained by the majority of both structural and functional psychologists, we should have to admit that there is a serious limitation on the side of method in behaviorism. Imagery from Galton on has been the inner stronghold of a psychology based upon introspection. All of the outer defenses might be given over to the enemy, but the cause could never wholly be lost so long as the pass (introspection) to this stronghold (image) could be maintained.

So well guarded is the image that it would seem almost foolhardy for us to make an attack upon it. If we did not perceive certain signs of weakening on the part of the garrison it would seem best to agree with Professor Cattell that the position of the behaviorist is too radical, and that we should better admit the claims of imagery and try to work out a scheme for behaviorism which will embrace the image. Suppose we consider this aspect of the question first: does the inclusion of the image weaken the claims of the behaviorist? It must be admitted that it does.

Take a case like that ordinarily urged. Some one suggests in words that you borrow one thousand dollars and go abroad for a year. You think over the situation—the present condition of your research problems, your debts, whether you can leave your family, etc. You are in a brown study for days trying to make up your mind. Now the train of thoughts going on in your mind, according to the upholders of the image, has no adequate behavior counterpart while it is in transit. The behaviorist, observing you, might note that your appetite had departed, that you were smoking and drinking more than usual, and that you were distrait. Finally, experimental tests might show that your ability to make fine coördinations had been seriously interfered with, and that your dynamometric threshold was lowered, and so on *ad infinitum*. The introspectionists would say that all of these tests failed to give anything like a complete record of your " mental content " or of the " totality of conscious processes." Indeed, they would urge that such tests have only an analogical reference. Only direct observation of the mental states themselves by the method of introspection will ever tell whether you are grieving over past sins or are really trying to reach a decision about going abroad! If we grant this, and such an impulse is very strong, the behaviorist must content himself with this reflection: " I care not what goes on in his so-called mind; the important thing is that, given the stimulation (in this case a series of spoken words), it must produce response, or else modify responses which have been already initiated. This is the all-important thing, and I will be content with it." I.e., he contents himself with observing the initial object (stimulation) and the end object (the reaction). Possibly the old saying, " half a loaf is better than no bread at all," expresses the attitude the behaviorist ought to take; and yet we dislike to admit anything which may be construed as an admission of even partial defeat.

Feeling so, it seems wisest, even at the cost of exposing the weakness of our position, to attack rather than to remain upon the defensive. We spoke above of certain signs of disaffection and mutiny among the ranks of the faithful. These signs manifest themselves in three different ways: (1) The attempt on the part of Woodworth, Thorndike, and others to question the dogma of the image and to show that thought processes may go on independently of imagery —or, indeed, even independently of peripherally initiated processes. To this last contention we do not accede, as we shall undertake later to show. (2) The failure on the part of the most earnest upholders of the doctrine of the centrally aroused sensation to obtain any objective experimental evidence of the presence of different image-types. Reference here is made to the researches of Angell and of Fernald. *Although these writers in no way suggest such a conclusion,* it seems to us that the way is paved, by reason of their findings, for the complete dismissal of the image from psychology. Furthermore, most psychologists themselves are willing to admit that introspection furnishes no guide for the determination of one's own image-type. In this field, above all others, introspection, if it is a legitimate method at all, ought to yield its best results. It is just here that it has failed, except in the case of a few fortunate men who seem to have become " adept " in the use of it. We who are less happy in its use must forever do without this wonderful Aladdin's lamp, which, upon demand, illumines the dark places of the human mind. (3) The attempts even of the structuralists to reduce the so-called higher thought processes to groups of obscure organic processes. We have in mind the recent work on recognition, abstraction, etc.

All of these tendencies, initiated by the psychologists themselves, lead directly over to our principal contention, viz., that there are no centrally initiated processes.[6]

The environment in the widest sense forces the forma-

---

[6] There are probably in most cases kinæsthetic substitutes for imagery. Concurrently with the faintly *articulated word apple* there arise associated kinæsthetic impulses in eye muscles. If these latter are strong one can see how the fiction of visual imagery might arise. Mead has already spoken for the existence of a strong tactual and kinæsthetic element (grasping, handling, etc.) in all forms of perception and in imagery. Dunlap has rejected the centrally aroused content in the image.

tion of habits. These are exhibited first in the organs which are most mobile: the arms, hands, fingers, legs, etc. By this we do not mean to imply that there is any fixed order in their formation. After such general bodily habits are well under way, speech habits begin. All of the recent work shows that these reach enormous complexity in a comparatively short time. Furthermore, as language habits become more and more complex behavior takes on refinement: short cuts are formed, and finally words come to be, on occasion, substituted for acts. That is, a stimulus which, in early stages, would produce an act (and which will always do so under appropriate conditions) now produces merely a spoken word or a mere movement of the larynx (or of some other expressive organ).[7]

When the stimulus produces either an *immediate overt response* (as, e.g., when John is told to go to the sideboard and get an apple—taking it for granted that he goes), or a *delayed overt response* (as, e.g., when an engineer is asked to think out and make an apparatus for the conversion of salt water into sweet, which may consume years before overt action begins), we have examples of what we may call *explicit behavior*. In contrast to behavior of this type, which involves the larger musculature in a way plainly apparent to direct observation, we have behavior involving only the speech mechanisms (or the larger musculature in a minimal way; e.g., bodily attitudes or sets). This form of behavior, for lack of a better name, we may call *implicit behavior*.[8] Where explicit behavior is delayed (i.e., where deliberation ensues), the intervening time between stimulus and response is given over to implicit behavior (to " thought processes ").

Now it is this type of implicit behavior that the introspectionist claims as his own and denies to us because its neural seat is cortical and because it goes on without adequate bodily portrayal. Why in psychology the stage for

---

[7] These substitutes are discussed in detail on p. 332.

[8] It may be said in passing that the explicit and implicit forms of behavior referred to throughout this book are acquired and not congenital.

the neural drama was ever transferred from periphery to cortex must remain somewhat of a mystery. The old idea of strict localization of brain function is in part responsible. Religious convictions are even more largely responsible for it. It is not meant by this that the men originally making the transfer were aware of this religious tendency at all. When the psychologist threw away the soul he compromised with his conscience by setting up a " mind " which was to remain always hidden and difficult of access.[9] The transfer from periphery to cortex has been the incentive for driving psychology into vain and fruitless searches for the unknown and unknowable. Had the idea of the image not taken such firm hold upon us we would never have originated the notion that we are seeking to explain consciousness. We would have been content to study the very tangible phenomena of the growth and control of explicit and implicit habits.

It is implied in these words that there exists or ought to exist a method of observing implicit behavior. There is none at present. The larynx and tongue, we believe, are the loci of most of the phenomena. If their movements could be adequately portrayed we should obtain a record similar to that of the phonogram. Certainly nothing so definite as this could be obtained, but we should get a record, at least, which would largely reveal the subject's word-habits, which, if we are not mistaken, make up the bulk of the implicit forms of behavior.[10]

[9] The tendency to make the brain itself something more than a mechanism for coördinating incoming and outgoing impulses has been very strong among psychologists, and even among psychologically inclined neurologists. A still wilder hypothesis is held in regard to the neural impulse. According to many psychologists we are taught that an incoming impulse may be held *in statu quo* for long periods of time, or at least that it may ramble around in the nervous system for an indefinite period of time—until it can " obtain possession of the motor field," at which time it exerts its effect. So far as we know no such thing occurs. The nervous system functions in complete arcs. An incoming impulse exerts its effect relatively immediately upon one system of effectors or another, as shown by inhibition, reinforcement, summation, phenomena in the muscle in operation, or by inciting wholly new effectors to activity.

[10] See the recent work of Anna Wyczoikowska, *Psychological Review*, November, 1913, p. 448. See summary, p. 326.

Now it is admitted by all of us that words spoken or faintly articulated belong really in the realm of behavior as do movements of the arms and legs. If implicit behavior can be shown to consist of nothing but word movements (or expressive movements of the word-type) the behavior of the human being as a whole is as open to objective control as the behavior of the lowest organism.

Affection as a form of instinctive behavior.—Affection is the other stumbling-block in the way of our main thesis. It is needless for us to enter into a lengthy discussion of the various views of affection. It is sufficient to call attention to the generally accepted position that affection is a mental process distinct from cognition. Both Angell and Titchener in this country admit the independence of the two. In Germany likewise, with the exception of the followers of Stumpf, the independence is admitted. Indeed, as it is well known, Wundt and his pupils are attempting to introduce into affection the same wealth of detail they have already succeeded in bringing into cognition. We refer to the addition to the elementary processes of pleasure-pain, those of strain-relaxation, excitement-calm.

In maintaining his position as to the independence of the two processes, Titchener states that affection and sensation are closely similar in the following respects. Both possess certain common attributes, viz., *quality, intensity, duration.* Sensation possesses the additional attribute of *clearness,* which affection lacks. " The lack of the attribute of clearness is sufficient in itself to differentiate affection from sensation; a process that cannot be made the object of attention is radically different, and must play a radically different part in consciousness, from a process which is held and enhanced by attention." Furthermore, the lack of *clearness* distinguishes affection from organic sensation —the cognitive processes with which it is most closely allied. On the whole, while sensation and affection are closely allied, " the difference is so great that we have no choice but to rank affection in human psychology as a second type of mental element, distinct from sensation."

Adherents of the view that affection is merely an attribute of sensation have not been lacking. Külpe has been given credit for demolishing this assumption.

There remains the view in contrast to the one first outlined, advanced principally by Stumpf and accepted and amended by Helen Thompson Woolley, viz., that affection is really organic sensation. The theory as advanced by Stumpf is all but unintelligible in view of the fact that the simplification that he obtains by his reduction is more than offset by the complexity he introduces when he states that the emotions, in addition to the complex of sensations, contain a mysterious " kernel.'' Mrs. Woolley, while rejecting the " kernel " hypothesis, insists that affection can be identified with sensation. She gives no clear reason for the solidarity and distinctness of the two groups, nor for the rather constant presence of the one or the other of these two groups. Stumpf no more than she meets these two points.

The Stumpf-Woolley view may be modified and stated in more definite terms. Every stimulus which calls out either overt or delayed response arouses concomitantly (reflexly) a definite and complex group of afferent impulses from tissue not specified definitely by the authors. We assume that the tissue in question belongs to the reproductive organs and to the related erogenous zones. The area involved in sex functions embraces a much wider zone than that of the sex organs proper. The erogenous zones are in infancy widely distributed throughout the body surfaces. Only gradually does the sex organ come to be looked upon as the focus of sex experience. Even in the case of most adults certain of these primitive zones remain functional, as, e.g., the nipples, etc.

This area as a whole may be looked upon as initiating impulses of two fundamental kinds: (1) a group connected with tumescence and rhythmical contractions of other muscular tissue and with increases in the quantity of the various secretions. This group, if functioning alone, as it does in cases of sex response, would lead to the expansive or seeking movements, and ultimately to the unfolding of the instinctive mechanism of the act of reproduction (ending in the orgasm). (2) A group connected with the shrinkage of the sex organs, relaxation of other muscular tissue, and with inhibition of secretion. These impulses, gaining the motor centers, would, if no others inhibitory in character were present, release movements of avoidance.

In order to bring this conception of the sensory character of affection in line with our general scheme, it is necessary to suppose that the impulses from the erotic tissues function as do the impulses arising from other receptors, i.e., looking at it from a neurological standpoint, there is a definite system of reflex arcs running from these regions (both enteroceptive and proprioceptive impulses are involved) to the muscles. This, as far as we know, is thoroughly established. In order to illustrate the point, let us take the neurophysiological situation at the moment of sex excitement.

When a definite sex object (female) appeals to any one receptor, the eye, the ear, or the nose of the animal, granting a certain physiological condition of the animal (i.e., the proper season of the year, period of sex excitement, etc.: in general, since seasonal rhythms are not so marked in the male, the animal must be in a receptive condition for such stimuli), several sets of arcs begin to function: (a) one leading from the distance receptor (aroused by the sex object) to the striped muscles, tending to produce a heightened tonus in the skeletal muscles. Movements in the striped muscles do not become overt until definite impulses are sent in from the sex zones. When these are present with sufficient intensity, overt seeking movements begin. The impulses from the sex zones are aroused by the second set of arcs: the initial impulse aroused by the sex object while arousing tonus in the striped muscle (b) passes out (via the white rami) also to the appropriate sympathetic ganglia. When these neurones are stimulated, changes are produced in the circulatory, glandular, secretory and muscular mechanisms, possibly of the character described in (1) above, p. 22. As soon as these effectors are thrown into activity they set up a characteristic group of afferent impulses (they represent a definite

set of bodily reverberations, to use William James' term,
and hence in current psychological terminology they are
the bodily substrata of the *emotion of pleasantness*), which
upon reaching the motor centers, produce the actual seeking movements in the striped muscles. When the situation
is prolonged, i.e., when definite receptors other than the
initial one become stimulated by the sex object by reason
of the seeking movements, the complete act of reproduction
follows. On the other hand, if the general physiological
condition is different (organism not receptive to sex
stimuli) there again arise (*a*) an increased tonus in the
striped muscles and (*b*) activity in the sympathetic
mechanisms, checking of secretion, lack of tonicity in the
muscles, etc., which arouse, in turn, a definite group of
afferent impulses ('' bodily substrata of unpleasantness '')
that tends definitely to set free the *avoiding reaction*. Since
the mechanisms involved in sex are fundamental, it seems
reasonable to suppose that every object, either instinctively
or through habit, tends to throw them into the one or the
other form of action, of which we have just spoken.[11]

Certainly many objects (non-affective stimuli, stimuli

[11] In fact we see no escape from such a conclusion, if the Stumpf-
Woolley hypothesis is adopted. By its own admission, this theory
must be able to account for several so-called observed facts. We state
them from the standpoint of current psychology.

1. That there should be two well-marked and opposite groups.
2. That they always accompany perceptions or images.
3. That they are evanescent and hard to observe (Titchener says
    they cannot be " observed ").
4. That the image carries its own tone which need not be, and
    often is not, the same as that given in the original perception.
5. That there should at times be neutral perceptions and images,
    and that tone tends to disappear with frequency of appearance
    of the stimulating object.

Were we interested in arguing for a structural psychology, we
could readily show how 1, 2, 4, and 5 follow immediately from our
premises. In regard to 3, it could be said (1) that evanescence would
be the character expected in all cases except that of direct sex stimulation, since these arcs are functioning only slightly along with the arcs
from distance receptors to voluntary muscles, which are functioning
at high intensity. Titchener's statement that they cannot be attended
to is a pure assumption in the interests of a structural criterion.
Pathological cases tend to support the view that at certain times
affective processes, or, on this view, affective sensations, are often the
only sensations which are attended to.

distantly or not at all connected with sex stimuli) do not, in the beginning, arouse these groups, *but through the ordinary mechanism of habit come later to arouse faintly the one or the other* (substitution, p. 272). There is evidence in sexual pathology to show not only that such habit connections are formed, but also that they can become more fundamental than the primal instinctive pathways, as is shown in the use of phallic symbols, fetishes, etc.

We thus seem to be able to connect so-called affective processes definitely with general processes of adjustment. Behavior, while possibly not immediately interested in such processes, need not escape its share of work in their study. On the one hand, the student of behavior, when some of the more pressing problems are solved, will be interested in the types of *stimuli* which jointly arouse movements in the striped muscles and in the unstriped muscles and glandular tissues in the sex zones, and in the finer analysis of the movements themselves. He will try to determine whether such stimuli arouse these movements by means of inherent connections or through habit. Furthermore, he will try to determine whether the movements of the glands, etc., actually set up sensory impulses in the sexual zones, and whether they have the effect called for upon his theory. This can be attacked in two ways: (1) probably by actual plethysmographic and galvanometric studies upon the sex organs themselves; (2) by the elimination of the sensory avenues which lead from these zones to the central system. His primary interest, however, will be engaged in determining the effect of these impulses upon overt movement, since it is highly probable that they are responsible for so-called preferences, which play such an enormous rôle in the daily life of the human being, and for the many forms of artistic, æsthetic, and religious modes of response. To those who have inherent objections to admitting that the æsthetic, artistic, and religious sides of life are at bottom sexual, this view will not sound convincing. Fortunately, thanks to the work of the scientific students of social phenomena we are fast losing our prejudices against admitting the sex reference of all behavior.

It must be confessed that wholly new methods will have to be devised for the pursuit of studies in this field. There is still hope, as was suggested above, for galvanometric and plethysmographic experimentation. You may object that expressive methods have already failed to show any constant physiological processes occurring in conjunction with the examination of " pleasant " and " unpleasant " objects. We have worked for years upon the expressive methods and no one is more ready to admit their failure in the past. Our present feeling is that we have taken our plethysmograms from the wrong organs. Whether there are too many technical difficulties in the way of the objective registration of the many delicate changes in the sex organs (circulation, secretion, etc.) remains for the future to decide.

The result of our examination into the nature of both image and affection seems to indicate that after all the behaviorist can bring them into his general scheme of work without in any way weakening his position. It would thus seem that there is no field which an introspective psychology legitimately can call its own.

Will there be left over in psychology a world of pure psychics, to use Yerkes' term? The plans which we most favor for psychology lead practically to the ignoring of consciousness in the sense in which that term is used by psychologists today. We have virtually denied that this realm of psychics is open to experimental investigation. We do not wish to go further into the problem because its future rests with the metaphysician. If you will grant the behaviorist the right to use consciousness in the same way that other natural scientists employ it—i.e., without making consciousness a special object of observation—you have granted all that our thesis requires.

Summary.—1. Human psychology has failed to make good its claim as a natural science. Due to a mistaken notion that its fields of facts are conscious phenomena and that introspection is the only direct method of ascertaining these facts, it has enmeshed itself in a series of speculative questions which, while fundamental to its present tenets, are not open to experimental treatment. In the pursuit of answers to these questions, it has become further and further divorced from contact with problems which vitally concern human interest.

2. Psychology, as the behaviorist views it, is a purely objective, experimental branch of natural science which needs introspection as little as do the sciences of chemistry and physics. It is granted that the behavior of animals can be investigated without appeal to consciousness. Heretofore the viewpoint has been that such data have value only in so far as they can be interpreted by analogy in terms of consciousness. The position is taken here that the behavior of man and the behavior of animals must be considered on the same plane; as being equally essential to a general understanding of behavior. It can dispense with consciousness in a psychological sense. The separate observation of " states of consciousness " is, on this assumption, no more a part of the task of the psychologist than of the physicist. We might call this the return to a non-reflective and naïve use of consciousness. In this sense consciousness may be said to be the instrument or tool with which all scientists work. Whether or not the tool is properly used at present by scientists is a problem for philosophy and not for psychology.

3. From the viewpoint here suggested the facts on the behavior of amœbæ have value in and for themselves without reference to the behavior of man. In biology studies on race differentiation and inheritance in amœbæ form a separate division of study which must be evaluated in terms of the laws found there. The conclusions so reached may not hold in any other form. Regardless of the possible lack of generality, such studies must be made if evolution as a whole is ever to be regulated and controlled. Similarly the laws of behavior in amœbæ, the range of responses, and the determination of effective stimuli, of habit formation, persistency of habits, interference and reinforcement of habits, must be determined and evaluated in and for themselves, regardless of their generality, or of their bearing upon such laws in other

forms, if the phenomena of behavior are ever to be brought within the sphere of scientific control.

4. This suggested elimination of states of consciousness as proper objects of investigation in themselves will remove the barrier which exists between psychology and the other sciences. The findings of psychology become the functional correlates of structure and lend themselves to explanation in physico-chemical terms.

5. Psychology as behavior will, after all, have to neglect but few of the really essential problems with which psychology as an introspective science now concerns itself. In all probability even this residue of problems may be phrased in such a way that refined methods in behavior (which certainly must come) will lead to their solution.

BIBLIOGRAPHY

ANGELL, JAMES R., "Behavior as a Category of Psychology," *Psych. Rev.*, 1913, XX, 255.

BODE, B. H., "Psychology as a Science of Behavior," *Psych. Rev.*, 1914, XXI, 46.

DUNLAP, K., *A System of Psychology*. New York, Scribner's, 1912.
———— "The Case Against Introspection," *Psych. Rev.*, 1912, IX, 404.
———— "Images and Ideas," *The Johns Hopkins University Circular*, 1914, No. 3, 25.

LOVEJOY, A. O., "On the Existence of Ideas," *The Johns Hopkins University Circular*, 1914, No. 3, 42.

MARSHALL, H. R., "Is Psychology Evaporating?" *Jour. Philos.*, 1913, X, 710.

MEAD, G. H., "Concerning Animal Perception," *Psych. Rev.*, 1907, XIV, 383.

TITCHENER, E. B., "Prolegomena to a Study of Introspection," *Am. Jour. Psych.*, 1912, XXIII, 427.
———— "The Schema of Introspection," *ibid.*, 485.
———— "A Text-Book of Psychology." New York, Macmillan, 1910.

WARREN, H. C., "The Mental and the Physical," *Psych. Rev.*, 1914, XXI, 79.

WATSON, J. B., "Image and Affection in Behavior," *Jour. Philos., Psych. and Sci. Meth.*, 1913, X, 421.
———— "Psychology as the Behaviorist Views It," *Psych. Rev.*, 1913, XX, 158.

WOOLLEY, HELEN T., "Sensory Affection and Emotion," *Psych. Rev.*, 1907, XIV, 329.

YERKES, R. M., *Introduction to Psychology*. New York, Henry Holt, 1911.

CHAPTER II

SOME PROBLEMS ENUMERATED

No lack of unity in the problems of behavior.—In the preceding discussion of the relation of behavior to psychology several problems which face the behaviorist were touched upon. In the present chapter the attempt is made to develop them in such a way that their unity may be traced. At the present time behavior appears to the casual observer to consist of a large number of rather isolated bits of research which may be classified here and there under sciences already well recognized. This is a serious mistake and one which will handicap advance in this subject in the years to come. The sketch of the problems given below may be looked upon as a program for unified and sys-

tematic work rather than as a complete expression of the
scope and aim of behavior. Even such an immature and
hasty sketch of the problems confronting us will, it is hoped,
offer convincing evidence that the work of the behaviorist,
while closely related to that of the zoölogist and the physiologist, is, nevertheless, independent.

Field *versus* **laboratory studies.**—Before presenting the
special groups of problems of behavior, it is necessary to
face one criticism often urged against the young science,
viz., that of the narrowness of its problems. In the last
few years behavior has become mainly a laboratory science.
This has led a large number of men who have devoted their
lives to the field activity of animals, such as Burroughs,
Wesley Mills, and a wide group of naturalists, to say that
the laboratory is not a suitable place in which to study
behavior. According to them only highly specialized problems can be attacked in the laboratories. True and un-
trammeled expressions of habit and instinct and of the
uses of the senses must be sought for in the field activity
of animals. Unquestionably it is a mistake to neglect field
work. It requires no lengthy argument to show that general orientation with respect to the daily routine of
adjustments of animals and an accurate knowledge of the
environmental conditions under which animals live can
come only through field observation. No one who has ever
used monkeys as subjects can help feeling how handicapped
we are at the present time in our laboratory studies of
simian life through lack of systematic knowledge of their
life in the open. What is true in the case of the primates
is true with respect to nearly every other animal form. It
is highly improbable that any of us could describe in a
really helpful way the daily routine of the domestic fowl
or the dog. We are even less familiar with the seasonal
routine of animals, such as hibernation, migration, etc. On
the other hand, it can hardly be claimed that mere observation of field activity, even when made by competent
students, can ever hope to answer in any scientific way the
basal questions which must be asked about the mechanics
of stimulus and response. Even the most superficial ob-

servation of field activity by the trained student raises at once a host of questions, the answers to which must be sought in the laboratory—is the cat visually stimulated by a moving object in steadily decreasing intensity of light for a longer time than the human being, or does this animal stalk its prey after it is lost to sight through a highly developed sense of smell? Do the birds which feed upon decaying animal matter sense it through smell or sight? A few minutes' observation will show that while many of our problems are raised in the field, the scientific answers to them come through the laboratories. But granting the indispensableness of the laboratory, it is well, after finishing with our animal, to observe him yet again in the field. One can readily conceive of some such situation as the following:—after years of analytical study upon the temperature, visual, olfactory, and auditory senses of a given species of bird, one might predict the utter absurdity of that bird's being able to get back to its home when carried out to sea for a distance of one thousand miles. Yet on specific test we find the bird able to do this. Of course our laboratory study was incomplete, or we should have been able to predict what actually happened. Yet the incompleteness of the laboratory study would be discovered only when we, so to speak, began to put the bird together again! Without developing the subject further, it would seem obvious that there is no conflict between field work and laboratory work. The field is both the source of problems and the place where the laboratory solutions of these problems are tested.

Grouping of problems.—The vast majority of the problems in both human and animal behavior may be grouped under one or another of three divisions: I. *Sense organ functions.* II. *Instinctive functions.* III. *Habit formation.* In addition to these large divisions in which the subjects for research lie, there remains the work of, IV. *Correlation:* first, among behavior data—giving both an ontogeny and a phylogeny of behavior; second, of behavior with structure; and finally the correlation of behavior and structure with physico-chemical processes. We shall take up these divisions separately and attempt to show in some detail what special questions gather around them. Later we shall discuss the apparatus and methods which are employed in attempting to return answers to them.

I. Sense-Organ Processes

Introduction.—The study of sense functions should come prior, logically, to the study of either instinct or learning, since neither instinctive action nor learning can be thoroughly understood until we have definite knowledge about the sense processes of the animal under experimentation. In actual practice, work upon instinct, learning, and the sense organs has been carried forward simultaneously. It is very difficult to study any one of these subjects by itself. In the learning of mazes and puzzle boxes both by animals and human beings, many facts appear which are of importance to a study of instincts and senses. On the other hand, our knowledge of sense-organ processes is obtained in two ways: (1) by forcing the animal to form sensory habits (p. 187); and (2) by noting the inherited modes of response to controlled stimuli. In the study of the spectral sensibility of the chick (limits) one finds that the chick is positive to light, i.e., will go towards a lighted compartment from the first, without learning. The relations among these three divisions seem at first sight to be too complicated for analytical work. It will be seen from the chapters that follow that the difficulties are more apparent than real.

1. *Vision*

Necessity for consideration of anatomical structure.— Before making an extensive study of vision in any particular animal form, it is essential to study carefully the structure of its eye and the visual conduction systems; and to have at least some knowledge of the animal's general anatomy. Questions as to the presence or absence of a fovea; whether both rods and cones are present, and their distribution; whether the animal has the essential structure for binocular vision; whether there are accommodation, convergence, and divergence—are met at every turn in our work. Not to have orientation with respect to them means a lack of thoroughness in the setting of problems for the study of vision. It is equally essential (where possible) to make a study of the animal's visual environment and of the field habits and instincts which seem to. depend upon visual stimuli.

Reflex responses to light.—In the observations of the movements of lower forms of plants and animals, one is often struck by the remarkable sensitivity of some of the organisms—Euglena, Stentor,—and by the equally noticeable lack of sensitivity in other forms, e.g., Paramecium. The general responsiveness to light is equally observable in the higher animals as well. The tern remains absolutely quiescent in total darkness. The chick's behavior on the sudden elimination of light is equally remarkable. It remains at first quite still, as though stunned, and then begins aimless movements,—pecking, turning, running against objects, etc. The rats, and probably other rodents as well, require separate laboratory work in order to tell whether vision is functional at all. Vision seems to function in some animals (nocturnal animals) only in very weakened intensity of light, strong light producing cessation of activity equally as well as absolute darkness.

General divisions of problems in vision.—The problems in vision proper may be considered under (a) white light vision; (b) monochromatic light vision; (c) the rôle of vision in daily life (mutual relations among the senses).

White light vision.—(a) One of the first problems in white light vision is the determination of the delicacy of the mechanism. What absolute intensity of light can the animal respond to with dark adapted eye, and with light adapted eye? What difference in intensity between two lights is it necessary to maintain in order to give a basis for a differential response? (Weber's law.) Are responses to light positive or negative? Under what conditions may a positive tendency be changed to a negative?

Can it be so changed in any of the vertebrates without involving habit formation? We are led over almost at once into a consideration of darkness and light adaptation in animals with cone retinæ and in those possessing rod retinæ, the difference in the response to white light between animals with image forming eyes and those with eye structures too undeveloped to form images. Another forward step in the work on vision is the determination of the animal's behavior with respect to form and size, vertical and horizontal lines, moving and stationary stimuli, patterns, etc.

Response to monochromatic light.—The difficulty of gaining accurate knowledge of animals' monochromatic light responses is very great. Heretofore the work has been carried out by methods and apparatus which can never yield accurate results. The first step in the study of any animal's color responses should be the determination of the limits of its spectral sensitivity. The second step should be the determination of the energy of stimulus necessary to yield threshold responses at various points in the spectrum. Enough places should be chosen to enable the experimenter to plot the sensitivity curve throughout the spectrum. This threshold curve will serve in several connections. In the first place it enables us to say immediately whether both lights used in the work on sensory habits lie above the animal's threshold, and consequently whether both are effective stimuli. We have learned the necessity for this after the loss of several months' work. In the second place it will largely increase our knowledge of the variations of intensity which it is necessary to make the monochromatic lights undergo in order to test for sensitivity to wave-length difference (color vision). Let us illustrate: suppose we have found that even at our standard intensity the red has very little stimulating effect upon the animal, i.e., that it is only slightly above its threshold. Now if one is confronting the animal with red and green it is perfectly evident that if we cut down the intensity of the red in only a small degree, it will cease to stimulate the visual receptors. This is only one of the features which make it desirable to obtain the limits of the spectrum and the sensibility curve for the animal whose vision we wish to study at length. The next step, logically, in the monochromatic light work, is the careful working through of the Weber law for intensity at several points in the spectrum. Our interest is not psychophysical here but methodological. We need to know for subsequent control of behavior, what difference in intensity one has to maintain between two reds of the same wave-length in order to afford a basis for a difference in response. The problem is simple enough in technique, as will be shown on p. 357. One allows a given bundle, red, for purposes of illustration, to come from the spectrum. This is then divided by means of a double image prism into two beams equal in intensity. The intensities are then controlled separately by means of smoked wedges (or rotating sectors). The tests on the animal are carried forward in exactly the same way as in tests on sensitivity to wave-length difference. The tests should naturally be repeated with different absolute intensities. The Weber-Fechner law may or may not hold. Regardless of the bearing of the work upon that law we will gain a clearer insight than we now have of the *relative stimulating value* of the different colors at low, intermediate, and high intensities. The results of these experiments upon differences in intensity should aid us in testing the possibility of response to differences in wave-lengths, which is the most difficult problem in animal vision. Since this problem is already well known, we leave a further discussion of it to p. 356 ff., where the results of tests on color vision are considered.

Finally, as a means of controlling visual response it is essential to test the relative effects of decreasing the intensity of light by the four different methods usually employed: (1) distancing the source of the light; (2) thinning the beam by the use of diaphragms; (3) by the use of the rotating sector; (4) absorption by means of smoked (neutral) wedges. As is well known, careful experiments have shown that in the human being it is a matter of indifference (Talbot's law) which method is used. This cannot be assumed to be true in the case of animals. This work should best be undertaken with monochromatic light.

2. *Audition*

Grouping of problems.—The problems in sound may be grouped under three general headings: (1) response to pendular vibrations; (2) to a-periodic vibrations; (3) to the ordinary sounds in the animal's environment (mates, other animals, etc.).

(1) Response to pendular vibrations.—As in the case of vision, so in audition, field observations ought to guide us in making our audition tests. We can do little more here than to enumerate the various problems which lie before us.

(*a*) *Range of sensitivity.*—The animal's range of sensitivity to simple pendular vibrations is probably the most fundamental problem in this field. The work can be carried out with good forks by forcing the formation of sensory habits. The method of making these tests is described on p. 81. The tests should be combined with threshold tests and with others designed to bring out differential sensitivity both with respect to pitch and to intensity. While there is no convenient standard of intensity at present, it is possible for the work to be carried out upon different animals in the same laboratory with the same apparatus. We can obtain in this way values which are strictly comparable for the different animals. Such work is, however, not reproducible in other laboratories unless some system of exchanging apparatus is adopted.

(*b*) *Localization.*—The localization of sound stimuli (in the case of bodies which give periodic and those which give a-periodic vibrations) is important both for obtaining knowledge of the experimental range of auditory sensitivity and for tests of the function of sound in the daily life of the animal.

(*c*) *Response to clangs.*—The question as to the ability of the animal to respond to differences in the timbre of sound complexes (analysis of chords) has an interesting bearing upon the nature of structural relations in the inner ear (complexity demanded in organ of Corti).

(2) **Response to a-periodic vibrations:** (*a*) *Stimulus threshold.*—The falling ball (some standard apparatus should be chosen) gives us the best means of testing stimulus thresholds. The tests would be very easy to carry out. It is surprising that this work has never been attempted.

(*b*) *Difference threshold.*—The differential sensitivity for sound intensity should likewise be worked out with a similar instrument, but in this case the problem is more difficult, since two stimuli must be employed. The tests of response to periodic and a-periodic vibrations are designed to give us the experimental range of auditory functions, and not the practical range employed in daily life. The problems which follow are connected with the practical range.

(3) **Response to the ordinary sounds in its environment (mates, other animals, etc.):** (*a*) *Instinctive repertoire of sounds.*—The instinctive repertoire of vocalization is important, if for no other reason than to guard ourselves against those enthusiastic but untrained investigators who would tell us that animals have a language. It is possible to obtain this instinctive repertoire only by isolating the animal until the native vocalizations have all been recorded, and then comparing the vocalizations of the isolated animal with those of an animal brought up in company with its fellows.

(*b*) *Modification of vocal sounds through social influence.*—The extent to which such vocalizations are modifiable by social surroundings may be illustrated by the work of Conradi, who reared English sparrows with canaries,— certainly with no hardship to the voice of the sparrows (p. 143). As a part of (*b*) we include the problem of finding to what extent animals can be made to respond correctly to articulate sounds made by the human being (note the behavior of the dog, Jasper; the chimpanzee, Peter, and of other highly trained animals, p. 299).

(*c*) *Influence of such sounds upon activity of mates.*— The extent to which animals are induced to engage in common activities by the voice of the mate, parent or companion (sex activity, feeding, flight, etc.). While these problems possibly may have the flavor of the " manufactured " or laboratory variety, a little field observation will quickly show that they are really fundamental. Hodge would have us believe that the deer has an almost unbelievably acute sense of hearing. How can we dispute it or confirm it in the deer or any other animal until we have made threshold tests under standard conditions? Kalischer tells us of the absolute pitch memory of dogs. Who can prove it or disprove it except by the laboratory type of test? Until these exact and rigorous tests are made and repeatedly confirmed by several investigators it is impossible to carry forward research upon the localization of pitch centers, experimentation upon the functions of the cochlea, and the like.

3. *Olfaction and Gustation*

Lack of definite knowledge of smell functions.—It is singular that the functions of the organ of smell have never been investigated in any complete way in any vertebrate. Several investigations have been carried out upon smell in birds and in fishes. These tests have had as their object the determination of the fact whether those animals use that receptor. Of the range and complexity of its uses we have nothing. That enormous differences exist among the smell functions of different animals there is little room for doubt. In addition to the problems connected with the general functioning of the organ of smell, there are many concerning the instinctive life of the animal which have never been explored. We have in mind here the positive reactions made to certain " nauseous " smell stimuli, and to the apparent lack of sensitivity to the odor of flowers and perfumes generally, etc. The human being seems to be the only animal which responds negatively to the class of odors which Zwaardemaker calls nauseous.[1]

[1] K. S. Lashley finds that an Amazon parrot in his possession will vomit at the smell of an old pipe (Class VI).

How much of this is due to social training and how much to fundamental biological tendencies is not known. From the study of primitive Australian tribes and from biological studies generally the conclusions seem to follow that social conventions and training are responsible for the negative tendencies which are so apparent in man. Still, the evidence is not completely decisive. Certain smells in the cultivated European are connected with definite reflexes: nausea and even vomiting being produced. That our ignorance of smell functions in general is almost colossal comes out clearly when we try to compare even in thought the delicacy of the average human being's sense of smell with that of certain varieties of dogs. Hunting dogs, bloodhounds, etc., must have an almost unbelievably delicate sense of smell. Yet when defective human beings have been forced to depend upon this sense, they have surprised us by the delicacy with which they use this organ. It is difficult even in field work to detect the actual uses to which smell is put by animals. In the case of the monkey it is quite clear that objects are rejected by this sense long before they reach the mouth. That olfactory stimuli start seeking movements in many vertebrate forms is also clear. The specific problems in smell are much like those in the other sense fields. There is need of field observations to guide us in setting problems for determining the interrelations of smell with other sense functions, and the rôle smell plays in the daily life of the animal. As in vision and in audition we need to test the animal's range of sensitivity. For this problem the best plan of attack would probably be that of taking several odors from each of Zwaardemaker's nine classes and testing in order whether the animal is positive or negative to them. Either form of response, provided proper controls were introduced, would show that that odor was an effective stimulus. If no such simple inherited mode of response were present we should attempt to force the formation of a sensory habit which would enable us to determine whether the odor lies within the animal's range. Extended experiments would be necessary for the determination of threshold intensities of different olfactory stimuli.

We shall sketch a method farther on (p. 89) by means of which such tests may be started at least with some hopes of results.

Function of olfaction in habit formation.—The extent to which smell stimuli influence the formation of habits in the daily life of most of the vertebrates is at present unknown. It is generally believed that smell forms the center of reference for most animals. What tests have been made do not confirm this. That smell data are utilized in habit would seem to be clear from the anecdotal literature, and yet in many of the tests on the formation of motor habits we have been enabled to eliminate this sense without decreasing the rapidity with which learning takes place.

Problems in gustation.—Gustation offers as its main problems: (a) the ability of animals to react differently to sapid substances either instinctively or through habit; (b) the delicacy of the organ in detecting taste substances in solution (and at a distance), and (c) the localization of the taste organs. The sense of taste offers a more inviting field to students of lower vertebrate and invertebrate behavior than to those engaged in work upon birds and mammals.

4. *Cutaneous, Proprio- and Entero-ceptive Systems.*

Difficulties in the way of making satisfactory tests.—We experience great difficulty in making tests upon the tactual, kinæsthetic, organic, and other internal systems of receptors. Some interesting work has been done in all of these fields, but we have not gone far enough in such investigations to talk very intelligently about the problems. Work here calls almost instantly for operative technique.

Proprio-ceptive system.—The maze experiments and those on the so-called delayed reaction (pp. 99 and 104) have been the most effective ones so far in yielding results. There still remains a very large number of problems in connection with the maze. The disturbance which results from rotating the maze after the animal has learned it is a case in point (p. 219). Many observers have noted this phenomenon. While it may possibly be explained in terms of the change in the balance which exists among the processes in the distance receptors, it may be due, on the other hand, to a change in the functioning of some of the internal receptors, possibly those lying in the semicircular canals and vestibule. The work which Carr and his students are doing upon the responses of animals to discrete impressions (delayed reaction)—e.g., exposing for one second a light in one of three places and then waiting a definite period, one, two, three, or five seconds, then releasing the animal to see whether it will go to the place where the light was flashed,—is showing us the extent to which kinæsthetic and organic receptors may function in ordinary situations (p. 224). The homing sense in birds is another problem which may lie within this field. No one can say definitely to the contrary yet. Our experience already noted in getting the terns to come back home from long distances over territory wholly unknown should make us hesitate at least in explaining the homing sense in terms of the visual landmark theory.

Entero-ceptive system.—The organic sense is especially hard to deal with in isolation. That it plays an important part in the daily activities of most animals is apparent. There is something in animals which functions like a time sense. Nest shifts among the terns and other birds show oftentimes a marked and regular rhythm. Hunger is probably the most compelling of all stimuli. Since the stimulus to hunger consists largely in the rhythmical movements of the muscles in the stomach, it would seem possible, by operative experiments, to eliminate the afferent impulses aroused by these movements. It would be exceedingly instructive to study the formation of habits, functioning of certain instinctive acts, etc., in animals which had undergone such operations.

Cutaneous system as a distance receptor.—Many problems remain to be attacked in the cutaneous mechanisms, when they are considered as distance receptors. For some time we have felt the need of accurate information upon the sensitivity of animals to changes in temperature, i.e., the extent to which associations may be formed between certain acts and certain temperature stimuli. The problem is surely not an insoluble one. Some preliminary experiments upon the sensitivity of squirrels to temperature changes have already been made. Further needed facts are those which relate to the animal's ability to detect differences in the moisture contents of two air columns, differences in pressure between two air columns, and the extent to which olfactory stimuli may be detected by the cutaneous receptors in the nasal cavities (experiments must be carried out upon anosmic animals). Such experiments, in addition to the light they will throw upon the function of the cutaneous receptors, will guide us and serve as a means of control in determining the animal's experimental range of sensitivity to olfactory stimuli. Furthermore, they will assist those of us who are engaged in the study of homing. As is well known, some of the homing theories maintain that the bird is guided back in its flight by responding to appropriate air currents, which may differ in their cutaneous and possibly in their olfactory values. Furthermore, problems concerning the presence of a '' common chemical sense '' and those connected with the functioning of the lateral line organs lie in this field.

II. INSTINCTIVE FUNCTIONS

Introduction.—In the chapter devoted to the special consideration of instincts, we shall discuss more intimately the nature of instinct, its origin, source, etc. In the present connection we are concerned with some of the broader questions which must be raised concerning the relation of congenital response to acquired forms of behavior, and to the study of the sense-organ processes.

Some types of instinctive response.—In the first place, it is essential to know the stimuli which have native and unacquired biological significance: those to which, apart from training, the animal responds either positively or negatively or by the inhibition of overt response altogether. These types (and many others as well) may be more easily observed oftentimes in the lower forms of animal life, but they are not lacking in the higher forms, as has been already pointed out. In addition to these there are those types of stimuli which produce first inhibition and then negative response, as the call of the mother hen to the chick when a shadow passes over the field of vision; flickering lights; certain types of noises; and sudden changes in the intensity and character of lights and sounds. The necessity of knowing the instinctive tendencies of our animals comes out clearly in experimentation. Suppose, e.g., we desire to test the retention of an association between a very weak light and a brighter light, or that existing between two colors: we find from our preliminary work that the animal is positive to the one or the other,—shows an instinctive tendency to go to the lighter or darker of two lights, or to the one or the other of two monochromatic lights. If the animal is allowed to obtain its food with the light to which it shows a strong instinctive tendency to react positively, we shall, after the lapse of the desired time, not be testing retention at all: we shall be showing simply that the native positive tendency still persists.

The animal's instinctive mode of attack on problems.—Furthermore, we have to be concerned with the animal's method of dealing with objects and problems. The rat and the squirrel will claw, bite, hold small articles with the forepaws and nibble at them, sitting the while on their haunches. The chick, under similar circumstances, will peck at objects too large to seize and swallow whole, and will move them all around the room without attempting to secure them with the feet. Carnivorous birds will hold the booty with the feet while they rend and tear it with the beak. The monkey will pick up small objects and carry them to the mouth with one hand and bite off small portions much like the human being. The list of these native differences in reaction is almost endless. It is desirable to have accurate knowledge of them in order to shape our problems for the study of these functions and of the animal's types of learning. The failure to take account of the instinctive capacities of animals has led certain naturalists and even scientific students of behavior to criticise many of the methods in use in the behavior laboratories on the ground of being unsuitable to a particular animal's mode of life. In some cases the criticism may be just.[2] On the whole, we think the behaviorist has not shown a lack of ingenuity in adapting his studies to the different forms of animals.

Instinct and habit.—It is because of the intimate connection between instinct and habit that one most desires to get a clearer knowledge of the animal's repertoire of perfected instinctive responses, his partial and incomplete adjustments, and even his tendencies towards adjustment before beginning controlled work upon habit formation. In the common acts of animals how much is hereditary and how much is ontogenetically acquired? The squirrel has the ability, apparently, to pick out a sound from a faulty nut. Some animals seem to have an instinctive endowment with respect to the choice of food. The everyday functions of drinking, catching, seizing, and swallowing prey or booty probably belong in the class of partially instinctive and partially acquired reactions. The chick, e.g., while apparently it can drink instinctively, needs habit to perfect the complex act of striking, seizing, and swallowing small objects. Only careful experimentations upon young animals will enable us to tease habit from instinct. The extent to which we have gone in this work will be taken up in Chapter IV. The problems in instinct have been little more than hinted at here. Enough has been said, it is hoped, to show the necessity for a wide knowledge of animals' instinctive capacities. We have literally hundreds of books upon instinct. Most of them are worthless. If only the naturalists who made them had been taught the patient habit of stating just what they saw and not enlarging upon it, what a mine such books would be to us! As it

[2] Criticisms have been several times directed against the carrying out of experiments in the dark room. These objections are pointless: first, because the behavior of the animal in darkness is just as important a part of our work as his behavior in light; and second, even those animals which ordinarily use daylight, work perfectly well in the dark room and remain in good physical condition throughout the course of the investigation.

is, we must begin all over again. Here, more than in any other place, we feel the need of careful field observations.

III. LEARNING

Introduction.—On account of its bearing upon human training, learning in animals is probably the most important topic in the whole study of behavior. Entirely apart from this connection, this division contains the behaviorist's most important group of problems, since by means of habit formation he finds the most direct way of controlling animal activity. The fundamental instincts cannot be easily changed, but habits which are just as efficient and just as economical in the matter of energy expenditure can be implanted alongside of them. There seems to be almost no limit to the number of habits which the higher vertebrates may form, or to the complexity of such habits. The work of Pfungst on " Clever Hans,'' and of Krall upon the Arabian steeds are examples. We cite also the training of Peter, Consul, and Roger, as well as a host of other less well known animals. But these animals have been trained for purposes of exhibition. Their acts are almost completely without scientific significance except in so far as they show the behaviorist the possibilities in delicate methods of training and the limits within which training may take place. Before beginning upon the simplest problem in learning, it is necessary, as we have already shown, to have some knowledge at least of the instinctive modes of response of the animal and of the receptors to which we are making appeal. In behavior up to the present time, we have largely put the cart before the horse. In entire ignorance of instinctive capacity and sense-organ functions, we have plunged *in medias res* and attempted to do satisfactory work upon learning. We have tried to point out under I and II that work of this character can never be final. Most of the work has been undertaken for the purpose of gaining orientation. We have felt the necessity of making broad and general studies. Nearly all of the longer monographs have treated of the senses, instinctive equipment, and the capacity for learning of each animal studied.   No one would attempt to study a new race of human beings in this whole-sale way.   While it is highly essential to have pioneer studies it is equally important for us to remember that such studies are purely provisional and temporary.   When we have finished our general survey, we are then prepared to begin really intensive work upon the animal.

Grouping of problems.—Problems of learning and reten-tion may be grouped under three headings: (1) the " per-severance " or fundamental method of acquiring control of skeletal muscles; (2) efficiency of training methods; and (3) complex forms of learning.

(1) The perseverance method.—The work on trial and error learning (better, " perseverance learning ") has been rather desultory.   It may now be safely taken for granted that every animal form from the Paramecium to the primate can learn by this method.   Any further work in this field ought to have a definite purpose: either that of establishing norms in a particular form for the learning of certain kinds of problems for comparing with similar re-sults from other animals, or, that of obtaining laws of plasticity with respect to age, sex, species, etc.   It seems quite essential, if we are not to waste time, to devise a set of standard problems which can be learned under stated conditions.   There is no agreement at present about the most serviceable kind of problems, but there are movements towards such a standardization.   In the chapter on methods several problem boxes will be suggested which seem to have a wide range of usefulness and adaptability.   In the work of establishing norms for inter-species compari-sons, similarity in the types of problems is all that can be hoped for, so different are animals in their structure, size, and action systems.   In the intra-species work all of the separate groups (the separate groups differing only in age or sex, etc.) of animals should learn the same problems under identical training methods.   There has been great laxness in this respect.   Many of the experimenters have not even felt the necessity of keeping the conditions started with rigidly the same throughout the course of the formation of the habit. Intercomparability of records should be the chief desideratum. Given the learning curves of these simple problems, we should next, under conditions as nearly identical as possible, determine the retention of the habit after varying intervals. It is unfortunate that this has never been done with care. To do it well requires a large expenditure of time and effort. It is also highly valuable to obtain records for the learning and retention of complex habits. This has already been partially attempted in the case of a few animals,—the monkey and the raccoon. The problem chosen was a complex puzzle-box consisting of a combination of latches, bolts, and levers (p. 98). This type of problem is, in a way, highly artificial and foreign to the daily life of the animals. However, it offers an interesting means of establishing a set of " unit habits " which may be found later to be of great service in tests on imitation (p. 277). It is hardly more foreign to the life of the animal than are nonsense syllables to the human being. All admit the value to the latter of taking material that is far removed from his daily sets of habits. Similar arguments hold for the necessity of choosing like material for the animals, since here, as in the case of man, we wish to study what might be called the crude or native learning and retentiveness (corresponding to the experimental range of functions as opposed to the practical range of everyday life).

(2) **Efficiency of training methods.**—With standard records on the learning of simple problems before us, we are in a position to take up what we may call, broadly speaking, the distribution of effort in learning. What is the most advantageous way to teach a problem to an animal? Should we allow him to work at it continuously? Shall we give him one trial a day? Three trials a day? Five trials a day? Shall we allow our animal to form three habits abreast? Or is it more advantageous and more economical in every way to allow him to form his habits serially? What forms of incentives should be used, food or reward of some kind, punishment or a combination of reward and punishment? Furthermore, how shall we regu-

late these incentives so as to obtain maximum but constant stimulating effect? We have been engaged in the study of these problems for some years now. That we are slowly gaining an insight into the efficiency of training methods may be seen from the summary of such work given on p. 228. It is at this point that the study of behavior has its closest contact with experimental pedagogy. On account of the numerous conventions which everywhere surround the human being, it has been next to impossible to introduce experimental methods into the teaching of children. We are content, as we have been in the past, to teach in the high schools four or five subjects a day and to spend thirty or forty minutes, as the case may be, on each of these subjects. Who knows whether we are right in this procedure? Surely here, if anywhere, animal behavior can be of practical service to the experimental student of education. In Chapter I it was urged that the results of experimental pedagogy should be put in such terms that they will be directly comparable with those gathered from animal experimentation. It is hoped that the reasons for urging this are now clearer.

(3) **Complex forms of learning.**—The third division in learning is connected largely with the social life of the animal. To what extent is the animal influenced in his learning, (1) through imitation of a mate; (2) through imitation of the experimenter; (3) by being put through an act; and (4) by various forms of encouragement? Finally, do we find that animals learn by methods which are closely analogous to those employed by the human being? A large amount of work has been done upon these various forms of complex learning. The problems are delicate. The results at hand are not harmonious. All of us have worked rather blindly. We have put our animals into strange and complex situations and have expected them to imitate acts of our own devising (which are oftentimes quite difficult), without being sure that the various simple coördinations (" unit habit ") are really parts of their sensory-motor equipment. Our procedure is on a par with asking a man who has never played the piano to

render " The Spring Song " on that instrument. It is useless to ask young children to imitate acts as wholes where the elementary coördinations are lacking or are ill-formed. There must be complete mastery of simple habits,—a readiness to respond to a difficult and complex environmental setting in a variety of different ways,—the ability to change responses ever so slightly to meet the slightest change in a heretofore well-known object. In order to do this our stock in trade of acts must be much more numerous than the objects to which we respond. Any one familiar with the early tentative imitations of children,—their failure to imitate at early ages the types of acts we call upon animals to imitate,—will not find fault with these statements. Apparently new coördinations are not established by imitation either in man or in animal. What is new is the combination or method of grouping. Where imitation appears there are found always groups of flexible responses to every object worked with. Furthermore, one is able to change the background or setting of the object (coincident stimuli) without breaking down the habit. It often happens that after an animal has learned to do a certain act, open a problem box, e.g., under given conditions, a change in those conditions,—removal of the box to another place in the room,—will produce a breakdown in the habit. There seems to be a lack of readiness on the part of all animals to shift responses to meet slight changes in objects oft-reacted to. Given enough coördinations of an elastic kind and it is hard to see how an animal can fail to imitate. Whether such conditions are realizable in the large majority of animals is the problem for experimentation to decide. The extent to which experimentation has thrown light upon such questions is discussed in Chapter VIII.

IV. CORRELATIONS

Introduction.—Studies upon the structure of sense organs and upon the nervous system generally seem to be somewhat out of fashion at present. We have never, in this country, paid the attention to the histology of the sense organs and to the comparative anatomy of the central nervous system which these subjects deserve. This condition of affairs is probably purely temporary. It is certainly devoutly to be hoped that the study of sense-organ structure, integrations in the nervous system, localization of function, etc., will, on some future swing of the pendulum, once more become central with the anatomists and neuro-physiologists. It seems discouraging that neurological conceptions are so backward. We sadly need working concepts of the nature of nervous impulses, of the anatomical and physiological nature of the sensory endings in the sense organs which are responsible for the different types of elementary functions and of the different chemical bodies set free by these highly organized structures: of fatigue products in the muscles, of the processes which make for the adaptation of sense organs and the like. In this day of advanced physiological and neurological technique surely the only difficulty in obtaining satisfactory answers to these questions is the lack of sufficient interest on the part of the men who are competent to carry out such researches. The interests of biological scientists are engaged chiefly in the study of evolution (variations, mutations, heredity, etc.), in the physiology of secretion, nutrition, and metabolism generally, and in experimental embryology. The absorbing interest which these subjects afford leads to the neglect of topics which are not connected with the direct life-subserving functions of the body.

Lack of behavior data handicaps the neurologist.—The lack of accurate knowledge of the range and delicacy of sense-organ functions, and of the integrations among sensory responses,—data which the behaviorist must supply,—makes the more careful neurologists draw back from the detailed work upon the structural elements which must be correlated with particular functions. A history of correlation studies shows quite clearly that the functional side has not been worked up with sufficient care to furnish anatomists and physiologists with the proper bases for correlation. There is little question but that a large number of correlations now adhered to between function and structure will have to be seriously modified or changed altogether. We call attention here to the work of Kalischer, Swift, and others upon the localization of the pitch center in dogs. The anatomical work was based upon the crudest kind of behavior work. At present the human psychologist attempts to correlate sensibility to wave-length differences with the functioning of the cones, and the finer sensibility to differences in white light with the functioning of the rods (and cones). The cortical projection centers for both sets of impulses are placed in the occipital region. The work of Franz, von Monakow, and others shows that we are not at all upon solid ground even with respect to the simple correlations which are used in psychology in everyday teaching. Simple working conceptions of what goes on in the nervous system when habits are formed will be very stimulating to the student of behavior. It would seem that the physical chemist and the physiological chemist might advance helpful facts bearing upon these questions. The behaviorist is ready to assist in the work. He is in a position to force the formation of simple habits in whatever sets of sensory-motor arcs the neurologist or physiologist may specify. He is willing to take animals at infancy and establish such habits in neural systems not previously largely exercised as, e.g., in association tracts in the cortex. Whether such work will ever throw light upon what happens at the surfaces of separation (synapses) through habit formation remains to be decided by future work. It is worth a thorough trial in some well-equipped neuro-physiological laboratory. It is quite possible that the increasing accuracy with which sense-organ functions are being isolated will give a very decided stimulus to structural work in this country. Until the returns from this work begin to assume large proportions, one can hardly blame the more careful neuro-physiologists for interesting themselves along other lines. Donaldson for many years has been amassing a wealth of detail upon the growth processes and anatomical correlations in the rat. These studies have taken many different forms,—from determining the total body weight and weight of the central nervous system (relation between central nervous system weight and body length or weight) of the animal at different ages, to that of the analysis of the chemical constituents of the nervous system at different ages. The work upon behavior has just reached the point where it may begin to take advantage of such material. C. J. Herrick has suggested the advisability of centralizing behavior and anatomical work upon some one species of animal, e.g., upon the rabbit.   While it is not advisable to limit behavior studies in any way, much good will come even from bearing such a suggestion in mind.   The problems singled out should be definite and simple, and designed to emphasize the functions of particular organs or parts of organs.   This would enable the anatomical work to proceed without waiting for complete returns.

General aim of behavior.—It is believed that the next few years will bring order out of chaos in the physico-chemical relations in the nervous system.   That the organism is a machine is taken for granted in our work.   The only point we insist upon is that the machine be made not too simple to perform the multitudinous demands which the behaviorist must make upon it.   There has been a strong tendency on the part of many biologists to assume that the mechanisms are exceedingly simple.   '' Having found that the ovum of the sea-urchin can be fertilized without the stimulus of the spermatozoön, they fail even to give the egg the credit which rightfully belongs to it! ''   It is hoped that the chemical and physical relations which exist in the egg itself can soon be so thoroughly understood that the egg too can be put together in the laboratory and then fertilized. The production of artificial protoplasm in the laboratory will in no way interfere with the study of behavior.   Even after we have made it, it is highly probable that nature will still be allowed to take her course.   As long as we have animals in the world it is hard to see how the demand for a study of their methods of living, moving, and having their being can ever grow less.   That such physico-chemical studies can ever undermine our work upon habit formation, efficiency of training methods, the reactions of human beings to one another (ethical problems, etc.), the retention of habits, etc., is hardly likely. The tendency towards too great simplification is manifested in another way. Because it is found in a few cases (or in many) that animals respond positively or negatively to a physical stimulus without training it is assumed that the mechanics of response have been put upon a simple physico-chemical basis, that there is no longer any pressing need for a study of the reactions of animals, and that further work along such lines must be looked upon as routine.

No one believes more thoroughly in the complete physico-chemical nature of all response, from the simplest to the most complex, than the author. We are prepared to state our belief in the view that we shall ultimately be able to trace the complete set of physico-chemical changes (quantitative energy transformations) from the moment of incidence of the stimulus to the end of the movement in the muscle. In fact it is one of the goals of behavior to assist in making this possible. But again we insist that all of the facts about response be considered. In very few cases have we reduced reactions to their simplest terms. When we have done so we shall have no quarrel with the label which is attached to them, be it that of " simple reflex " or " tropism." Analysis of reaction must end somewhere. The simple reflex is a convenient hypothesis. It may not be a final goal any more than was the atom in chemistry or than the electron of the physicist may be twenty-five years from now. Both the electron and the simple reflex work well enough at present as convenient means of expressing the results of scientific analysis. The present end of analysis, then, in behavior will be the reduction of complex congenital (instinct) and acquired (habit) forms of response to simple reflexes. Having reached the goal it follows that complete predictability, both of stimulus and response, will be afforded.

Furthermore, behavior is interested in synthesis as well as in analysis.[3] The building up of habits from simple re-

[3] It must be remembered that synthesis is essential to complete analysis of even tropism-like responses. Cole, Holmes, and others have

flexes for practical and theoretical (and ethical) purposes is as important as tearing them down. We should be able ultimately to formulate laws of habit formation (effect of punishment, of different training methods, retention, etc.). In the invertebrate realm wonderful progress has been made towards reducing complex responses to more elementary forms. Progress has been much slower in the case of the responses of the higher vertebrates. That some advance has been made appears clearly in our studies of instinct, and of sensory and motor habits.

Summary.—In this chapter we have attempted to throw the problems of behavior into three great classes,—sense-organ functions, instinctive functions, and learning. We have enumerated some of the separate problems in each division. It is interesting to consider now for a time what we would have before us if a large number of such problems were solved: a group of isolated facts or a system of behavior? As was pointed out in Chapter I, psychology, as it is at present adhered to, would say that the results would lack coherence and that the needed coherence could be obtained only by interpreting the facts in terms of consciousness. But introspection likewise gives us isolated facts (?). Titchener [4] points out that introspection is only a method. A method, even a legitimate one, can give us only facts. Inferences, generalizations, theories, hypotheses, all are necessary to a science. But these are open to us. We shall obtain first a systematic grouping of results which will constitute the phylogeny of behavior; second, a similar grouping to constitute the ontogeny of behavior; and thirdly, correlations between structure and function which will be worth while. These three strata of facts will furnish the neurologist, trained in physical and physiological chemistry, with a set of phenomena which is tangible enough to guide research. Finally the raw material will

shown that in the case of certain insects and frogs, the tropism-like responses to light (positive or negative reactions to size and intensity differences) fail to appear when definite objects are in the range of the visual receptors.

[4] *American Journal of Psychology*, XXIII, p. 447.

be at hand whereby behavior can be regulated and predicted. The behaviorist will have his theories, his inferences, and his generalizations. A limited set of observations upon the visual responses of animals possessing a fovea compared with a similar set upon animals possessing only a modified retinal area may lead to the generalization that only animals with a fovea are capable of responding to differences in the wave-length of light. We may then hazard an explanation of the phenomenon in terms of the lack of development of certain sensory structures, or of certain photochemical substances. In general, we have ahead of us problems which, while not sharply separated from those of the experimental zoölogist, the physiologist, and the physicist either in subject-matter or in methods, are yet nevertheless distinct and independent. We have divided their labor and have marked off our problems. They are not likely to object to this or ever to claim any portion of the province which we are likely to want. Rather, they will gladly relinquish all claim upon many of the problems which are ordinarily classed as belonging to their fields. There should follow a constant interchange, among these sciences, of behavior material, data on evolution, neural structure, and physiological chemistry. The behaviorist has no need to fear that this close contact with other biological and physical sciences will injure him. His field is too independent and too necessary to the other sciences for him to have misgivings about its future. If he becomes lost in a general biological mirage some other cause than his rejection of a psychology based upon introspection must be advanced to account for it.[5]

BIBLIOGRAPHY

THORNDIKE, E. L., *Animal Intelligence.* New York, Macmillan, 1911.
WASHBURN, M. F., *The Animal Mind.* New York, Macmillan, 1908.
YERKES, R. M., *The Dancing Mouse.* New York, Macmillan, 1907.

[5] It needs to be emphasized here that training in behavior should be accompanied by training in histology, physiology, and experimental zoölogy, and preceded by training in chemistry and physics. It is hoped that the day is past for considering philosophy to be the proper subject to pursue along with behavior. In saying this we do not mean to underestimate the value of philosophy in any way.

CHAPTER III

APPARATUS AND METHODS

Introduction. I. Stimulus to general activity: stimuli to locomotion. —(a) General stimuli positively responded to.—(b) General stimuli negatively responded to. II. Methods of studying the receptors of animals: forcing the formation of sensory habits.—Control box.—Pawlow's method.—Methods dependent upon instinctive response.—Control and auxiliary methods.—Criticisms of the methods for determining the sensitivity of receptors. III. Apparatus for obtaining specific stimuli: apparatus for obtaining monochromatic light.—Use of apparatus.—The selenium cell.—Device for securing a purified spectrum.—Apparatus for testing response to white light, form, and size.—Apparatus for producing auditory stimulation: apparatus for obtaining constant air supply.—The Helmholtz system of tandem-driven forks. —Animal control box for work on audition.—Yerkes' apparatus for testing hearing in frogs.—Apparatus for obtaining olfactory and cutaneous stimuli.—Yoakum's temperature apparatus. IV. Methods of studying motor habits: introduction.—The problem box method.—Description of boxes.—Description of maze experiments.—Apparatus for the study of the " delayed reaction."

Introduction.—In this chapter only the more general methods and apparatus used in the study of behavior can be considered. The books of Jennings, of Mast, and of Loeb give adequate descriptions of the technical methods and the apparatus employed in the study of invertebrates. The presentation of the technique used in investigations of the behavior of vertebrates must necessarily be meager and incomplete. This field has been developed rapidly and the motives for development have been very varied. These differences in standpoint have had their effect upon the types of apparatus which have been devised and upon the methods employed in conducting experiments. In past years only the roughest kind of preliminary work has been attempted. In more recent times there has grown up a strong tendency to do more careful work with better instruments and by methods which are capable of being standardized. This is shown by the general tendency on the part of investigators to standardize their stimuli and to adopt iron-clad rules concerning the physical control of the animal and the objective recording of results. Up to the present time we have had to be content with a small beginning in the various laboratories. There has not been sufficient general interest in the subject to justify large expenditures for apparatus. It is hoped that the next few years will bring decided improvement in the equipment and housing of behavior laboratories. What is said here about apparatus and methods must be looked upon as suggestive. It is frankly confessed that probably too much consideration is given to those used in the personal work of the writer.

I. THE STIMULUS TO GENERAL ACTIVITY [1]

Stimuli to locomotion.—The first and most obvious need in behavior is to provide some form of stimulation which will make the animal *move* in some way. Unless the animal will work steadily we are powerless to force habits upon him. We have as yet explored only a few of the various forms of stimuli which may be used for the purpose of calling out desirable general activity. As will be shown in Chapter VII, we have attempted to establish habits on the basis of providing " satisfiers " or " dissatisfiers " for the animal. This point of view is anthropomorphic and one which cannot be applied, or rather it is one which no one would apply in the realm of animals below the vertebrates. In many of the lower forms general activity of the kind we obtain by using food as a stimulus with vertebrates, can be called out successfully by many different kinds of stimuli. Light, e.g., can be so adjusted in intensity that we

[1] We necessarily use the term stimulus rather loosely in behavior at present. We employ certain objects to make the animal move. Let us call such objects *general stimuli*. While moving in response to the general or primary stimuli (e.g., food or electric shock) we find that we can make him respond positively or negatively to light stimuli, sound stimuli, etc., that we can make him learn to open a problem box, etc. We shall call these latter objects *specific* or *secondary stimuli*.

can call out at will (1) general but undirected activity (shock movements), (2) an immediate positive response, or (3) an immediate negative response. We never think in such cases that the animal goes towards the light because it is a satisfier or away from it because it produces dissatisfaction. For this reason we prefer to speak of stimuli positively and negatively reacted to in discussing the means by which we evoke general response in the animal of a kind necessary to the formation of habits. We shall consider under two heads the more common forms of stimuli which we have found to work in a satisfactory way. (A) General stimuli to which the animal responds positively; e.g., food and objects connected with the sex life, etc. (B) Those to which the animal gives a negative response; e.g., the electric shock, extremes of temperature, intense light, etc.

(A) General stimuli positively responded to.—Food has been the most commonly used form of stimulus for inducing general locomotion. The use of food requires a rather careful technique. If a large amount of food is given on one day the animal will be sluggish on the following day. If too little food is offered the animal becomes too eager. Long-continued experimentation with light feeding produces a starved and unsatisfactory animal. The most thorough way to go about the problem of food control is to surround the animal with the food which is necessary for its well being and then determine the length of feeding period required properly to maintain metabolism. The maintenance of metabolism can be determined by weighing the animal. It is not fair to talk of the cruelty and inhumanity of keeping the animal hungry, as has been done by several writers, until there is some factual support for the charge. There is not the slightest difficulty in keeping the animal in perfect condition and at the same time hungry enough to work properly. We have found no animal (as used under ordinary laboratory conditions) which does not work well when food is used as the general stimulus. Yerkes states that he was unable to use it satisfactorily with the dancing mouse. We repeated the maze experiment on the dancer with food as the stimulus. So far as we could judge the method was as satisfactory, from the standpoint of the rapidity of learning and from that of the well being of the animal, as the punishment method of Yerkes. Observers have stated that certain reptiles and amphibia are not commonly in a physiological state where food is positively reacted to; e.g., some of the reptiles eat as infrequently as once a month. Furthermore, in working in the field it often happens that the animal under observation is not under our control to the extent where we can regulate its food supply. Under these conditions some other form of stimulation must be employed. Sex objects will certainly work well as a general stimulus in the case of some animals. This was shown by Dr. Kimball at the University of Chicago in his work upon rabbits. (This work was never published.) We have gone far enough in repeating his experiment to show that the female can be put in the problem box in the place of food. The male will attempt to get access to her by the same methods which he will employ in the case of the food. The male monkey will attempt not only to get at the female, but also, if at all aggressive, to reach other males in the same way. The difficulty with using sex objects as a general stimulus is due to the fact that sensitivity to such objects is as a rule seasonal. It is extremely difficult to use such a form of stimulation in the case of most animals where experimentation is to extend over a long period of time. The rabbit forms a notable exception to this rule. Even with that animal only the male can be experimented upon in this way. With some birds, not directly under the control of the experimenter, and possibly with other animals as well, objects connected with the reproductive function are the only ones which can conveniently be used for motivation during the breeding cycle. This is especially true with the terns. It was found that during the nesting period the nest and eggs could be used in place of food. The activity induced was fully as great, apparently, as that obtained in other animals by using food.

(B) **General stimuli negatively responded to.**—A few years ago Yerkes advanced the view that '' punishment '' formed by far the best single method of motivation. Punishment was obtained by means of an induction shock administered by a metal grill connected with an inductorium. This punishment method has not worked any too well. It has been criticised by Hamilton who found that it made his dogs restless and hesitant; by Lashley, who found that it made rats, where association was difficult, after a time refuse to work. Under ideal conditions, where the problem offered is easy, it apparently does hasten association. Hoge and Stocking found that discrimination between a 16 c.p. and a 2 c.p. light was hastened by administering food as a reward, and punishment for failure. I.e., a combination of the food and punishment method, in their experiments, seemed to be most satisfactory.[2] In discrimination work generally troublesome position habits are very soon set up. At first glance it would appear as though punishment were extremely useful in eliminating such habits. In actual practice it does not always have this meritorious effect—the animal becoming sulky under continued punishment. Animals differ greatly in their sensitivity to the induced current. Rats are oftentimes badly disturbed by a current which is too weak for the human being to feel. Other animals are extremely resistant even to fairly high currents. The rabbit is not disturbed in the smallest degree by a current which is unbearable to the human being. Even when all possible objections are urged against the use of punishment it must be admitted that in some problems (especially in the formation of sensory habits) where the animal is neither too resistant nor too sensitive, the use of the induction shock is to be recommended.[3] In addition to the electric shock, other forms of stimuli which are reacted against have been tried. In sensory habits (with monkeys) where two specific stimuli are employed we have tried the experiment of putting sharp needlepoints (not visible) upon the handle of the food box placed immediately underneath the color to be reacted

[2] For a discussion of habits arising under controlled incentive, see p. 204.

[3] On the quantitative use of faradic stimulation, see Martin.

against. This method does not work as well as the electric shock. The reason is not hard to see. The avoiding reaction should be aroused at such a point that the *animal when turning away from the grill can immediately turn towards the right stimulus*. This makes the right response on each successive trial the one which was last executed (*recency*) and also the one most often executed (*frequency*). The rôle played by recency and frequency in the fixation of arcs in habits is discussed in Chapter VII.

II. Methods of Studying the Receptors of Animals

Forcing the formation of sensory habits.—The sensory range of animals and the sensitivity of their receptors can best be studied by forcing the formation of sensory habits. The method for establishing these has taken several different forms. In forcing such habits it has been usual to confront the animal simultaneously with not more than two specific stimuli, although this method has by no means been universally employed. Multiple stimuli methods are sure to be found useful in certain types of work.[4]

The general procedure is as follows: the animal is placed in an experiment box. This box has a home compartment

[4] Multiple stimuli methods have not been worked out as yet in any great detail. Hamilton has made a series of tests upon mammals (p. 111). His method places the subject in an experimental situation which may be reacted to in many different ways and with varying degrees of satisfactoriness or adequacy. The subject of the experiment is placed in a small room on one side of which there are four doors. From experience he learns that he may escape by one of the doors and one only, but which of the four to choose is his problem, for it is the plan of the experimenter to lock, in a given trial, the door through which the animal escaped in the previous trial and two others. Any one, then, of the three doors may be unlocked in a given trial. The animal has absolutely no way of predicting which is unlocked. Yerkes's method is similar in purpose to that of Hamilton but it offers a somewhat wider range of usefulness. It consists essentially in the presentation to the subject—bird or mammal; young or old; normal or abnormal—of a bank of twelve keys numbered from left to right, one to twelve. The subject is given to understand verbally, or through actual experience with the apparatus, that pressing some one of the twelve keys will yield certain desired results such, e.g., as the displaying of a picture, the presentation of food, the ringing of a bell. Success in the experiment means simply pressing the key which brings the desired result. The

where the animal is restrained until the experimenter is ready to make the test. At the will of the experimenter the door of the home box is opened and the animal is then confronted with both stimuli simultaneously; e.g., a circular and a square translucent plate illuminated from behind, each by lights of known candle-power. The circle and the square are separated from each other usually by a distance of 25 cm. A partition divides one end of the stimulus chamber into two compartments. The animal, leaving the home box, may respond by entering the compartment illuminated by the square or the one illuminated by the circle. Usually several preliminary responses are taken to see if there is any instinctive tendency to respond positively either to the one or the other of the two stimuli. Where experiments upon retention are to be carried out later, there is general agreement that the animal must be trained against his positive tendency,—i.e., he must be trained to respond positively to the stimulus primitively reacted against.

The fact that a general stimulus must be used in connection with the specific stimuli has already been stated. In using this method it is always necessary to have the apparatus so arranged that the positions of the two specific stimuli may be interchanged at will. This is necessitated

experimenter sees to it that in no two successive trials is the same key the one to be operated. He is, further, able to push back out of sight any number of keys and thus to present the subject with as few as one or as many as twelve. Let us assume that in any given experiment the observer decides that the key the fourth from the left shall always be the correct one. It then becomes the task of the subject of the experiment to suit his reactions to the number chosen by the experimenter. Only if he discovers the "guiding idea" of the experimenter can he succeed, trial after trial, in pushing the right key at first. It is obvious that both Yerkes's and Hamilton's methods serve to illustrate *general reactive tendencies* rather than to analyze reactions minutely and carefully. The methods are intended to bring into clear light those modes of responding to a given situation which are characteristic of different types or conditions of living beings, and thus to furnish a basis for a profitable comparison of reactive tendencies. (See Hamilton, G. V., "A Study of Trial and Error Reactions in Mammals," *Jour. Animal Beh.*, 1911, 1, 33. In this description we have quoted largely from Yerkes's "The Study of Human Behavior." Contribution from Psychopathic Hospital, Boston, Massachusetts, No. 25, 1913. This article appears also in *Science*, 1914, XXXIX, 625.)

by the fact that the animals very easily form position habits, i.e., go repeatedly to the same side regardless of the stimulus to be found there. These so-called position habits are not always easy to detect. The animal often learns to respond to the rhythm of the shift in the position of the stimuli. The experimenter has always to be on his guard against the use of secondary criteria on the part of the animal. In control tests the series of shifts to be made on any given day should be determined by throwing a die. Since the highest number which can be thrown is six, the animal will not be forced to go to the one or the other side too often in succession. It is of the utmost importance for the experimenter to be out of the sensory range of the animal during all the control tests. An error which occurs by reason of the experimenter's presence might almost be called the "Clever Hans error." With slight modification of the above description of an experiment in vision the method may be adopted for use with olfactory, auditory, and cutaneous stimuli.

Control box.—Much time has been spent in devising a box for controlling the animal which, without too much modification, can be used with all the animals likely to be used in laboratory work. The box shown in Fig. 1 is the most serviceable one we have at the present time for experiments upon the sensitivity of animals to light.

The box we employ is 94.5 cm. in length by 74 cm. in width by 25.5 in depth. It is divided into a home compartment, H, 31.5 cm. in length by 25 cm. in width, and a response chamber, C, 40.5 cm. in width, which is partially separated into two smaller compartments by a partition. The length of the partition is 25.5 cm. The distance from the door into the response chamber to the stimulus patch is 69 cm. The distance between the stimulus patches is 25 cm. The dimensions of the face of the stimulus patch are 3 cm. by 5 cm. The other divisions of the box are not important. It can readily be seen that it offers two alleys which lead into food compartments, F and F_1. Two doors, D and D_1, permit one to confine the animal in the chosen food compartment. By a special mechanism the doors can be closed from without the apparatus by pulling the knobs, K and K_1. Two doors lead from F and F_1 into H. It is thus possible to work with the animal without touching it and without being seen by it during its reaction. By means of a special signaling device the movements of the animal can be recorded without the necessity of watching the animal. Two miniature lamps blackened, except for an opening about 1 mm. in diameter, are connected with the platforms, S, S₁ and S₂. When the animal crosses S and goes into the response chamber both lamps are caused to wink (break circuit). If then he crosses the right hand platform, S₂, the right lamp goes out until "choice" is completed and the animal goes into R. If the animal goes across S₁, the left lamp goes out, etc. In the drawing the stimulus light falls upon the right stimulus patch, X, conse-

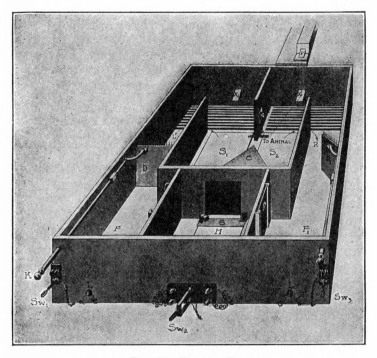

FIG. 1. CONTROL BOX

H, home box; C, response chamber; F, F₁, food compartment; X, X₁, stimulus patches; S₁ S₂, platforms causing lights L, L, to wink; S, platform causing both lights to wink simultaneously; D, D₁, doors leading to food compartment; K, K₁, knobs controlling these doors.

quently food may be obtained by passing around R through the open door D₁. It will be noted that the door D is closed. If the animal makes the wrong turn it must pass S₁ around into alley L; there finding the door closed, it must retrace its steps and pass S₂ and into R through D. The apparatus as a whole can be shifted so that the light can be made to fall either upon X or X₁ at will. The box is shown with punishment grill in each compartment.

When made according to the above specifications the box is suitable to carry out experiments upon the following animals: pigeons and other birds of like size, half-grown chicks, young monkeys (small species), guinea pigs, rabbits, rats, and squirrels. It enables one to control the factor of smell; to prevent the animal from returning to the home box; from getting access to the food if an error has been made; and to take a record of the time elapsing between the exit from the home box and a right or wrong choice. These are essential points in every method of physical control. When the box is to be used in connection with the apparatus shown in Fig. 3 and Fig. 6 the end bearing the stimulus patches is replaced by one in which two circular openings, 15 cm. in diameter and 25 cm. between centers, have been cut (the height of the center of these openings above the floor is 10 cm.).

For the auditory and olfactory work slightly different types of control boxes are demanded. Fig. 12 and Fig. 14 show respectively the forms which we have used.

Pawlow's method.—While properly belonging among physiological methods, Pawlow's salivary secretion method has been widely used in animal behavior, by Russian students especially. This method is used to determine the efficiency of animals' receptors. The possibility of using it depends upon the fact that when certain animals (the dog has been largely used) are stimulated by chemical processes (the specific stimuli for secretion, food, etc.) a secretion of saliva occurs. The chemical property of food, which acts directly upon the receptors in the mouth, thus starting the flow of saliva, is the essential " property." This property produces an " unconditioned reflex." In addition to the essential property of food there are certain non-essential properties, such, e. g., as its color, brightness, smell, etc., which may, under certain conditions, produce conditioned reflexes.

In actual practice the method is worked as follows: a healthy animal is chosen—one in which salivary secretion is abundant. The duct of one of the salivary glands is exposed on the outer surface of the cheek and a salivary

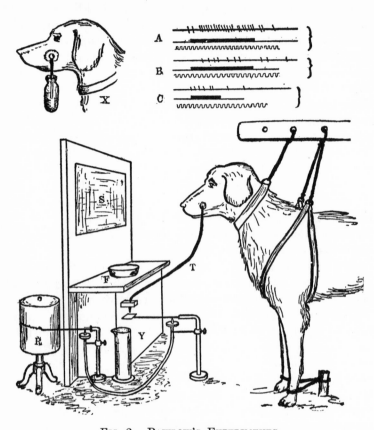

FIG. 2. PAWLOW'S EXPERIMENTS

The upper left hand corner, X, shows the graduate attached directly to a small funnel fastened over the duct of the salivary gland. The lower part of the drawing shows Nicolai's method. The dog is held in position by comfortable bands. The tube, T, runs directly from the funnel over the salivary gland to the recording apparatus, Y. Careful records are made at R. S shows the position of the stimulus (color, sounds, etc.) and F the food dish. At A, B, and C are shown three sets of records: A, the number of drops, the total amount of the secretion and the temporal relations when food is placed in the mouth; B, when the food is sensed by sight, smell, etc., C, when the color green is shown after the conditioned reflex has been established. (After Nicolai.)

fistula is formed. After this heals a small glass funnel or metal canula is attached to the opening of the gland.

There are three methods of making determinations: (1) As the secretion flows from the tube into a graduate the drops are counted individually and the total flow of saliva read from the scale of the graduate; (2) the saliva is allowed to flow into a graduate tube attached directly to the funnel over the duct and the amount of secretion determined by reading the scale of the tube. Under these conditions the tube must be replaced after each experiment and carefully cleansed. This method is shown at X in Fig. 2. (3) A metal canula is inserted in the duct of the gland and connected by rubber tubing with the small glass tube. The saliva drops from the tube directly upon the lever of a Marey tambour (Y in Fig. 2). As the drops fall upon this lever a record is made upon a smoked drum, R. From this record the experimenter may read the quantity of the secretion in drops or the total amount of secretion from the graduate, and also the temporal distribution of the drops. This latter method is the one used by Nicolai.

The animal is next subjected to a course of training. If light response is sought, an " association " between the given light and food is established by exposing the eye of the animal to the light and then immediately feeding him. This light stimulus in time causes a flow of saliva. A conditioned reflex has thus been established. Suppose it is now desired to test the animal's sensitivity to differences in wave-length. A green light, e.g., is exposed and food is given. This is repeated constantly until the reflex is established. Control tests are then introduced—white light or some other color is substituted for the green light. If the reflex occurs only (or mainly) when the green is exposed and inhibited when the other stimuli appear, we have presumably just ground for assuming sensitivity to wave-length differences.

It is quite clear that Pawlow's method, in theory at least, is designed to give the behavior student the same set of facts as the " discrimination method " (better *sensory habit method*) now so widely used. As a matter of fact it has nothing like the general range of usefulness of the method first described. In the first place there are only a few animals which can be successfully experimented upon in this way. While the dog lends himself very readily to such a type of experimentation, it is very difficult to see how the method could be worked upon the primates. The monkey, unless severely trussed, would not allow the canula to remain in place very long. In the case of birds, fish, reptiles, and amphibia, the use of the method is out of the question. Furthermore, the flow of saliva in many of the small animals is not sufficiently great for the method to be used successfully. In addition to these differences, which are dependent upon the anatomical and physiological nature of the animal, there are several inherent difficulties in the method. In the first place, these reflexes tend to disappear after the animal has been subjected to the same stimuli many times. In the second place, these reflexes have not the precision-like character which the students of Pawlow at first maintained. It is quite unusual for secretion to be inhibited entirely by the confusion stimuli. Positive results obtained by this method are certainly of value. It is doubtful if behavior students, in testing for sensitivity to various stimuli, will be satisfied with obtaining negative results.

Methods dependent upon instinctive response.—There is no doubt but that sensory habits arise much more rapidly where the food or other general stimulus is made to convey also the specific stimulus. As an example of the use of this method we cite the experiments in which Shepherd colored cubes of bread with different aniline dyes and soaked the cubes to be responded negatively to with quinine. Modifications of this method appear in the work of Hess and of Katz and Révész. In the study of the chick, e.g., red-dyed rice grains are fastened to the floor, while the green-dyed grains scattered among these are left free. In determining the limits of sensitivity in the red and in the violet food grains are illuminated by spectral rays from above. The animal is supposed to peck at grains which reflect rays to which its retina is sensitive. In the case of those animals which either collect or disperse when light falls upon them, we may use a similar method. With fish which collect in the light it is possible to start with rays from the middle region of the spectrum and then gradually to lengthen or shorten the wave-length of the incident beam and thus determine the limits of sensitivity in the red and in the violet, as shown by the fact that the animals swim about " aimlessly " as they do in darkness when the wave-length is such that it no longer offers stimulation (p. 341). In work of this character no food is employed.

Control and auxiliary methods.—In all sensory habits it is necessary to show definitely to what stimulus the animal is responding. In the case of two or multiple stimuli methods the animal may be responding only to one stimulus. If this directive stimulus is removed the habit breaks down. If one or all of the other stimuli are removed no breakdown in the habit occurs. In order thoroughly to control sensory habits it becomes constantly necessary to be able to remove or add stimuli. Besides the normal methods of controlling the stimulating factors in the environment, we have another very serviceable one; that of removing the sense organs not employed specifically in the task set the animal. Further discussion of control methods is given on p. 209.

Criticisms on the methods for determining the sensitivity of receptors.—General criticisms of the exact methods which have recently been employed have been urged on account of the slowness with which habits arise. It sometimes requires as many as 500 to 600 trials to train an animal to respond positively to the brighter of two lights and negatively to the darker in the apparatus we recommend for such work on p. 78. On account of this difficulty we have been criticised for setting the animal a task so far out of line with its everyday adjustments. The investigators who criticise the more rigorous and exact methods on this score have had resort to direct food methods. As we have already stated, the habits arise very quickly under such conditions. Unfortunately the more rapid method does not yield results which can be interpreted. In the case of dyed food we have no large control over the range of wave-lengths and intensities. If the food is directly illuminated we have no control over the relative absorptive powers of the food stuffs for the different wavelengths. Many other objections to direct food method may be urged. While we admit that the exact methods tax the time and the patience of the experimenter greatly, yet their use is certainly to be recommended in all cases. It is to be hoped that some means of hastening the speed of the formation of sensory habits will shortly be found. At present the following devices are being tried out:

(1) Attempts to increase the stimulating effect of the one or the other stimulus. E.g., we confront the animal with red and green and put a rotating sector in the path of the red. The sector is rotated so slowly that the red is made to flicker. If the animal, on his preliminary trials, is held by the flickering light and tends to seek it, we make red the positive or food color. If, on the other hand, another type of animal is frightened by the flickering red, we make green the positive or food color. Gradually the sector is made to rotate more and more rapidly until the flicker disappears. We are then ready to make our control tests.

(2) Attempts to increase the stimulating effect of one stimulus over the other by making the one differ from the other in several particulars. We may be working upon the animal's ability to respond to differences in the intensity of two white lights. Finding that the discrimination arises slowly, we make the two stimuli differ in size and in form as well as in the brightness and then gradually eliminate all differences except that of intensity.

(3) We may use only one stimulus and get the animal to respond either positively or negatively to that. We then very gradually introduce the second stimulus.

III. Apparatus for Obtaining Specific Stimuli

Apparatus for obtaining monochromatic light.—The apparatus for obtaining monochromatic light is somewhat complicated and expensive. If there were any other way

of testing, in a satisfactory way, the color responses of animals, we certainly should not go to the spectrum for our
stimuli. Investigators have tried various other methods
but with such indifferent success that it seems now all but
a waste of time to attempt to use any but spectral light.
Without going into details it seems worth while to sketch
the apparatus which we have found serviceable and then
to take up the technique in presenting these stimuli. This
will be done in the fewest possible words and without entering into needless technicalities. In order to obtain spectral
bands relatively pure and of the greatest possible intensity,
a prism spectrometer should be used. The prism should
be large in size. The intensity of the light, too, is dependent upon the size and speed of the lenses. We have usually
chosen second-hand compound photographic lenses (por-
trait lenses) of large aperture (4 inches) and relatively
short focus (8-18 inches). We sketch below (Fig. 3) the
simplest apparatus which will care for all the color work
which is likely to be done in any of the behavior laboratories.

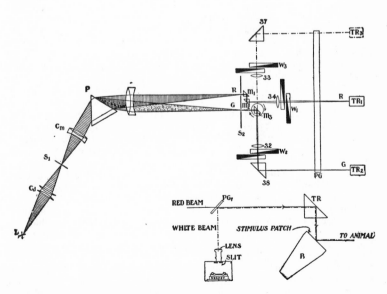

FIG. 3. GROUND PLAN OF MONOCHROMATIC LIGHT APPARATUS

(1) SOURCES: For testing differential sensitivity, limits of spectral sensitivity, etc., where high intensities are needed in control work, the automatic arc light has proved the most serviceable source. In determining thresholds, difference limens, etc., the Nernst filament has been most frequently employed. It is possible now to have made a tubular tungsten source in a nitrogen-filled bulb which has a very much greater intrinsic brilliancy than the Nernst. When these can be more conveniently obtained, they should prove more satisfactory in every way than the Nernst.

(2) DESCRIPTION OF SPECTROMETER: The condensing lens, Cd, Fig. 3, gives an image of the source upon the slit in the collimator, S_1. The collimator is of such a size as to give a cylinder of parallel light which approximately fills the face of the prism, P. After refraction the light passes through the objective, O_1, and is brought to a focus upon the (double) slit in the objective, S_2. This slit will admit any two desired regions of the spectrum.

(3) SPACING, REVERSING, AND PROJECTING DEVICES: Immediately behind this slit are situated a series of spacing and reversing, total reflection prisms and three small projection lenses. In the drawing, red and green beams are designated. In order to permit reversing the two beams (no matter from what region they are admitted) must be brought within 8 mm. of each other. This is accomplished by introducing the two small reflection prisms, M_1 and M_2. The arrangement of these is clear from the drawing. The red beam, upon reflection from M_2, passes through its projection lens, 34, to the face of the large total reflection prism, TR_1, thence downward to the plaster surface immediately below (not shown in the upper drawing but in the auxiliary drawing; the plaster surface is marked " stimulus patch "). The red beam does not change its position, consequently in order to reverse the right-left position of the two beams, the green must be made to appear now to the right of the red, now to the left. This is accomplished very simply as follows: Immediately behind the slit, S_2, one finds the small total reflection prism M_3. The green beam is shown entering this. It is reflected and made to pass through its projection lens, 32, then to reflection prism 38 and to reflection prism TR_2, and downward to the plaster surface. Prism M_3 is mounted upon a small revolving table. When the table is rotated in the direction of the arrow nearest the slit, the green beam is reflected in the opposite direction, through lens 33 to prism 37 to prism TR_3, downward to plaster surface.

(4) REGULATION OF INTENSITY: One of the most important things in making tests upon the color responses of animals is the means of controlling the intensity of the light. Rotating sectors are extremely accurate and results from them are easy to duplicate in other laboratories. The principal difficulty with them is that the angular opening cannot be altered while the sector is rotating. At least this is true with all but the most expensive sectors, such as the Brodhun. Since two or three sectors are required, the cost of the latter is prohibitive. The Nichol prism is always exceedingly expensive in large sizes, and furthermore, when it is set to give the maximum transmission not more than 50% of the light is admitted. Another disadvantage arises from the fact that it is not possible to

use the prisms except with parallel light (at least the angle of divergence must be quite small). We have finally come to the method of using the smoked wedge. These are shown at W_1, W_2, and W_3 Each wedge is paired and mounted in such a way that the movement of a single screw will cause both wedges to move synchronously. The beam is not deviated by the introduction of the wedges (they are purchased connected to a strip of clear optical glass as shown in the diagram). The wedges are calibrated in pairs from the point of greatest transmission to the point of least transmission, by the Bureau of Standards, which furnishes a curve of wave-lengths on the one hand plotted against percentage transmission on the other. The wedge enables us to get over one difficulty which we have experienced in our color work, viz., that of getting higher intensities of light than that given by the standard intensity, as measured by the selenium cell (p. 75).

(5) INTRODUCTION OF WHITE LIGHT: It often happens in monochromatic light work that one desires to introduce a certain amount of white light into monochromatic light or to substitute a white light for a monochromatic light. Both ends can be met by the very simple device sketched in the lower part of Fig. 3. A 4-inch strip of fine French plate glass, PG (upper drawing), is introduced at any chosen point in the pathway of the three beams. This plate is inclined at an angle of 45° to the incident beams. The monochromatic lights pass on through the plate glass with relatively little reflection to the plaster of Paris surface. Immediately underneath the plate glass one places a Nernst filament properly housed and supplied with a slit for controlling intensity. By means of a small lens an image of the Nernst can be projected vertically upward to the plate-glass surface, PG. The plate-glass surface reflects the beam (about 10%, which is ample), on to the plaster surface. On any of the plaster surfaces one can use at will (1) a pure monochromatic light, (2) a white light, (3) a light obtained by superposing a monochromatic light of any desired intensity (stated in terms of energy) and a white light of any desired intensity (stated in photometric terms).

Use of apparatus.—The description so far has been concerned with obtaining suitable stimuli which appear upon the plaster surfaces. In any given test as we have stated only two surfaces are illuminated. As Fig. 3 is drawn the *green* light falls upon the extreme left surface and the *red* upon the central one. A suitable control box (Fig. 1) is placed in front of the plaster surfaces. This control box can be shifted to right or left synchronously with the reversal of the right-left relation of the two lights described above. On p. 220 ff. we have described some tests made with this apparatus.

The selenium cell.—One difficulty in the way of using

monochromatic light hitherto has been the lack of any convenient means of obtaining uniformity of stimulation. Apparently the only wholly satisfactory method of affording
reproducibility of conditions in the various laboratories is
to state (1) the wave-length, (2) the energy carried by
the monochromatic band, and (3) the dimensions of the
stimulus patch. With these constants given no difficulty
need be experienced in repeating the work of another investigator. On account of the small energy carried by such
bands as are used in behavior work and the nature of the
apparatus, great difficulty is experienced in adapting the
ordinary methods of determining energy to our needs.
The selenium cell, on account of its very great sensibility,
seems at present to afford the best solution of our difficulties, however complicated and cumbersome its use may be.
In order to use the cell its " sensibility " curve must first
be obtained. When a cell connected with a suitable source
of current is exposed to light its resistance changes. It
varies with length of the wave of the incident light. If now
a galvanometer is inserted these variations in resistance
show as deflections of the needle of the galvanometer. It
is obvious that if we allow a given monochromatic band
(e.g., red) whose energy is known to fall upon the cell, a
given deflection of the galvanometer will appear. This is
then noted. The wave-length of the bundle of light next allowed to fall upon the cell is shifted, but its energy is kept
constant. This again produces a deflection which is noted.
This routine is repeated from one end of the spectrum to
the other. When completed we are enabled to plot the
sensibility curve of the cell in terms of galvanometric deflections on the one hand, and the wave-length of the
incident beam on the other (the energy carried by each
bundle of monochromatic rays being constant). The
selenium cell has to be thus calibrated in some physical
laboratory where a suitable radiation meter is at hand. It
may be used though when no stable base is at hand. The
drawing and description given below (Fig. 4) give the facts
necessary for installation and use of the system.

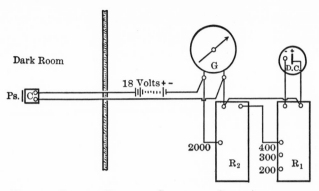

FIG. 4. GROUND PLAN OF SELENIUM CELL APPARATUS

INSTALLATION AND USE OF CELL: A selenium cell in the dark permits so large a current to pass that the resulting galvanometric deflection is liable to go off the scale. In order to remedy this defect the potential fall across the galvanometric terminals is compensated for by the introduction of a dry cell, DC, connected to the terminals of the 10,000-ohm. resistance box, R_1. To one of the plugs a wire is soldered and by means of this connection is established with a similar resistance box, R_2, which is finally connected with the galvanometer, as indicated by the drawing. This second resistance box, R_2, is shunted around the first for two reasons: (1) the necessary small potential drop across the galvanometric terminals may be attained; (2) a high resistance is shunted around the terminals of the galvanometer, hence, but little of the current from the circuit containing the selenium cell is diverted. In the drawing, all plugs in both R_1 and R_2 are removed with the exception of those indicated. While these particular resistances apply only to a particular selenium cell, it is readily possible to apply this method to any selenium cell, for by changing suitably the relative resistances in R_1 and R_2 it is always possible to bring about the desired condition, that the galvanometer shall show no deflection when the selenium cell is in darkness. In using the instrument as installed above we first allow the current to run through the cell for approximately one hour. By the end of that time the slight heating effect so produced has reached a constant. We next test the cell under the influence of a standard carbon lamp. In the original calibration we established the fact that the cell gave a deflection of, say 60 mm., when exposed for 12.5 seconds to a standard 8-c. p. carbon lamp at 1 meter's distance. If, when we come to use the cell for equating energies, we find that the standard lamp gives a slightly different reading (due to temperature changes, etc.) we alter the sensibility of the galvanometer by shunting another 10,000 resistance box (not shown) around its terminals. When we are sure that our system as a whole is in the same condition as it was during the moment of calibration we are ready to equate our stimuli. Monochromatic light of known wave-length is allowed to fall upon the " stimulus patch " S for a period of 12.5 seconds. By altering the intensity of the light through the use of the smoked wedges (Fig. 3) we finally get the desired reading upon the galvanometer. We then repeat the procedure for the green light. In order easily to expose the cell for the desired length of time (12.5 seconds) the author has devised an automatic electric clock which starts the instant the light is turned on and breaks the circuit at the end of this period. By convenient switches the clock may be made to break the circuit through the standard lamp or to actuate a magnetic shutter which works over the face of the slit in the collimator, S_1 (Fig. 3), (thus excluding the monochromatic light except for the 12.5 seconds interval).

Device for securing a purified spectrum.—The spectrometer system, as above described (p. 71), is arranged to test the sensitivity to differences in wave-length. An additional device is needed when we come to test the limits of spectral sensitivity and to do threshold work generally. In such work great purity of the beams (freedom from white light) is demanded. It is well known that the spectrum obtained with any single spectrometer contains white light. The intensity of this light varies in different spectrometers and in the different regions of the spectrum of any given spectrometer. Ordinarily this does not matter, since where two beams are employed at high intensities, the intensity of the white light in each may be independently varied by the method shown in the auxiliary drawing in Fig. 3. In testing limits of sensitivity in the infra-red and ultra-violet it is obvious that the presence of white light in the beam would lead to results which could not be interpreted. White light may be excluded by the introduction of a second spectrometer. The apparatus then takes the form shown in Fig. 5.

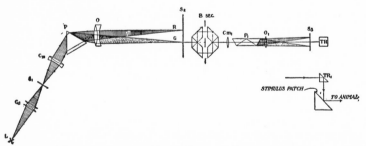

FIG. 5. GROUND PLAN DOUBLE SPECTROMETER

In this sketch the arrangement of parts up to S_2 is the same as in Fig. 3. After issuing from S_2 the light (illustration shows that green is admitted) G_1 takes the following course: It passes first through the Brodhun sector, B sec. (which by a series of prisms rotates the light around a *stationary* sector, the angular opening of which can be adjusted so as to admit all gradations in the intensity of the light), then through a (1-inch aperture, 8-inch focus) single achromat which serves as a collimator, thence through a direct vision refracting prism (1-inch face), through a (1-inch aperture, 8-inch focus) single achromat which serves as an objective. As shown in the diagram, the white light in G is dispersed into a faint continuous spectrum along S_3. The green appears as a very intense band. The slit opening at S_3 is made just wide enough to admit this band. It passes to the total reflection prism, TR, and is reflected down upon the plaster surface below (shown also in Fig. 1). Examination with a pocket spectrometer of the beams so purified shows that the white light has been completely excluded.[5] A spectrum so obtained is known as the " purified spectrum of Helmholtz."

Apparatus for testing response to white light, form, and size.

—Fig. 6 shows the apparatus required to test differential sensitivity to white light, to form, and to size. This apparatus consists of three chief parts: (1) a light box (Fig. 6), A; (2) an experiment box suited to the animal to be tested (Fig. 1), and between the two (3) a stimulus adapter, by means of which two illuminated areas are simultaneously exposed to view. This appears as the end (front) of the light box.

The wooden light box, A, is divided into two compartments, C and D, by the partition, B. The sides, ends, and partition of the box are $\frac{7}{8}$-inch planed and seasoned lumber. The inside dimensions are as follows: Length, 3 meters; width (between sides), 52 cm.; depth, 30 cm. The bottom is $1\frac{3}{4}$-inch planed stock, dowelled and glued. It is made 2 feet longer than the box, as a provision for the support of the experiment box. To the middle portion of the box are hinged two lids, E and F, of $\frac{7}{8}$-inch lumber. The edges of the box and lids are grooved and rabbeted. When the lids are closed, the two compartments, C and D, are light-tight with respect to one another. Two cast-iron carriages, G and H, carry incandescent lamps, which serve as sources of photic stimuli. Each carriage rides on a pair of steel tracks, IJ and KL, placed on the floor of its compartment. To the floor of each compartment is attached a Starrett steel tape, M and N, from which the position of the source of light may be read directly in millimeters. In order that daylight, instead of artificial light, may be used when it seems desirable, a hole 12.7 cm. in diameter is cut in the end of each compartment. These holes are fitted with Aubert diaphragms, as shown at O and P.

[5] I.e., only a single bright band appears in the field.

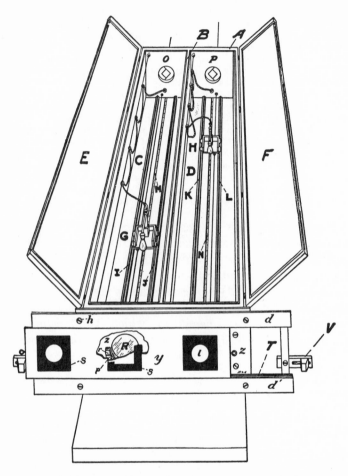

FIG. 6.   PERSPECTIVE OF LIGHT OR "BRIGHTNESS" APPARATUS

A, light box; C, D, compartments of A; B, partition between C
and D; E, F, lids of A; G, H, metal carriages carrying tungsten
lamps; IJ and KL, tracks for G and H; M, N, Starrett steel millimeter tapes; O, P, apertures covered by Aubert diaphragms; R,
Bausch and Lomb cooling cell in light box; d, d', metal straps; y,
aluminum plate sliding between d and d'; T, tracks for y; V, stop
for y; z, steel plate bolted to wooden end of light box; h, screws
attaching y to z; s, s, standard brass stimulus plates; p, brass frame
about aperture in y; r, hard rubber ring screwed to p.

The completed apparatus carries a system of ball-bearing pulleys, cords, and levers, not shown in Fig. 6, by means of which the experimenter may shift the lamp carriages without approaching the light box or experiment box. Against the experiment box end of each compartment of the light box is placed a water cell, R, to serve as an adiathermal screen. The cooling cells used by Bausch and Lomb in their projection lanterns prove satisfactory. They are circular metal cells of at least 11 cm. diameter with a water space of 4.8 x 12.5 cm. The stimulus adapter is a device by means of which the experimenter is able to regulate the size, form, and position of the visual stimuli. A steel casting, $\frac{3}{8}$ inch thick, carefully planed, and firmly bolted to the light box, is shown at z (Fig. 6). This sheet of steel contains two circular apertures, 10 cm. in diameter, through which the light passes from the light box to the experiment box. To the metal plate, z, the stimulus adapter is attached by four bolts, one of which is labeled as h. The essential parts of the stimulus adapter are: (1) A metal frame composed of the straps d and d' and the two vertical straps (not shown). The inner edges of the horizontal straps are rabbeted and into them is fitted (2) the aluminum plate y, which slides smoothly on a pair of tracks (which do not appear in the figure), which are screwed to d and d'. y moves on six rollers. It contains three windows, each 12 cm. square, located 25 cm. apart (center to center). These windows receive the standard stimulus plates. (3) Back of each window is attached by four small screws a square frame of 1-16-inch sheet brass, p, 9.3 cm. on its inner edges and 13.3 cm. on its outer edges. A flange is thus created which serves to hold in each window (4) a brass plate, s, 12 x 12 cm. and 1-16 inch thick. This plate contains an accurately cut opening. It is held firmly in position by two screws through diagonally opposite corners of the metal frame, p. At any time by loosening the screws, the experimenter may readily remove a plate and replace it by another with an opening of different size or form. The set of standard plates is fully described in connection with the table on p. 80. Between the frame, p, and the standard plate, s, is inserted a piece of opal-flash glass, l. This serves as a diffusing surface and constitutes the stimulus area. It is held against the brass plate, s, by two screws. (5) To the metal frame, p, is screwed a ring of hard rubber, r, $\frac{1}{8}$ cm. thick, 2 cm. wide, with a circular aperture 10 cm. in diameter. To this rubber ring is glued a ring of piano felt about $\frac{1}{2}$ cm. thick. These hard rubber and felt rings serve to fill in the space between the metal front, z, of the light box, and the aluminum plate, y, which carries the stimulus plates. (6) By means of the bolts at h, and corresponding positions in the three other corners, the stimulus adapter may be brought into the necessary proximity to z to prevent light from passing from one stimulus opening to the other, between z and y. Each of the four bolts (h) at the corners of the stimulus adapter carries, between z and y, a coiled spring which serves to press y away from z. By putting the proper amount of pressure on the four springs the experimenter can so adjust the surfaces of the rings of piano felt to the planed front of the steel plate, z, that the light cannot pass between the two, while at the same time the surfaces may be moved over one another freely whenever it is necessary to move y. (7) At either end of the frame of the stimulus adapter a stop, V, is attached so that y shall not run beyond the track, T. The most important part of the "brightness" apparatus is the set of accurately made brass stimulus plates which is briefly described below. The set, as used by us at present, consists of 26 plates. These plates fall into three groups: (1) Plates to test white light vision—three plates with a 6-cm. circular opening and three with a 5-cm. circular opening. This provides a plate for each of the three windows of the stimulus adapter with a diameter of either 5 or 6 cm. (2) Plates to test size vision—this group consists (including those of group 1) of plates with circular openings, which, between 6 cm. and 5.5 cm., differ by 1 mm. in diameter, and between 5.5 cm. and 3 cm. by 5 mm. (3) Plates to test form vision—there are in this group four plates whose openings differ in form, while being equal in area. They are (a) the 6-cm. circle; (b) a hexagon 3.299 cm. on the side; (c) a square 5.317 cm. on the side; (d) and an equilateral triangle 8.081 cm. on the side. The area of each opening is 28.2743 sq. cm. In addition to the above there are provided three forms which are inscribed in the aperture of the 6-cm. circle. They are (a) a hexagon 3.000 cm. on the side; (b) a square 4.243 cm. on the side; and (c) an equilateral triangle 5.196 cm. on the side.

DESCRIPTION OF STANDARD STIMULUS PLATES

Each Plate is a 12 cm. square of 1-16 inch Acid Blackened Brass, Containing an Accurately Cut and Centered Opening

Description of Openings

USE To test response to	Form	Diameter or side	Area	Number of plates needed
white light	Circle	6.000 cm.	28.2743 sq. cm.	3
	"	5.000 cm.	19.6350 sq. cm.	3
The 6 and 5 cm. circles (as above) and				
	Circle	5.900 cm.	27.3397 sq. cm.	1
	"	5.800 cm.	26.4208 sq. cm.	1
	"	5.700 cm.	25.5176 sq. cm.	1
	"	5.600 cm.	24.6301 sq. cm.	1
To size	"	5.500 cm.	23.7583 sq. cm.	2
	"	4.500 cm.	15.9043 sq. cm.	1
	"	4.000 cm.	12.5664 sq. cm.	1
	"	3.500 cm.	9.6211 sq. cm.	1
	"	3.000 cm.	7.0686 sq. cm.	1
	Circle	6.000 cm.	28.2743 (as above)	
	Hexagon	3.299 cm. (side)	"	1
To form	Square	5.317 cm. "	"	2
	Equil. triangle	8.081 cm. "	"	2
Openings inscribed in 6.000 cm. circle				
	Hexagon	3.000 cm.	23.382	1
	Square	4.243 cm.	18.003	2
	Equil. triangle	5.196 cm.	11.691	2
			Total................	26

The apparatus as thus described is probably better adapted to test white light vision than to test form and size vision. Criticisms have been urged against it on account of the fact that when a 5-cm. circle is contrasted with, e.g., a 6-cm. circle, there appears a difference not only with respect to size but also with respect to the amount of flux. H. M. Johnson is at present using a modification of the Ive's grating which changes the size without altering the total flux. In regard to its adaptability for testing form, Hunter has likewise urged that " pure form " has not been offered to the animal: that what is offered is really a difference in pattern. We cannot here enter into the details of these criticisms (but see p. 366).

Apparatus for producing auditory stimulation.—The auditory work in this country has been very backward largely because satisfactory apparatus have been very expensive and hard to obtain. One of the serious handicaps has been the lack of a constant air supply for the Stern variators, pipes, and other wind instruments. It is highly desirable to make the finer tests on auditory sensitivity of animals with good tuning forks. At the same time it is essential to have control tones which can be substituted for the forks. The variators serve this purpose very well. The need for a constant air supply has been felt not only by the behaviorist but also by the human psychologist as well. The standard tuning forks are very serviceable and very accurate but they are almost useless in behavior work, unless they are actuated by the method Helmholtz devised. We shall describe first the air supply system which has been in use in the Hopkins laboratory for some years, and then the Helmholtz system of tandem-driven forks.

Apparatus for Obtaining Constant Air Supply

Figs. 7 to 10, inclusive, show the complete installation necessary for constant air supply. Figs. 7 and 8 show the interior construction of the Dureco O positive pressure blower, which is the essential part of the system.

The drum of the blower is eccentrically mounted in the case of the machine and the vanes are so arranged as to slide in and out of this drum. These vanes are supported at the ends by shoes or rollers, depending upon the size of the machine, which run in a raceway near the outside circumference of the casing heads. The purpose of these shoes or rollers is to hold the vanes in position so that they cannot come in contact with the outside casing and thus cause a great amount of friction; they also hold the vanes in a steady position so that they can slide in and out of the drum without jerk or vibration. As the drum revolves the shoes or rollers in the raceway keep the vanes in approximate contact with the outside casing, but at all times there is a clearance. On account of the position of these vanes as the drum revolves the air in the casing is displaced and

FIG. 7. END VIEW SHOWING INTERNAL CONSTRUCTION OF DURECO POSITIVE PRESSURE BLOWER

B shows vane in "out" position. The other two vanes are shown forced back into the drum.

FIG. 8. SHOWING SHOES (*a*, other two not lettered) RUNNING IN RACEWAY NEAR THE OUTSIDE CIRCUMFERENCE OF THE CASING HEAD

the vanes force the air out of the discharge opening, at the same time sucking in the air at the intake opening. By reason of the special construction described above the machines are practically noiseless in their operation, have very little friction and require only a small amount of power.[6]

Fig. 9 shows the method of installation. The pulley, P_1, of the blower is belted to P_2, the pulley on the shaft of an electric motor. The (1½-inch) outlet pipe, OP, of heavy fireman's hose runs into the bottom of a galvanized iron tank, 2 feet in diameter and 4 feet in height. The top of this tank is supplied with a spring pop valve, R, which regulates the pressure when no air is being used. The iron

[6] We are indebted to the National-Standard Company, Niles, Michigan, for the above cuts and description.

supply pipe, Sp. P (1½-inch), leads directly down (or up) to the room in which the air is to be used. A cord, C, is attached to the valve, R, and runs over pulleys to the room where the air is to be used. This cord is attached to a screw control at H (Fig. 10). By

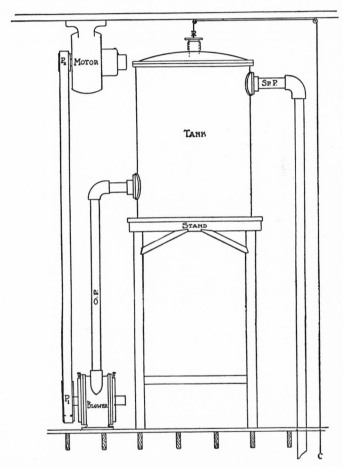

FIG. 9. SYSTEM OF INSTALLING BLOWER, MOTOR, AND AIR TANK

means of this control the air, when in use, can be held at any pressure. After the blower has run for a time the whole system warms up and the pressure rises somewhat. When the rise in temperature has reached a maximum the valve is adjusted to give the needed pressure. It will run indefinitely with a variation in pressure too small to be detected by a water manometer. Fig. 10 shows the method of using the air system with a Stern variator.

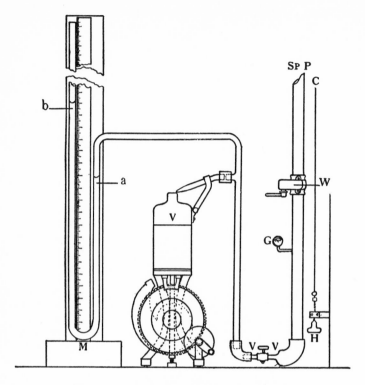

FIG. 10. METHOD OF USING AIR SUPPLY

As in the previous figure, Sp. P and C represent, respectively, the supply pipe and the cord controlling the pop valve. The opening of the heavy gate valve, L, admits the air. The valve is opened up until the gauge, G, shows about 3 pounds pressure. (The higher the pressure within certain limits the less the variation in the manometer.) By means of the small cock, vv, the air which supplies the variator, V, can be accurately regulated. The pressure required to produce a clear tone in the variator shows in the water (or coal oil) manometer, M. The manometer shows extremely small changes in pressure. A pressure change which cannot be detected by a change in the pitch of the variator will show readily on the manometer. In attempting to test changes in pitch or intensity one must be constantly on one's guard against changing the position of the head, standing waves, etc. Adaptive changes in the sense organ are also likely to produce apparent changes in pitch and in intensity. By making the proper double connections at vv it can readily be seen that the apparatus lends itself to the uses suggested on p. 90 as well as to carrying out tests with two variators upon auditory sensitivity in animals.

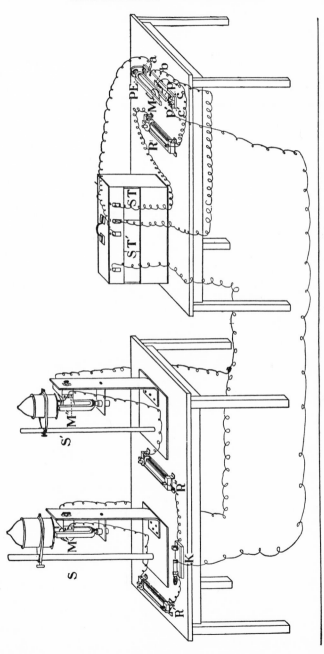

Fig. 11. Johnson's Modification of Helmholtz's System of Tandem-Driven Forks

The Helmholtz system of tandem-driven forks.—Fig.

11 shows Johnson's modification of Helmholtz's method of actuating tuning forks. The c-64 d. v. primary fork is mounted in a room 100 feet distant from the room in which the experiments upon the animals are being conducted. This fork runs continuously without attention from the experimenter during the whole course of the tests. Upon the table (Fig. 11) are placed the two stimulus forks S and S'. The system is connected as follows:

The primary fork, PE, is actuated by a current passing from the positive pole of a 2-volt 6-ampere storage cell, ST, through the rheostat, R, to the binding post, a; thence through the fork, through the platinum contact, p', with the mercury cup, c, through the magnet, M, to the binding post, b; thence to the negative pole of the storage cell. When the current is made at the platinum-mercury contact the prongs of the fork are attracted by M, thus withdrawing p from c and breaking the circuit, which releases the prongs of the fork and permits the circuit to be made again at p and c. The primary fork is thus driven at its natural frequency. The secondary forks are driven by a current passing from the positive pole of a 4-volt 6-ampere storage cell, ST', to the binding post, a; thence through the fork and platinum contact, p', with the mercury cup, c', to the central pole of the double key, K; thence through an extreme pole of K through the rheostat, R, the magnet, M', of S to the negative pole of the storage cell. For S' the current passes through the corresponding connections from the other extreme pole of K to the negative pole of S', etc. By means of the double throw switch, K, the experimenter can actuate either fork at will and for any given length of time. Since there are no electrical contacts on the two stimulus forks the tone produced is almost absolutely pure.[7] As will be seen from the drawing, each fork has placed over the ends of its tines a König adjustable resonator which must be accurately tuned. By varying the height of the resonator a very great variation in the range of intensity is afforded. The only drawback to this system comes from the fact that a primary fork will actuate only forks the vibration frequencies of which stand in simple ratio to that of the primary. By choosing a primary of low frequency, 64 d. v., a fairly large number of secondary forks in the middle region of the scale will be at our disposal (256, 320, 384, 448, 512, 576 d. v., etc.) for testing differential sensitivity, response to clangs, etc.

[7] If the forks are placed directly upon a solid surface one can hear faintly the undertone. If the fork is suspended and its resonator properly tuned the undertone cannot be heard beyond a distance of two or three feet. In cases where great sensitivity in the deep tone is suspected the stimulus forks themselves may be placed some distance away.

Animal control box for work on audition.—A special form of control box is desirable for use in connection with the above method. It is shown in Fig. 12.

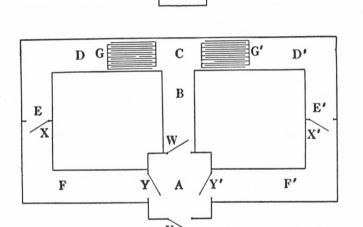

FIG. 12

A, home-box; B, introductory alley; C, opening into alleys D and D'; E. E', alleys entering food compartments F and F'; G. G', punishment grills; T, table containing stimulus-forks. V, W, X, X', Y, and Y' are doors, automatically swinging in the direction indicated. The experimenter's place is in an adjacent room by window O in front of door V of the home-box. (After Johnson, *Animal Behav. Monographs*, Ser. No. 8, p. 32.)

A is the home-box, 4 by 4 feet, in which the animal is placed between tests. Entrance is made from without by the door, V; B is an introductory alley, 6 feet long and 2 feet wide, leading to the alleys, D and D'. These alleys are each 10 feet long and open to alleys E and E', which are shut off by the two doors, X and X'. These doors are made to open from the animal, and are closed automatically by a small coiled spring. Each is provided with an iron lift latch, which is heavy enough to catch when the door is closed. A string is fastened in a small hole drilled in the end of the lever of each of these latches, and run through an eye-screw in the door above, then through a pulley attached to the side of alley

E or E', as the case may be, then to the operator's place, so that by pulling the string the door may be unlatched and pulled open without the operator having to leave his place. When the string is released the door closes and latches itself. Alleys E and E' open into two food compartments, F and F'. The covering of these boxes is provided with two doors, located near the end of alleys E and E', through which food is dropped. Y and Y' are two doors opening from food compartments, F and F', into the home-box, A. These doors are not provided with latches, since they close behind the animal, flush with the jambs, and cannot be opened by an animal which has not free use of its hands. They are provided with coiled springs, like those on doors X and X'. The animals would usually open these doors from the food compartments, merely pushing their way into the home-box, but it is well to provide a means of opening them with strings, as are doors X and X', for the sake of timid animals. Door W is opened by means of a spring. A heavy gut cord is fastened to an eye-screw near the top of door W, and run through a small hole near the top of the outside framework of home-box A, to the operator's station, where it is hooked until door W is to be released. G and G' are two punishments grills— strips of brass about 3 feet long, secured to a white pine board 3 by 2 feet. Alternate strips are connected with the respective poles of the secondary coil of an inductorium, leaving the other end free. When the current is switched in, the animal's foot must rest on two or more of these strips, which are only 1 cm. wide and 1 cm. apart, thus completing the circuit and causing the animal to receive a shock. The inductorium should be placed outside the room where the animal is being worked, and far enough away so that the sparking noise will not disturb the experiment. The current may be shifted through G or G' by a double-throw switch at the operator's station. The framework of this cage is constructed of yellow pine 1 inch by 3 inches; the top and sides are covered with woven steel wire, having a mesh about 1 cm. square. Food is kept in both the food compartments, F and F'. The animal is given the problem of choosing a turn to the left into alley D, leading to food compartment F, at one tone, and a turn to the right into alley D', to food box, F', at the other tone. The stimulus tone may be sounded while the animal is in the home-box, A, and the animal released after it has been damped; or the tone may be sounded after the animal's release, say one-half second before he can reach the end of the introductory alley. If punishment is to be administered the animal should receive it the moment he makes the wrong turn.

Yerkes' apparatus for testing hearing in frogs (air and water).—Fig. 13 shows the simple apparatus for testing the auditory responses of frogs under the following conditions: When tympanic membranes are (1) in air, (2) half submerged, and (3) wholly submerged. As will be shown on p. 388, no direct response to sound is exhibited by frogs. In order to show that auditory stimuli are effective it is necessary to utilize an indirect method. When tactually stimulated the frog will jerk up its leg. Repeated observations show the magnitude of this reaction. When a bell is sounded at definite intervals (i.e., within one second) before the tactual stimulus is given the height of the leg reaction may be (1) reinforced or (2) inhibited,

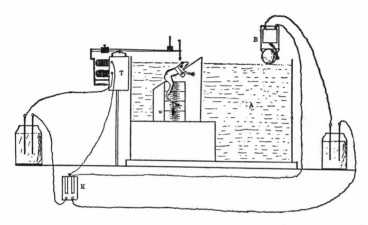

FIG. 13. AUDITORY APPARATUS FOR TESTING HEARING IN AIR AND
IN WATER

A, aquarium; B, electric bell; T, tactual stimulus apparatus; K, hand key for giving stimuli; W, weight to hold leg. (After Yerkes, *Jour. Comp. Neu. and Psych.*, 1905, XVI, p. 297.)

depending upon the temporal relations of the stimuli. This apparatus may be used in connection with a pendulum for automatically regulating the intervals between bell stroke and tactual stimulus.

Apparatus for obtaining olfactory and cutaneous stimuli.—Fig. 14 shows a rough apparatus for studying (1) olfactory responses. It can be used only where there is a steady air supply. It is designed to be used in connection with the air system sketched above. In addition to its use as a device for testing olfaction it may be used for testing sensitivity to (2) differences in temperature, (3) differences in the moisture content of two air columns, and (4) differences in the pressure of two air columns.

The manometer shown in Fig. 10 should be used to control the stimuli in all this work. As drawn the apparatus is ready for use in olfactory work.[8]

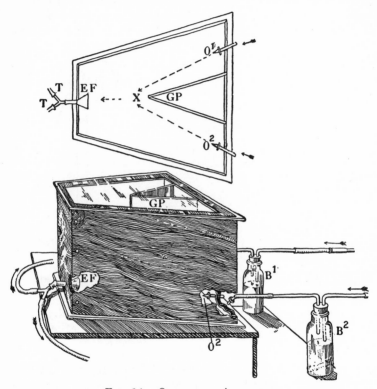

FIG. 14.   OLFACTORY APPARATUS

The whole apparatus rests upon a glass plate and the inside walls of the stimulus compartment are lined with glass. The cover is also of plate glass for ease in observing the behavior of the animal. Two air columns shown by the two arrows on the extreme right of the lower drawing come directly from the air system, each being connected with a separate manometer. They pass over the surface of two fluids, in which appropriate olfactory substances have been dissolved, B^1, B^2. After passing over the olfactory substances the

[8] As may readily be inferred, we may pass one air source over a dry chamber and another over water if our purpose is to test sensitivity to differences in moisture content. Or if it is to test differences in temperature, we may pass one through a small constant temperature air chamber. On the other hand, if we are testing differences in pressure, the two air sources are sent directly into the stimulus compartment.

air is piped separately into the stimulus box through the fine pointed nozzles, O_1 and O_2. The nozzles are placed at an angle such that the two air columns escaping from them converge at a point, X— the apex of the two glass partitions, GP. It is at X that the animal is stimulated simultaneously by the two stimuli. Electric grills may be placed in front of O_1 and O_2. At EF is shown a funnel, to which are attached two tubes. These tubes are connected with an aspirator attached to any convenient water faucet. This serves to partially prevent diffusion of olfactory particles. As sketched above, two serious defects are inherent in the apparatus. There is no convenient way of admitting the animal and there are no exit compartments. Food should not be used in the chamber but in the exit boxes. The entrance should probably be placed underneath the box in such a position that the animal would have to enter near X. Since opening this door would introduce variations in the direction of the currents O_1 and O_2, the animal should be placed first in the ante-chamber, the door to which should immediately be closed. The air should then be turned on at once and the animal admitted. Immediately upon its correct response the proper exit door should be opened. Unfortunately no careful work has so far been published upon these forms of sense modalities, and investigators are working more or less blindly in trying to devise proper apparatus. Dr. Jean Weidensall carried out a series of experiments upon rats with this apparatus but the work was never completed. It was carried far enough to show that with the modifications suggested we may safely begin work upon olfactory and cutaneous sensitivity. There are many methods of conducting simple qualitative tests upon smell, taste, and cutaneous sensitivity. Such methods will be taken up in the chapter devoted to those senses.

Yoakum's temperature apparatus.—Fig. 15 shows the apparatus used by C. S. Yoakum for testing the temperature sense of gray squirrels and white rats.

The construction of the apparatus is as follows: Two galvanized iron boxes, A and B, are made with outside dimensions of 9 x 9 x 24 inches. The inner opening or tunnel, running the entire length of the box, is 5 x 5 inches. The space between the outer and inner jackets is 2 inches deep. It entirely encloses the central cavity with the exception of the ends. This enclosed space is supplied with three vents, an inlet, I, an outlet, O, for the water circulation, and an air vent, V, to relieve the pressure when water is admitted to the system. The outlet is placed at the bottom of the encircling jacket and brought to a level with the upper part of the box. Thus arranged it can be used to syphon out the water after the day's experiment is over. In the bottom of each tunnel small cubical food pans are sunk flush with the floor. They are placed near the end farthest from that used by the animal as an entrance. The back of each box is closed with a piece of ground glass. Separate electric lights EL, illuminate the tunnels. The temperature of these boxes is regulated by forcing hot or cold water of the desired temperature through them. A triple faucet is used; two vents to give hot and

cold water, respectively; the third to give a mixture of hot and cold.
The respective temperatures of the two boxes cannot be maintained
with extreme accuracy. The variation is sometimes as great as
2° C above or below the standard. The two boxes can be interchanged by means of a rope and pulley, P. The animal is admitted
from behind, the arrow showing its probable course.

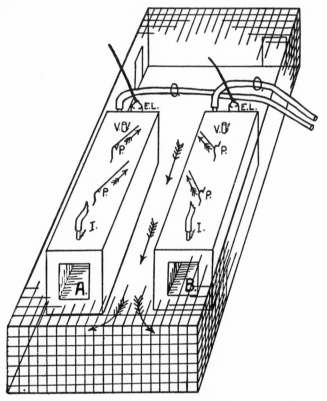

FIG. 15. YOAKUM'S TEMPERATURE APPARATUS. (*Jour. Comp. Neu.
and Psych.*, 1909, XIX, p. 561.)

A and B, galvanized iron boxes; I, inlet for water supply; O,
outlet; V, air vent to relieve pressure when water is admitted; EL,
electric lights illuminating the tunnels (through ground glass); P,
attachment for cords used in shifting position of boxes.

IV. METHODS OF STUDYING MOTOR HABITS

Introduction.—Motor habits do not differ fundamentally
from sensory habits, yet they are distinct from them in one

respect. In sensory habits the investigator attempts in general to bring out particularly data bearing upon the stimuli to which the receptors of the animal are sensitive. In motor habits he attempts to bring out particularly data concerning the action system of the organism. In thus examining first one end of the reflex arc and then the other there is introduced no change in standpoint or in method of interpretation. Further discussion of the resemblances and the differences between sensory and motor habits may very well be left to Chapter VI, where the concrete experiments upon them are presented.

The problem box method.—The problem box method in animal behavior in one form or another is as old as civilization. It remained for Thorndike, in 1899, to perfect the method and to make it serviceable for bringing out certain facts connected especially with what one roughly calls learning in animals. The forms of puzzle boxes in use in the various laboratories are very numerous. Their size has had to be varied with the size of the animal and their nature to suit the particular instinctive capacity of the animal. It is obviously impossible for the English sparrow to learn to manipulate all of the problem boxes that may be offered to the monkey. On account of the differences in the action systems of animals no standardization of types has thus far been suggested. Each experimenter has devised problem boxes which he thinks will be suited to his animals' capabilities. On account of this difference in the boxes themselves and in the technique of experimentation there is no uniformity in results even in the same laboratory where different animals are used; and no hope at present of work being duplicated in other laboratories. Much better results could be obtained if groups of boxes could be devised which would be suitable for a large range of animals. E.g., it is possible to devise boxes of the same dimensions and which are manipulated in an identical way, that may be commonly used for mammals of small size—monkeys, cats, dogs, raccoons, squirrels, porcupines, etc. Another set could be used for birds; still another for fish, etc. The method of using problem boxes is somewhat as follows: some form of general stimulus is provided. This has usually been food particularly sought by the animal. It is placed inside the box. Some form of restraining cage is usually placed over the box (see Fig. 19). Usually one allows the animal to feed in the open box for a few days before attempting to give it the problem of opening the door. The general stimulus to work is thus strong by the time the animal begins its attack upon the specific problem. The mode of the animal's attack upon the box while solving the problem depends upon its instinctive equipment and upon the type of problem selected. The animal is allowed to eat a small amount of food after opening the box and is then removed in preparation for another trial. The number of trials given per day alters both the form of the learning curve and its length. The subject of the distribution of effort in forming motor habits will be taken up on p. 228. The recording of errors in the formation of habits of manipulation is almost impossible. The time curve furnishes the best criterion of the learning of the simple boxes usually offered.

Description of boxes.—Below we show some of the boxes which have been used with success in the animal work. All

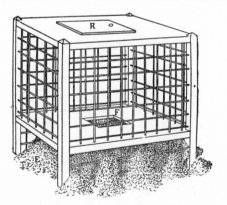

FIG. 16.   THE SAWDUST BOX

that we maintain for them is that they are serviceable and have a wide range of usefulness. We do not maintain that they are better adapted to the study of motor habits than others which have been employed. Nor do we claim that placing the food inside the box is more advantageous than Thorndike's method of placing the animal inside and allowing it to escape.

Box I (Fig. 16)—the "sawdust box"—is one of the simplest forms. It has been widely used in work upon rodents. It may be looked upon as standing between the maze and more definite forms of problem boxes in regard to the type of activity demanded for its solution. The sides of the box are constructed usually of wire mesh. This extends to the floor of the containing cage on two sides and one end. On the remaining end, E, the wire netting extends only to the floor of box I. The animal enters under this floor and pushes its head into the interior of the box through the opening, F. It is usually banked upon all sides with sawdust to a height corresponding to the level of its floor.

Box II (Fig. 17)—the "latch box"—requires on the part of the animal a narrowly circumscribed movement. It is made of the same material and in the same general way as box I. The fastening, L, shows clearly in the drawing. Care must be taken to have

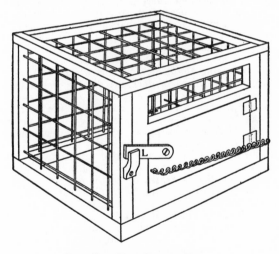

Fig. 17. The Latch Box

the hinges on the door work very easily, to have the socket which holds the latch very shallow, and the spring which opens the door work very gently. This box has been used largely on rodents and dogs.

Box III (Fig. 18)—the "inclined plane" box—is shown in two forms. In its simplest form (Fig. 18), as used by the author and by Richardson, it does not work well. The animal may chew the string or it may throw the plane by pulling on the string without necessarily touching the plane. Basset has greatly improved upon the original plan. Fig. 19 shows the form employed in his work

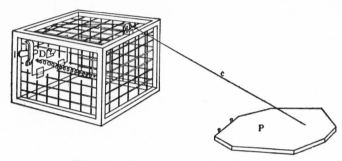

FIG. 18.   THE INCLINED PLANE BOX

and the details in construction and method of operation. The food box, A, is formed of wood, 11 x 12 inch base, 11 inches in height, and is covered on top and sides with ⅜ inch heavy wire mesh. It is fitted with a hard rubber door, d, 3-16 inch thick, 5 inches high, and 4¼ inches wide. To the inner side of the door is fastened a cord which passes over a pulley, p, and is weighted at the other end with a piece of lead, l, of sufficient weight to insure the opening of the door upon releasing the latch. B, shows the device for latching and releasing the door. A short distance above the door is fastened a 3-inch electrical magnet, m; directly below that is a steel wire, s.w, surmounted by a steel disc, s.d, of the same diameter as the core of the magnet. The steel wire holds the door by dropping through holes in two brass plates, g, which serve as guides, to a point, behind another brass plate, which is set at the top of and behind the door, 1½ mm. below the top. The setscrew, s.s, placed on the steel wire above the lower guide prevents any further drop. When the steel wire holds the door the disc is 2 mm. below the magnet; when the disc is drawn up to the magnet ½ mm. clearance is allowed for the door to swing back. Back of the feeding box, A, is placed the inclined plane, I.P. The inclined plane has a hard rubber base ⅜ inch thick, 6 inches long, and 2⅜ inches wide. Upon pivot standards rising from the middle of the base rests the plane itself. The plane is of wood fibre and of the same dimensions as the base. It is weighted at the end nearest the feeding box in order to insure its return to position after use. At the end opposite the weight and farthest from the feeding box, platinum electrical contacts, e.c, are placed in both base and plane. The power is provided through wires connecting the regular electric lighting system, 115 volts, direct current, with the wired apparatus. A 32 candle-power lamp is placed in the series in order to avoid any danger of short-circuiting. To make the contact and allow the current to pass through the magnet, thus raising the steel wire and releasing the door, it is necessary for the rat to step on the point of operation, o, which lies well out towards the end of the plane. On account of a certain amount of latency in the operation of the magnet, the rat must not only make the contacts touch, but must also inhibit further action, remaining on the point of operation until click of the disc meeting the magnet is heard. Over the food box and plane is placed a cage, C, constructed of ½-inch heavy wire mesh, the base measurements of which are 24 x 24 inches and the height 14 inches. This allows the rat ample

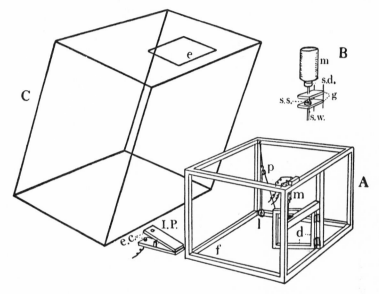

FIG. 19. THE MODIFIED INCLINED PLANE BOX
(After Basset, *Behavior Monograph*, Ser. No. 9, p. 25)

room to explore all sides of and above the food box. When the rat is placed within, the entrance, e, to the cage is closed.

Box IV (Fig. 20) shows the box used by Porter in the work on birds. This likewise is made of wire netting. As used by him the box was tilted forward so that the door would swing open when released. The bar, L, drops into a shallow socket. A string is attached to the end of the bar. This string runs upward through a ring at the upper edge of the box, thence along a wire arm, through a ring on the end of this arm, down to a loop, B, which is placed within reach of the animal. Another method of opening the box is shown. The string attached to the latch is fastened to a stud, C. The bird, in climbing over the side of the box, pushes in the string, raises the latch, and the door swings open.

Box V (Fig. 21) shows a relatively simple combination of fastenings. The animal, in order to open this box, must: bear down lever at left (1), push in bar at right (2), lift up latch in front (3), and pull out string behind (4).

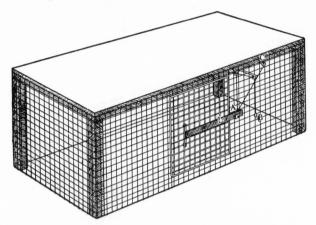

FIG. 20. PROBLEM BOX USED BY PORTER ON BIRDS
(*Am. Jour. Psych.* 1906, XVII, p. 257)

Box VI (Fig. 22) shows a similar but more complicated set of fastenings. It is an interlocking device. The door is fastened by a vertical hook (5) at the upper left-hand corner which cannot be un-

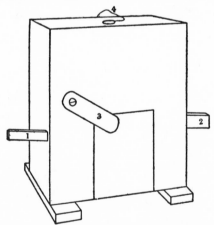

FIG. 21. SHOWING BOX WITH SIMPLE COMBINATION OF FASTENINGS

hooked until the button (4) near it is pushed back. But the button cannot be moved until the bolt on the right side of the door (3) is pushed back. This in turn requires the removal of the plug at the left (2) which again cannot be moved until (1) is pulled out. The only order which brings success is 1, 2, 3, 4, 5. Once worked, however, the fastenings cannot accidentally be replaced.

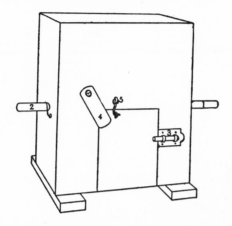

FIG. 22. BOX WITH MORE COMPLICATED FASTENINGS
(Both boxes after Kinnaman, *Amer. Jour. Psych.*, 1902, p. 123)

Description of maze experiments.—The technique of the maze experiment is quite similar to that of the problem box. The animal is fed for a few days in the center of the maze without being allowed to explore any other part than the food compartment. After habituation to this environment, regular tests are begun: the animal is admitted to the maze and allowed to find its way to the food. Both the errors (false turns, returning, and partial returning, etc.) and the time spent in going from the entrance to the food should be recorded. A record of errors made in the maze can be taken very accurately and conveniently by two different methods. In the writer's study of the terns the maze floor was lightly covered with a thin layer of coral sand. The tracks of the bird could be seen plainly and the length of the excursions into the alleys, etc., could be measured. The tracks were obliterated by brushing the sand lightly with a whisk-broom. A better method for obtaining the same results is the camera lucida method, which will be described in connection with the circular maze.

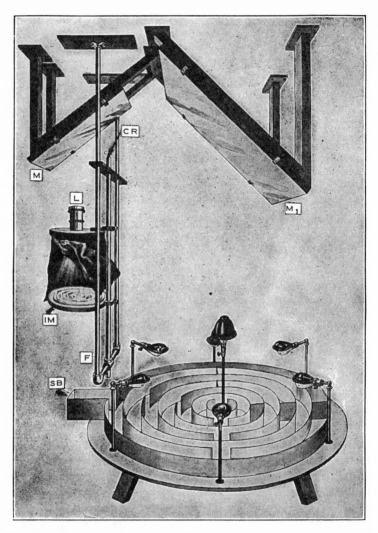

FIG. 23. THE CIRCULAR MAZE WITH CAMERA LUCIDA ATTACHMENT
SB, starting box; M, M₁, mirrors; L, lens; IM, image of maze.

THE CIRCULAR MAZE: The circular maze shown in Fig. 23 is
made with wooden base and aluminum walls. The base is 150 cm.
in diameter and 4 cm. in thickness, and is constructed as follows:
Two wooden discs 150 cm. in diameter and 2 cm. in thickness are
first sawed out. These two discs are finally glued together. Before
gluing, however, the upper disc is marked off into a series of con-

centric circles. The diameter of each of the circles is as follows, beginning with the outermost one: 140 cm., 120 cm., 100 cm., 80 cm., 60 cm., 40 cm., and 20 cm. The circles are then sawed out upon a band saw. The width of the saw is made just equal to or slightly wider than the aluminum sheets used for the walls. After sawing, the disc as a whole is converted naturally into a series of concentric rings. These are fastened down to the lower disc with hot glue and screws. The lower surface of the base is thus solid, while the upper surface shows a series of grooves into which the aluminum walls may be slid. Soft aluminum bought in rolls is used for the latter. The height of the aluminum is 18.5 cm., the thickness, .8 mm. The aluminum is unrolled and cut into the proper lengths. Each strip is cut just 10 cm. shorter than the length of the circular groove into which it is to be fitted. This gives an opening into the alley. By means of this arrangement it is possible to slide the aluminum around in its groove and thus to place the entrance in any desired position. Fig. 23 shows clearly the construction of the maze, the number of alleys, the placing of the entrances, and the radial stops. This maze offers several desirable things in work of this character: in the first place, it can be used on the unit plan, in that only the home-box and the surrounding segments need be used when a very simple maze is desired. The addition of other segments, then, merely increases the complexity in an, at present, unknown ratio. The coefficient of increasing complexity could be determined by allowing one group of animals to learn the maze in its simplest form, another in its next most complex, etc. Secondly, the ease with which complications can be introduced makes the maze very desirable. This is brought about by the flexibility in the arrangement of the entrances and radial stops. The camera lucida attachment is easily installed: it is simple and permanent. A large plate-glass mirror, M_1, 91 cm. wide, 121 cm. in length, is placed at an angle of 45° directly over the center of the maze. This mirror is strapped by small clamps to the edge of the surrounding framework. At a certain distance from this mirror a second mirror, M, 60 cm. $\times$ 75 cm., is placed at an angle of 45° above the maze and at such a distance from M_1 that the light reflected downward from M falls outside of the maze. Below M, and in the path of the light reflected from it, is placed a single achromat, L, 6 cm. in diameter and 50 cm. focus. The lens is placed in a barrel and the barrel is attached to a wooden disc 30 cm. in diameter. This board is attached to an iron collar which slides freely up and down the rod, CR. This gives a very easy means of adjusting the size of the image, focusing, etc. Below this first disc will be found a second disc similar in character and controlled in the same way. A pad of circular paper is laid upon this disc.[9] A reduced image, IM, of the maze appears upon this paper. Extraneous light is excluded by means of a soft black flannel curtain attached to the disc which supports the lens, L. As may readily be seen from the figure, the maze must be illuminated quite highly in order to produce a clear image. The illumination is obtained by means of six lights

[9] It is convenient to cut out several sheets upon a disc cutter and to stamp a hole 13 mm. in diameter in the center of each for the reception of a stud 13 mm. in diameter and 1 cm. high placed in the center of the board, IM.

placed symmetrically around the maze and by one light in the center of the maze. The six lights on the periphery are supplied with opaque half-shades, the light in the center of the maze with a similar opaque circular shade. These shades are of aluminum, blackened on the upper surface. The floor of the maze is covered with imported white linoleum. This serves to reflect the light upward to M_1, thence to M. Passing through the lens the rays are brought to a focus at IM. The ratio between the maze and the image is 6.4 to 1. The image appearing at IM is extremely clear when proper precautions are used to sensitize the eye. Even the smallest mouse can

FIG. 24. CHARTOMETER

be seen quite clearly. The movements of the animal are traced upon white paper with a soft pencil. In the early stages of learning several sheets of paper are used on each animal at any given trial in order to avoid a too complicated tracing. Each sheet is marked with the number of the animal, the number of the trial, and the serial number of the tracing. The length of the lines so traced is measured by means of a chartometer (Fig. 24). This instrument is surprisingly accurate even in measuring lines which are tortuous in their course. The error in measuring the length of the charted line is about 1 per cent.[10]

OTHER FORMS OF MAZE: Fig. 25 shows the "modified Hampton Court maze," which is too well known to require description. It has

[10] Yerkes and Kellogg have described a similar apparatus. See *Journal of Animal Behavior*, 1914, p. 150.

been used extensively in the animal work—upon rats, birds, squirrels, monkeys, and man. It is generally considered to be a very complicated maze. Yet actual experience shows that the circular maze just described is probably equally difficult, at least for the rat. The dotted line shows the true pathway.

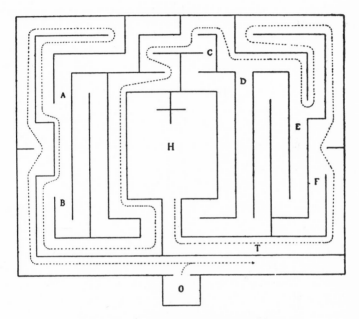

FIG. 25.   THE HAMPTON COURT MAZE

Complicated blind alleys, or *culs de sac*, are shown at A, B, D, E, F. It will be noted that C is not a blind alley but an alternate and longer way to the food. The animal is admitted at O. Food is placed at H. After the maze has been learned with the alleys lying in the directions indicated the maze as a whole may be turned 90°—180°, etc., to test the effect upon the animal of changing the absolute direction of the turns. Fig. 26 shows a maze constructed for the special purpose of determining the function of the kinæsthetic sense of the animals.

As constructed for the rat the alleys are of wood 6 inches in width and 6 inches in height. The maze was constructed so that it could be sawed across the dotted lines a-b. It will be seen that by removing or inserting the middle section, a-b, we can convert the maze respectively into its short or long form. The change merely increases the length of the four alleys without altering the relations of the turns leading to or from them. Particular attention is called to the fact that Q in the lengthened form comes to the point Q' in the shortened form; and that the distance S-B in the extended maze equals the distance S-B' in the shortened maze.[11]

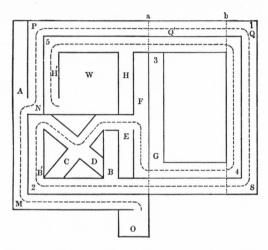

FIG. 26. SPECIAL FORM OF MAZE WHICH CAN BE LENGTHENED OR SHORTENED WITHOUT ALTERING THE RELATIONS OF TURNS

Apparatus for the study of the " delayed reaction."— The delayed reaction has recently been studied at the University of Chicago by Hunter. On p. 224 we present the more important results which have been obtained. Fig. 27 shows the needed apparatus.

It consists of a chamber, G, of suitable size, made with glass sides. The animal is confined here while being stimulated by lights coming from the food compartments, L, L, L. The entrances to the three food boxes are equidistant from G. Any one of the food boxes may be illuminated at will by closing the switch at M. Grills for electrical stimulation are shown at a, b, c. The current from the secondary of a Porter inductorium may be sent through any one of these at will by the switch system shown at N. The use of the apparatus in brief is as follows: The animal, previously habituated to the apparatus, is confined in G. A light, e.g., in box A, is turned on for a definite interval and then turned out. After an interval (during which no visual stimulation is offered) the animal is released at G. His problem is to enter only the box in which the light last appeared

[11] An animal, having learned the short form of maze in terms of kinæsthesis, should, when the maze is suddenly lengthened, attempt to turn into the blank wall at Q'; and run into the *culs de sac*, B, G, and H. Similarly, when the animal has learned the long form, it will, when the maze is shortened, butt squarely into the end of the alley, e.g., at 1.

(A in this instance). If he goes wrong he is punished. The delay
(from moment of turning out light to moment of releasing animal)

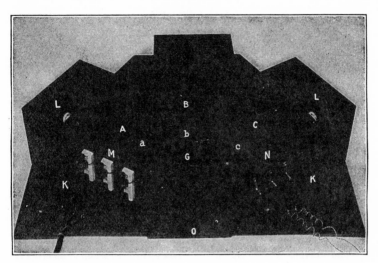

FIG. 27.   APPARATUS USED IN STUDYING THE DELAYED REACTION
(After Hunter, *Behavior Monographs*, Ser. No. 6, p. 25)

is gradually lengthened until a limit is reached beyond which the
animal cannot successfully react.

BIBLIOGRAPHY

HESS, C., *Vergleichende Physiologie des Gesichtssinnes*.   Jena, 1912.
MAST, S. O., *Light and the Behavior of Organisms*.   New York, J.
    Wiley & Sons, 1911.
PFUNGST, O., *Clever Hans*.   New York, Henry Holt, 1911.
YERKES, R. M., and MORGULIS, SERGIUS, " The Method of Pawlow in
    Animal Psychology," *Psych. Bull.*, 1909, VI, 257.
YERKES, R. M., and WATSON, J. B., " Methods of Studying Vision
    in Animals," *Behavior Monographs*, Ser. No. 2.

CHAPTER IV

OBSERVATIONAL AND EXPERIMENTAL STUDIES UPON INSTINCT

Use of term.—Modern writers have given no fixed meaning to the term instinct. The word is in common usage in a number of different departments of study,—philosophy, psychology, and biology. These separate divisions use the word in widely different ways. Probably no other term, unless it be that of consciousness, is more handicapped by its history. As one wades through the enormous literature and meets the widely different meanings attached to it, one is almost tempted to employ some other word. But in spite of its past the term is short, useful, and convenient. The student of behavior has come to look upon instinct as a combination of congenital responses unfolding serially under appropriate stimulation; the series as a whole may be " adaptive " in character (always adaptive from the Darwinian standpoint) or it may be wholly lacking in adaptiveness. Each element in the combination may be looked upon as a reflex. An instinct is thus a series of concatenated reflexes. The order of the unfolding of the separate elements is a strictly heritable character. Instincts are thus rightly said to be phylogenetic modes of response (as contrasted with habit, which is acquired during the lifetime of the individual). Such a series of reflexes, or an instinct, is best illustrated by the young bird's egress from the egg, and its later attempt at building a first nest; the first fighting responses in young animals, and in general the first attempts of young animals to capture, kill, and eat their prey. The act must be observed upon its first appearance if it is to be seen pure, i.e., without modification through habit.

Broader definition of the term reflex demanded.—If reflexes and instincts, by our definition, are to cover all forms of acquired movement not included under habit (p. 184) it is necessary to add that the term reflex should include not only the more definite and fixed types of reflexes with which we are already familiar through our studies in physiology, but also those which are less constant, and less predictable (i.e., less predictable in the present state of our knowledge of the physical and chemical processes taking place in the organism). Jennings, Mast, Yerkes, and other American writers have shown that even the responses of protozoa and the lower metazoa are not reflexes in the customary sense in which that term is used, i.e., in the sense of being absolutely fixed and wholly stereotyped forms of reaction. Every one will admit with Loeb that, given the same stimulus and the same organism, the reaction will be the same. Every one who attempts to work out a mechanical theory of life processes must admit this position, unless, along with his physico-chemical concepts, he is prepared to admit the possibility of the indeterminate action of entelechies and X-entities (see the work of Driesch and of Genung). But as a matter of observation we are not able in behavior, at present, to reduce all responses to reflexes of this stereotyped kind. The organism is constantly changing. We may be able to control one element in the total system of stimulation of the animal at any given moment (e.g., the energy and wave-length of incident light) but we cannot control the internal physiological processes which are also essential parts of the total stimulation and which also affect markedly the state of the effector. The two factors, extra-organic stimulation and intra-organic stimulation, together determine the nature of the observable response. If either state changes, the overt response changes also; e.g., the Stentor may react in several different ways or in the same way but with a greater or less amplitude to the same (extra-organic) stimulus, provided the physiological state of the animal be different at the different moments of stimulation. In a similar way it may be shown that the so-called simple segmental reflexes in the higher forms of animal life are not unalterably fixed in character. Yerkes has shown that the amount of reflex movement of the leg of a frog called forth by an electric shock can be greatly increased by introducing an auditory stimulus simultaneously with the electric, although the auditory stimulus calls forth no observable movement when given alone (see p. 388). Similar conditions hold in the case of the human knee jerk, and other reflex-like phenomena. The physiologist as a rule has investigated certain definite types of reflexes which are usually adaptive in character, such as the pupillomotor, those connected with respiration, circulation, the action of the glands and the muscles, etc. In general, while he looks upon these simple, direct types of response as calling, on the structural side, for the presence merely of an open pathway from receptor to effector (or from sensory surface to muscular mass where a nervous system is lacking), he knows, as has well been brought out by Sherrington, that there are many influences at work which alter the perviousness of this pathway (blockage or the reverse at synapses, momentary or more lasting differences in the tonicity of the musculature, etc.), and thus alter the intensity and to some extent even the character of the so-called simple reflex. The simple reflex, then, even to the physiologist, as he observes it in a spinal frog, is a general term to cover the more simple cases of segmental response. There is need, furthermore, to modify our notion of the reflex in still another direction. In reading genetic psychology, biology, and physiology, we are likely to be misled into thinking that all so-called reflex responses bear as definite and orderly a character as do those of which we have just spoken; and that their adaptive value can be as easily caught sight of. If we look at any young animal at birth we cannot fail to be struck by the inchoate mass of muscular response, such as the random movements of hands and other motile organs of the body, the wrinkling of the facial muscles, etc. None of these movements is stereotyped and none is adaptive in the sense that it " puts the subject in the control of the stimulus," to use a phrase often quoted by the psychologist. It is rather interesting that the Darwinian, who must find adaptive value in all instinctive activity, has not scrutinized random movement more carefully. If we examine the congenital movements of the young of any species from birth until the instinctive equipment is complete, we find (1) that, while there is no quantitative study at hand, mere observation shows that the number of random and unadaptive acts is far greater than is the number of organized adaptive reflexes and instinctive acts; (2) that under the influence of natural environmental demands or training many of these separate random acts can be organized into acts which are usually, but not necessarily, serviceable to the animal (habit formation, p. 184); and (3), finally, that many of them lie unorganized throughout the life history of the individual. In regard to this latter point it needs to be said that habit formation ceases after a time; the exigencies of environment (or the stimulating factors in the environment) are not sufficient, as a rule, to call forth all of the latent possibilities of organization. These random and spontaneous reflexes, unscrutinized by the physiologist,—the ceaseless movements of hands and arms, the facial muscles, and the turning and twisting of the trunk muscles and head as a whole, and later, climbing movements, running, jumping, etc.,—are of vital importance to the behaviorist, in view of the fact that every habit which is later put on by the animal must inevitably be analyzable into just such units. What is new in habit is the organization. The elements, in general, are as old, or as new as the race.

Content of term reflex as used in behavior.—Reflex, then, as a unit of analysis of instinct (as also of habit, as a matter of fact, see p. 184), in the modified sense in which we use the term, embraces (1) the fairly definite and generally predictable but unlearned responses of lower and higher organisms to stimuli. As examples of such acts among the invertebrates, we cite the responses of Euglena to the electric current, to gravity, to light, etc. These responses may consist of a definite movement towards or away from the stimulus. A characteristic but less general type of response of this kind is shown when Paramecium collides with objects: cilia are reversed, the animal swims backward, turning on the long axis of its body towards the aboral side; it then reverses the cilia again and starts in a new direction and repeats the above movements until forward movement can be continued without hindrance. Among the acts of vertebrates similar in definiteness and predictability we cite the reflexes of physiology such as the pupillar, plantar, patellar, etc. But we must be careful even in these cases not to over-emphasize the concept of invariability and predictability, since depending upon the physiological state of the organism we find, in extreme cases, the situation where a stimulus which at one time produces positive response may, under other conditions, produce negative response, e.g., when the frog is in a temperature of 10° it is positive to light, below 10°, negative. (2) We have in the case of both vertebrates and invertebrates many examples of highly unstable and indefinite responses. The picture here is in part kaleidoscopic, neither the elements nor the grouping possibly being the same twice. In this class would fall the unadaptive and abortive types which have been more or less neglected: movements of head, trunk, etc., and in the undirected (i.e., so far as simple physical stimuli under the control of the investigator are concerned) movements of lower organisms. The latter can be illustrated by the ceaseless swimming movements of Paramecia, the loping walk of Amœba, etc. These responses as a rule have been called "random" both in the literature on vertebrates and in that on invertebrates. It is evident, though, that the random movements when viewed *en masse* are congenital responses typical of the series. The random movements of the chick are quite different from those of the tern, and those of the Amœba are different from those of the Paramecium. Turning now to instincts which are made up of these reflex units, we should expect to find them at least as lacking in fixity as the units which compose them; and yet, just as there are many reflexes which, when examined in isolation, are found to be fairly permanent and stable so far as their qualitative features are concerned, just so do we find certain consolidations of reflexes which are stable and as much a permanent possession of the animal as its arms and legs. Possibly the argument can be most readily advanced by examining some of the typical instincts of the higher vertebrates.

General types of instinct.[1]—It is impossible, with the survey of animal activity which has been made, to give anything like a complete inventory of the various classes

[1] On *reaction types* see Hamilton, *op. cit.*, p. 62. In his study of mammals—human beings, monkeys, dogs, cats, and horses of different ages—he finds five reaction types, A, B, C, D, E.

Type A.—This reaction must include a single definite effort to open each of three inferentially possible doors (for description of the method see p. 62), and must not include an effort to open the inferentially impossible door. It is called the *rational inference type* and is displayed only by adult normal human subjects.

Type B.—This tendency involves trying all four doors but in an irregular order: *the unmodified searching tendency.* It is exhibited by only defective human individuals and by all of the animals in the following order with respect to frequency of its display: monkeys, dogs, cats, horses.

Type C.—Striking once each of the four doors in succession starting at either left or right: *the tendency to adopt stereotyped modes of searching.* This is especially exhibited by monkeys.

Type D.—This involves the error of making more than one separate continuous effort to open a given door during the same trial but always with an interruption of such repetitions of activity by an interval of effort to open some of the other doors: *searching tendency modified by recrudescent motor impulses.* This tendency regularly increases as we descend the phyletic scale.

Type E.—This includes several modes of behavior which have a common objective characteristic, viz., automatism. It is a relative implastic unadaptive mode of behavior: *the tendency toward perseveration of active impulses and inhibitions.*

of instincts, or to give a classification which will be accepted by any large number of investigators. Nevertheless, we should expect to find, and indeed we do find, certain characteristic instincts in every species of vertebrates. If the animal has survived at all, it is necessary for it to have certain instincts which relate to food, shelter, reproduction, defense, and attack, etc. The table below may be found helpful in holding together the mass of material which one finds when examining the work of students of behavior, and naturalists.

I. Structural characteristics, action systems, etc.	Bodily characteristics by means of which species are determined; methods of locomotion, such as creeping, crawling, walking, etc.
II. Obtaining food.	Taking food from beak of parent; sucking, pecking, scratching, diving; selection of food (when not determined by habit, e.g., herbivorous, carnivorous, etc.); the use of salt instead of fresh water; washing the food; methods of drinking, etc.
III. Shelter.	Stretching the wing to escape the sun; sunning, huddling, ruffling the feathers when cold, etc.; burrowing, taking up of abodes in hollow logs and trees; boring into timbers; hibernation, etc. Overlaps to some extent the group on sex and food.
IV. Rest, sleep, play, etc.	Night and day periods of activity, purely instinctive, since no structural peculiarities account for the differences; length of periods at nest, brooding or caring for the young; habits of sleep, i.e., bodily attitudes chosen; play; hibernation, etc.
V. Sex.	Mating; copulation; nest site; material of nest; methods of building nest; number of eggs laid or young cast; length of mating period or period in which partnership endures; care of the young, etc.

VI. Defence and attack.	Methods of attack, as lying on back; springing upward (to head and throat); spurring, goring with the antlers or horns, etc. Here belong also the hunting, stalking, seizing, and rending of live prey; shamming death; inflation of body; ejecting secretions, etc.
VII. Special forms of instinct.	Migration (possibly homing in general) as exhibited by birds, mammals, fish, reptiles. Possibly overlaps sex and food, but may be wholly independent of either. Mimicry.
VIII. Vocalization.	Calls, cries, sounds uttered in receiving food; during sex activity, etc. Shown in almost all vertebrate forms, but especially in the monkeys of the higher types and in birds.
IX. Unclassified and non-adaptive but complex and complete acts.	Strutting, dancing, inflation of cheek pouches; secretion of musk; elaborate nodding (as in the noddy tern).
X. Unclassified and non-adaptive, in this case random and abortive, sometimes appearing in one and sometimes in another combination, and sometimes in isolation.	(Discussed under reflexes, p. 110.)
XI. Individual peculiarities in response.	Reference is made here to very definite phenomena but ones hard to describe, such as persistence or the reverse in an attack on a problem (as shown in learning); boldness, individual tricks of hands, beak; ambidexterity or preponderating use of either right or left hand by any animal below man; probably hereditary but not known to be.

As may be seen from this list, no attempt is made to produce a logical arrangement of instincts. This has been tried many times, but it is certainly impossible to get a classification at present based upon any other grounds than that of general convenience.

Methods of studying instinct.—Two general lines of attack upon instinct are open to us. The first method is that of field observation. The work of the Peckhams on the social and solitary wasps, and that of Wheeler upon ants, serve both to show the working of the method and its general usefulness. Unfortunately there is no work on the study of the higher vertebrates comparable in completeness with those we have on the invertebrates. Instead, however, we have a series of publications more or less restricted in scope which deal with separate species of vertebrates. There is a fairly large number of more or less chance observations on mammals in captivity in the works of Allen, Richardson, Slonaker, Small, Lashley, Watson, and Waugh; upon fish in the works of Bauer, Hess, Parker, Reighard, Romeis, Sheldon, Sumner, and others; upon birds in those of Craig, Strong, Herrick, Hess, and Porter; and upon reptiles and amphibia in those of Hess, Newman, Schaeffer, and Yerkes. Completely worked out, this method would give us the life-history or field activity of animals. The second method is that of isolating the animal and observing the order of appearance of the instincts, measuring the degree of their perfectness, the progress towards perfection through supplementation by habit, variations in their life-history, such as recurrency, waxing, waning, possible loss through disuse, etc.

Various results obtained by the method of field observation.—We can attempt to do no more here than illustrate a few of the more common instincts appearing in various representatives of the vertebrate phyla. In so far as possible we shall take one individual species and attempt to present a picture of its various modes of instinctive response. These responses are naturally given in their unanalyzed form, just as the animal exhibits them in its native habitat.

Instinctive activity of birds; the noddy tern.—(I) The general bodily form, action systems, and taxonomic relations of the noddy tern need not concern us here. (II) On the first day after hatching the young bird strikes feebly its parent's beak. The movements are exceedingly poorly directed. Probably little food is obtained from the parent at first. Very rapidly the strength of the stroke becomes greater and at the same time ability to open the beak increases commensurately. More and more food is obtained. Finally, at the end of fifteen to twenty days the young can take the food from the parent as rapidly as the latter can regurgitate it. In eight to ten weeks the young bird leaves the nest, and after wing practice, strikes out in search of food. Minnows of several different species are eaten exclusively. As the adult flies over the water its eyes meet schools of minnows hopping over the surface. It darts downward, seizes them in the beak, and swallows them. As the crop becomes filled it will often fly upward and swallow with extra force, giving a peculiar twisting spiral-like movement to the throat. As soon as the crop is well filled the bird goes to brood the egg or to feed the young; or if a male and no egg has been laid, to feed the female. The search for food is again taken up at intervals ranging from two to five hours. The method of drinking is characteristic. As the bird flies over the water it darts down and skims the surface with open beak. Often it darts down and wets its breast feathers, especially on hot days when brooding the egg. Rarely, when soiled and possibly at other times, it dives completely under water. Occasionally it is found swimming in the water. (III) In its typical habitat the noddy needs no shelter or extensive protection from the weather. When young, the bird huddles under the wing of the parent, both to escape the cool wind and rain and the too fierce rays of the sun. Even while young it shows a peculiar response which persists throughout life: when the sun is particularly warm it spreads out one wing fan-wise and remains standing for long periods of time with head directed always towards the wind. This response begins very early, at about eight to nine days. Sunning is another characteristic mode of response. The adult birds collect on the beach or house-tops with head to wind, standing always a few inches apart. (IV) The bird is diurnal, sleeping apparently from dusk until dawn. Nothing is known of its sleeping attitudes. One bird occupies the nest at night while the other stands on a nearby limb. (The neighbor of this bird, the sooty tern, apparently sleeps in short snatches during the day and night. It is continually flying around the island at night, screaming and calling to mates and young. It has been nicknamed the " wide-awake tern.'') The noddy, both after its turn to brood the egg and after obtaining food, often goes to a house-top, the shore, a stake, or a piece of driftwood, and stands motionless for long periods of time. (A common response of terns, boobies, pelicans, etc.) (V) Nothing is known of the process of mating, since they reach the breeding ground apparently already mated. The choice of the nest site is a very simple matter; almost any place which will hold together a few sticks, seaweed, or shells may be chosen. Both animals (mates) work vigorously during the period of nest construction. Sometimes a very elaborate nest is built; at other times only a few sticks are thrown together on the ground or in the fork of some low bush. Often, as the animal brings in its single stick or shell, it will sit in the nest and turn round and round, thus giving the structure a characteristic shape. Quite frequently a half dozen shells and bits of seaweed are put in at the bottom of the completed nest. The impulse to pick up straws persists for a long period of time, almost throughout the brooding period. During the period of active nest construction, both birds go out to feed. As soon as the nest is fairly well constructed the female sits on a nearby limb usually very close to the nest. She " guards " this nest practically the whole day long, leaving only momentarily to drink. The male, on the other hand, goes out and fishes. On his return he bows elaborately to the female and she in turn begins to strike at his beak. If he has food in his crop he regurgitates it and the female eats from his bill. Only one egg is laid. As soon as the egg is laid the instincts of the birds again change. Before the egg is laid the birds are timid and will fly up at the slightest disturbance. After the egg is laid the birds become exceedingly bold. They will fiercely attack the encroachments of any other bird and will even attack the human intruder. A large number of the birds will actually sit on the nest and allow themselves to be removed bodily from it before offering to fly. The two birds take turns at brooding the egg. The nest shifts occur sometimes with remarkable regularity, two hours being about the preferred time. A number of interesting movements in the matter of caring for the egg appear; it is constantly covered. They turn it round and round with the beak; they go to the water to wet the breast feathers to keep it moist; they shove one another aside when the shifts are made without exposing the egg for any length of time, etc. When the young bird appears, there is again a marked change in the type of response. The birds again take turns in feeding the young one (of this, however, we are not sure). Probably the most interesting set of changes is that in their "dispositions." As the young bird grows older the parents no longer attack the human intruder but leave the nest much more readily than during the brooding season. (VI) The noddy has an exceedingly sharp bill and depends largely upon it in attack. When fighting on the ground it strikes vigorously with its wings. The blow of the beak of the tern is severe enough oftentimes to draw blood from the human hand. The beak is serrated on the inner edge, which enables it to hold quite firmly to an object. Two terns, in fighting, will strike vigorously with the beak and then lock beaks, and turn and twist, striking strong blows with the wings. It is no unusual sight to see a noddy chasing a large man-o'-war bird from the island. He flies under the man-o'-war bird and strikes him on the breast until he soars up and leaves the island. These fights between the noddies and the man-o'-war birds are brought about by the latters' attempts to roost over the nests of the noddies. Fights among the noddies occur when a strange bird attempts to usurp the nest; to have intercourse with the female of the nest; to steal straws; or in general to encroach upon the neighborhood of a nest. They will also attack any strange birds that come to the island, with the exception of the hawks. (The young sooty, which is hatched upon the same island, exhibits an interesting case of death-shamming. When one, two, three, and four days of age it will not leave the nest upon the open sand at the intrusion of a human being, but will lie in the nest perfectly motionless with head outstretched. Oftentimes when the little fellow is picked up and then put down again he will dart off rapidly to the shelter of a neighboring bush.) We have never noticed death-shamming in the adults nor a simulating of lameness (for the attraction of the hunter, as is so often mentioned in the literature by the naturalists.) (VII) The noddy is migratory, wintering somewhere along the shores of Central America. Some time in April, they leave there in a body for Bird Key, Dry Tortugas, reaching that island often about the 27th or 28th of April. There is wide variation, though, as has been found lately, in the time at which they reach Bird Key. The time of arrival will vary as much as a month to six weeks. Some time in September, again the time is variable, but the 20th was once actually observed, they leave Bird Key and go again to their winter home. If the ability to home is instinctive, this bird exhibits a wonderful development of such an instinct. We have been enabled to get the noddy to return to its nest from all distances up to eight hundred miles over an open water pathway (Galveston to Bird Key). (VIII) While young the noddy gives a gentle peep exceedingly like that of the chick. The variety and range of its vocal accomplishments are exceedingly limited. The adult bird is almost silent, day and night. Occasionally as one approaches its nest it will give a hoarse hiss-like warning cry, and then again a purring, unbird-like kind of noise, during periods of feeding and sex activity. (IX) This bird shows some interesting unadaptive types of response. The most interesting one is its inveterate system of nodding to every bird that comes near it and to its mate. This nodding is often preliminary to a fight; to a shift at the nest between the mates; and to sex activity. The photograph, Fig. 28, shown below, gives some idea of the elaborateness of the process. Another form falling under this head is that of complete cessation of activity for long periods of time. This has already been mentioned under another head. It is possible that there are a large number of such acts ex-

hibited during the mating period, but since we have not
been able to observe this, no record can be given. (In
a number of other birds elaborate dances are gone through
with as well as certain peculiar antics which are described

FIG. 28.   NODDIES IN THE ACT OF BOWING

by Fisher.[1]   Another example of such peculiar responses
may be found in the inflation of the cheek pouches exhibited
by the man-o'-war bird.)   (X) There are so many random
acts exhibited by the young birds of this species that an
enumeration or classification of them is impossible in this
connection.   (XI) Very great individual differences were
noted in the persistency of certain of the birds in working
at a problem, e.g., where entrance to the nest was denied.
There are also very great differences in the boldness of the
birds.   At certain nests the birds will always fly up at the
observer's approach during the entire nesting period; at
others, the birds will remain in the nest even after very
rough handling—often after they have been picked up
and sent off on trips they will suffer themselves again to be

[1] Birds of Laysan and the Leeward Islands, Hawaiian Group.
Bull. U. S. Fish Commission, Vol. XXIII, 1903, pp. 767-807.

caught and sent off. Many tricks, such as pecking at the toes, idly pecking at the nest material, tricks which might serve to identify the birds, were observed.

Instinctive activity of reptiles.—Very little is known concerning the phylogenetic modes of response of the reptiles. We shall mention some of the more common types of response found in the tortoise. (I) Aspidonectes (the " soft-shell " tortoise) runs swiftly on the land and when in the water swims with powerful strokes. It is almost impossible to overtake it by running. The essential form of the tortoise, etc., are too well known to require a separate description. (II) Aspidonectes is carnivorous, feeding upon crayfish and the larvæ of large insects. It crawls or swims along, thrusting its snout into masses of aquatic vegetation, picking up now and then a crayfish, etc., swallowing the booty whole and, when needed, using the forefeet to force the food down. It is rather interesting that fish often accompany this species of turtle in its wanderings after food. The turtle often stirs up and dislodges food which it cannot capture but which the fish can take with ease. (III) This animal, at the onset of cold weather, buries itself in the mud, and hibernates until the warm spring days of April come. It buries itself in the mud in a peculiar way, by rocking the body from side to side and throwing the mud up in such a way that it settles on the carapace and covers it quickly from sight. It sinks deeper and deeper until it gets well below the frost line. It comes out in April in a very much weakened condition. (IV) This animal has a tendency to lie on floating objects. On approach, it invariably slides off into the water. When on a floating object, it always lies facing the water; consequently no time is lost in turning when danger approaches. At times it crawls out on a bank and basks in the sun. Lying in shallow water, which is of course always warmer, is another favorite mode of response. By this process the turtle obtains both rest and warmth. From Newman's description of its activity, it would seem that this variety is diurnal. In the case of the loggerhead turtle, during the period when the eggs are laid, the animal is usually noc-

turnal in its land habits. The general mode for catching
the green and the loggerhead turtle is to walk around the
shore lines of the small islands on moonlight nights. The
turtles crawl out at night to lay their eggs and if seen
quickly enough can be turned over on their backs in such
a way that they are helpless. When large numbers are
captured they are taken to the various marketplaces and
sold. (V) Little is known of the process of mating, sexual
activity, etc., in the case of the turtle. Aspidonectes begins
to lay early in June. These animals are exceedingly wary
in their choice of times and places for laying. This species
apparently lays its eggs during the daytime. The animal
comes to the surface many yards from the shore and carefully reconnoiters before coming ashore. On reaching it
the turtle comes out on the sand, extending the head at
its full height and remaining motionless for some time.
If at this time a slight movement or faint sound alarms the
animal it dashes back into the water. When undisturbed, it proceeds slowly and cautiously to the nesting
ground. The female scratches out foot-holds for the fore-
feet and excavates with the hind-feet, using the right and
left foot alternately with a circular gouging movement. At
intervals she pushes aside the accumulated earth with her
hind-feet. In less than 40 minutes (single observation)
the nest is completed and she commences to lay the eggs.
After laying several eggs, she arranges them with the hind-
feet and rakes in earth previously wet with water from the
accessory bladders. The earth is generally packed in before any more eggs are laid. The remainder of the eggs
are laid and the earth is tramped upon quite firmly with
the knuckles of the hind-feet, the right and left foot being
again used alternately. The treading movements continue
for some minutes. No attempt is made to cover up the
traces of the feet. It has been said on good authority that
the tortoise cannot be frightened away when making her
nest. This apparently is not true with the various species
studied by Newman. However, if laying has actually begun, the animal will hesitate long enough to cover up the
eggs more or less completely when surprised. Yet again,

nests may be found with eggs completely exposed. The number of eggs laid ranges from nine to twenty-four.

Instinctive activity of fish.—There has been very little work done in the way of systematic and continuous observation of fishes. The most striking work which has yet appeared upon the instincts of fish was reported by Jacob Reighard upon the breeding behavior (V) of the dogfish (*Amia calva Linnæus*). During the last week in April the male of this species fixes on the nesting location. This is usually a place in a quiet bay or inlet well grown with water plants. He constructs a saucer-like excavation 30 to 90 cm. in diameter and from 10 to 20 cm. deep. The bottom of the excavation is covered with the fibrous roots of water plants, which form a spongy mass. At times the bottom is of gravel, sand, or black loam. Occasionally one finds in it water-soaked stems or leaves of cattails or other similar water plants. The sides of the nest are usually of rootlets and growing plants. The fish usually selects a relatively plantless area surrounded by a wall of growing plants and from this area removes the few young shoots. The nest is constructed entirely by the male without assistance from the female. The method of constructing the nest is to fan away the vegetation and ooze so as to expose the underlying material, and to rub down and bite away the scant vegetation. The nests are built usually at night, each nest being the property of an individual male. After the nest is constructed the male guards it for a period of usually 24 to 36 hours, but such a period may be extended to six days or possibly longer. At times the male will leave the nest. If females do not appear, he finally abandons the nest. The sexes seem to be able to detect one another at considerable distances (smell?), and the females apparently seek the nests prepared by the males. After the female reaches the nest, spawning may be observed. The male is very active at the time of spawning. He circles around the female in such a way as to meet her head on and travels towards her tail. In passing over her body he bites her on the snout and sides of her head and body as far back as the middle. At times during this period both animals leave the nest. On each return the male reëngages in the circling movement. The female usually lies quietly upon the nest. After 15 to 20 minutes of these circling movements the female is sufficiently stimulated to deposit the eggs. The male then approaches the female and lies by her side. This marks the completion of spawning. Spawning is done intermittently and usually at night. Apparently more than one female may spawn in the nest with an individual male. Then begins the guarding of the eggs, also by the male. The male lies at times directly over the nest, while at other times he is concealed in the natural openings of the adjacent vegetation. At these times one can approach within a very short distance of the nest. Usually as the observer approaches the male moves towards him, but not usually beyond the limits of the nest. If frightened, he dashes away. After a time he returns slowly and quietly to the nest. When the male guards the nest he lies, for the most part, quietly, or with only slight movements of his fins, but at intervals he moves over the nest, and thus by the movement of his fins keeps the eggs free from sediment which would otherwise soon smother them. He also keeps away other animals that try to occupy the nest. Fierce fights between the males are described by Whitman and Ecleshymer. The male also has to keep off the minnows and sunfish. The eggs hatch in from eight to ten days. When the larvæ are about 12 to 13 mm. in length they leave the nest. Observations have been made upon behavior during nest forsaking. The movements of the swarm of larvæ when leaving the nest suggest that it follows the trail of the male by scent.[2]

Special forms of instinctive response in fish.—Mention

[2] To test this matter a rough model of an adult *Amia* was made and covered with black rubber cloth. A freshly killed male fish was then trussed up and attached to the end of a stick so that it could be moved about in the water. The male was then taken to a nest where the larvæ were about ready to leave and made to pass several times over a course leading from the nest to a distance of about a meter. The larvæ soon followed this course and assembled about the male. When the model was substituted they paid no attention to it.

should be made of some highly specialized instinctive modes of response in fish which have been studied in detail by Sumner, Mast, and by several German investigators (Hess, Frisch, etc.). These responses are of such a character as to make the surface of the animal appear visually like the background upon which it rests. While present to some extent in other fish, it can best be observed in the flatfish.

The flounders ordinarily lie on the bottom and the skin assumes a color and pattern so nearly like that of their environment that it is frequently difficult to see them. On a black bottom they become dark; on a white bottom, pale. Whether similar changes occur with monochromatic light is not so well established. Mast states, however, that the fish when placed on a yellow bottom appear yellow; on a blue bottom, bluish; on a red bottom, reddish, etc. All of these changes in the skin are regulated through the eyes. If the bottom is finely mottled the pattern in the skin assumes a fine grain; if coarsely mottled, it assumes a coarse grain. But there is no evidence indicating an actual reproduction of the configuration of the background. If, after the skin has become adapted to a given bottom, the fish are moved to a different bottom, they tend to return to the original. The reflex mechanism by means of which such changes are accomplished has not been ascertained (see p. 354).

Results of the experimental study of instincts.—The study of the instinctive development of young animals reared in captivity has been exceedingly fruitful. The results so far accomplished may be considered under one of the following heads:

I. The initial performance of some instinctive acts.
II. Serial unfolding of instinctive repertoire of animals.
   A. Guinea pig,
   B. Rat,
   C. Monkey,
   D. Sooty tern.
III. Quantitative study of improvement of instinctive functions.
IV. Modification of instinct by means of social influences.

V. Hereditary character of certain instinctive traits.

VI. Waning of instinct; loss through disuse, etc.

I. The initial performance of some instinctive acts.—
The current notion of instinct is that it is an act which
takes place (without previous exercise or training) whenever the proper stimulus is first presented. The common
notion further states that the instinct, even upon its first
appearance, is just as perfect as during the later performances. Under the present heading we wish to take up
some initial instinctive performances and view them entirely
apart from the consideration of their perfectness or accuracy. We shall delay such discussions until p. 138 is
reached. Certain scientific writers are inclined to doubt
even the existence of instincts. To illustrate this type of
conception we cite the work of C. S. Berry. Some years
ago he reported that the young of the Manx cat learn to
catch and kill mice by imitating the parents. He concludes that:

"Cats are credited with more instincts than they really possess.
It is commonly reported that they have an instinctive liking for mice
and that mice have an instinctive fear of cats. It is supposed that
the odor of a mouse will arouse a cat and that the odor of a cat
will frighten a mouse. My experiments tend to show that this belief
is not in harmony with the facts. When cats over five months old
were taken into a room where mice were they did not show the least
sign of excitement. A cat would even allow a mouse to perch upon
its back without attempting to injure it, nor did the mouse show
any fear of the cat. I have seen a mouse smell at the nose of a cat
without showing any sign of fear."

This work of Berry's did a good deal of violence to the
common notion of instinct. The later work of Yerkes and
Bloomfield seems to reëstablish our faith in instinct. They
made their tests upon two litters of common cats. The
animals were carefully fed upon milk, beef, usually cooked,
and fish. They were housed in a room free from mice. In
the first week of life the kittens showed no special interest
in mice. Shortly after they gained their sight (12 days
of age), they were again tested, but the presence of the
mice did not elicit the instinctive response sought for.
When slightly over 4 weeks of age, 3 of the first litter of 4 failed to exhibit the instinct, as before. One of

the kittens, now, however, exhibited a type of behavior quite in contrast with that of the other 3. She noticed the mouse soon after it had been placed in the cage, as it moved near her, and quickly seized it, growling the while. The mouse escaped and the kitten gave chase but failed to recapture it before it had climbed to the top of the cage.

Five days later the kittens were again tested. Nos. 1, 2, and 3 acted as before; No. 4, as in the above test, made efforts to catch the mouse. Two days later the tests were repeated. Kittens 1, 2, and 3 showed a marked interest in the mouse, but behaved as in the other tests. No. 4 exhibited almost a complete repertoire of movements used by the adult cat in catching and killing mice. The mouse was pursued, caught, worried, killed, and partially eaten. The tests were continued upon the remainder of the kittens belonging to the same group as No. 4, and upon 4 kittens belonging to a second litter. All the animals tested, at slightly varying ages, exhibited the characteristic instinctive behavior of No. 4. The instinct to kill commonly appears at about the end of the second month. It may appear as early as the first month. Since Berry worked with kittens 5 months old it is just possible that his negative results were due to the fact that the instinct had waned through disuse.

Two definite things came out of this study: (1) as regards method, it shows quite clearly the possibility of being able to note the first appearance of an instinct and the variation in the time of its appearance among the same litter of animals; (2) it shows that the initial performance of an instinctive act may be fairly complete even though the act as a whole is enormously complex.

One of the most interesting of all responses, performed only once in the life of the individual, is that exhibited by the young bird in gaining egress from the shell. The technique of its method has long been known and may be described somewhat as follows:

"The chick chips the egg a little at a time with its bill, and as it does so it turns around inside the egg shell, the axis of its rotation being precisely the long axis of the egg. The consequence of this turning is that the tip of the bill, chipping the shell as it goes, describes a very exact circle around the end of the egg, and thus the large end of the shell is cut off.[8] The time which it takes to finish the cutting is very variable. When the opening has been extended nearly or quite around the egg, the chick pushes and separates the two sections of the shell, tearing in two any shreds of membrane which may have been holding them together. Thus the little bird effects its escape." (Craig.)

It has recently been shown by Craig that the young pigeon opens its egg in the same manner as the chick. The activity of the young bird actually under observation is extremely interesting. We quote from this author:

"No. 46, April 19, 1911. 8:30 A.M. My wife found egg chipped and called me to see it. While we watched it the young chipped the egg about one-third the way round (120°) in about ten minutes. The young made a strong movement, then rested for several seconds, then made another strong movement, and so on. Each movement seemed to consist (1) of pushing out the large end of the egg, i.e., pushing lengthwise of the egg; (2) thrusting the bill through the shell, the bill coming just far enough to break through, in fact many times not breaking through but only bulging the shell; (3) turning around a few degrees. We could see this turning through the hole in the shell; also we could see that each thrust of the bill appeared a little beyond the previous one. With the egg large end up, the turning was anti-clock-wise."

In the drinking and eating responses of many animals we should expect to find a high degree of completeness even in the initial performance. Chickens when left to develop naturally in the vicinity of water and food usually find the water by accidentally pecking at the dish containing it. The contact of the water on the beak sets off the rest of the mechanism. At times, apparently, drinking may be hastened by imitating other chicks. When the intra-organic stimulation becomes sufficiently intense, which is brought about by keeping the chick from water until the third day, almost any form of extra-organic stimulation will set off the act of drinking. Under this condition neither imitation nor fortuitous pecking at objects in the water are necessary to obtain the response. The dove does not instinctively give a drinking response to the sound

[8] Breed, however, denies that egress is accomplished mainly by pecking. He maintains that lifting movements are chiefly responsible.

of water or sight, nor to the touch of it on distal parts of the body. The young dove, like the chick, gets its bill into water probably chiefly by pecking, either at objects in the water which attract its attention, or in imitation of the old birds. When studied in detail it was found that for the first three or four times the bird has accidentally to peck at the water and to get it inside the beak before the drinking response is set up. But on the fourth time and always thereafter the response was perfect. Certainly in the case of the terns the feeding responses are quite indefinite at first, and on the part of many birds it is wholly a passive kind of process; the bird merely opens the beak and waits until the food is dropped in.

The young guinea pig is born in a highly developed state. Even at the end of the first day the animal is able to eat grass, bread and milk, and nibble at a carrot. It is able to run around and can find the breast of the mother unaided. This is quite in contrast with the case of the white rat. The young rat is extremely helpless and the mother takes the active part in feeding.

In the case of many vertebrates there seem to be no inherent methods of responding actively to different food stuffs. The young chick will peck at almost any small object. The young tern, shortly after hatching, will peck at its own toes, at small bright objects, and at fecal matter, and will even attempt to swallow matches. Even up to 10 and 12 days after being fed by hand upon minnows, they have to be watched constantly to prevent the swallowing of shells, seaweed, and other objects.

II. Serial unfolding of instincts in young captive animals.—We shall attempt to give in this connection a summary of the development of a few animals that have been carefully observed in captivity.

A. Guinea pig.—The guinea pig at birth is well covered with hair; its eyes are open; smell, touch,. and taste apparently all function; movement is not well coördinated and muscular weakness is apparent. It is able to run at birth, but after running a short distance and stopping, one leg is left sprawling behind it. There is no fear at birth of an approaching object, such as the hand held in front of the eyes, nor of persons. A shrill squeak, like that of a rat, caused first an instantaneous jump with a twitching of the muscles. This is the immediate reaction to such a stimulus. It may be followed by hiding under the mother: A carrot or other vegetable food produces no positive response at birth, but after the end of the first day these objects will be eaten. Small guinea pigs put outside of the experimental cage in which the mother was placed ran around quite freely and contentedly for an hour or more without the mother. In one case where the young one was removed from the mother for five hours, it gnawed a little at the wire. The mother does not seem to be a specific stimulus to the young, but after they have been returned from an absence of several hours they will seek her and suck. At 38 hours, the guinea pig's squeal, in its infantile form, is fully developed. The movements are almost as well coördinated as in the adults; there is great activity. The movements around the cage are similar to those of the adults when hunting food: the fore-feet creep forward, the belly flattens to the ground, and the hind part of the body is dragged forward. The peculiar movements of the guinea pig, so characteristic in the first three weeks of existence, begin to appear on the second day. At the age of 62 hours evidence of the mother acting as a specific stimulus is given in the act of the young in making real attempts to get to her through the wires of the cage. The small guinea pigs rarely play together. It is probable that the guinea pig at 3 days of age is as mature as the white rat at 23 to 27 days of age.

B. Rat.—In marked contrast to the precocious development of the guinea pig stands that of the white rat.

First day.—The young white rat is born destitute of hair. There is no external ear and there is a membrane over the eyes. The nose seems to be fairly well developed. Their movements, except sucking, are incoördinated, the mother crouching over them. When held in the hand they roll up into a ball; when placed on their backs outside of the nest they hitch and kick and wriggle over upon the belly or the side. They are generally unable to maintain the belly position for any length of time. When lying upon the belly they stretch out their paws in a turtle-like manner. The tail is often moved. Vocalization consists in a clucking sound, a fine high-pitched squeak, and a sort of chirp. Avoiding types of reaction are present such as brushing and pushing away with the paws; averting the head; movement of the whole body, etc.

It will thus be seen that there is very little that is definite in the way of instinctive activity. From birth until the fifth day there seems to be a steady increase in motor development. But no new instincts appear.

Fifth day.—The rats crawl with considerable vigor on the fifth day.

Twelfth day.—Walk, but unsteadily. Characteristic act of " face washing " appeared on this day in fairly perfect form.

Fourteenth day.—Running, climbing, characteristic movement of rearing on hind legs, lifting head, and sniffing. It is at this age that the young becomes sensitive to sounds.

Fifteenth day.—The eyes open. When removed from nest, can run back to mother with great rapidity. Scratching in sawdust to get back to mother when entrance was closed with sawdust was clearly noted.

From this period until full sexual maturity is reached, about the sixty-fifth day, the development of play activity is a most interesting phenomenon to watch. They are exceedingly active during this period. Small, from whose records the above notes are in part taken, states that the whole repertoire of play activity is complete at the age of 25 days. He enumerates the play acts as follows: running, jumping, climbing, fierce sham fights with biting, clawing, running over the mother and biting her ears, digging in corners, gnawing at the cage, sex movements (mounting one another—not complete). This catalog of play is very incomplete, as Small himself admits.

Of the instincts in this animal not exhibited until after sexual maturity is reached—such as construction of the nest, caring for the young, assembling them, storing food, etc.—very little is known.

C. The monkey.—One is bewildered by the very complexity of the responses in the young monkey, just as is the case in similar observations upon the child. There seems to be great progress in the development rather than the putting on of very definite instincts at any given time.

First week.—On the first day the little monkey was very still, moving only when forced to do so by the movements of the adult. However, certain reflexes seemed to be well established even at this age. Those observed were sucking, grasping, nuzzling, crying, sneezing, winking (not in response to visual stimuli), incoördinated movements of the legs when the stimulus for grasping was removed; and an increased muscular tension of the legs in response to the mother's movements. During the second day there appeared to be a slight unadaptive response to sound. (In the human infant this varies in the time of appearance from the second to the tenth day.) By the third day his strength had increased so that his grasp upon his mother's hair had become secure. The head and eyes were at this age first turned to follow a moving object. Two days later appeared the reflex grasping at a visual object.

Second week.—By the end of the first week his muscular activity was greatly increased, although most of his movements were still of the non-adaptive type. Complex coördinated movements of the limbs, as in jumping, appeared, as also those connected with reaching out towards moving objects. The scratching reflex was established. On the eleventh day he reached out and grasped small objects. By this time his response to sound indicated some degree of localization. On the twelfth day he first attempted to walk. The movements were very badly executed and showed a lack of coördination.

Third week.—The third week, the first week of walking, was marked by a tremendous increase in muscular control. The movements of the larger muscles of the limbs became fairly well adjusted to the demands made upon them. The first definite play activities appeared with contraction of the facial muscles in pursing the lips.

Fourth week.—Play rapidly changed from simple pull-ing and grasping to the more complicated stalking and capturing of objects in the cage. This was closely connected with his increased interest in scraps of solid food, which he first attempted to eat at this time. The scratching reflex was perfected. The very complex behavior displayed by the adult in this act appeared quite suddenly in the young animal. There is some evidence to show that habits of reacting to food by sight arose within a few days after he first tasted it.

Fifth week.—Apposition of the thumb and fingers was first observed, muscular coördination spreading peripherally. He attempted to draw the mother into his play.

Sixth week.—Movements connected with attack and defense appeared, as shown by his violent attempts to shake and tear apart the cage. This is a very characteristic act of adults. The thumb was used much more in grasping.

Seventh week.—Movements connected with care of the body, removal of insects, etc., were first observed.

Eighth week.—The use of the cheek pouches was acquired.

Ninth week.—Different vocal sounds were first distinguished. The method by which they were learned is not known, but from their sudden appearance they seem to be instinctive rather than imitative. . Stroking of the sex organs resulting in erection was noted during this week.

Fifteenth week.—From the tenth to the fifteenth week the progress noted was almost entirely motor. Play activities were still very marked but unadaptive movements persisted.

Approximately one year.—The group connected with the act of reproduction appeared very suddenly at the age of one year. So far as could be seen all of the essential reflexes were perfect.

D. Sooty tern.—The young sooty is born in a very helpless state. On the 7th of June eight young sooties were taken, all born on that day. They differ slightly as regards their development. This is due to the fact that the birds dwell for varying lengths of time in the shell after it has become pipped. In passing through the bushes when the birds are beginning to hatch one often hears quite lusty " peeping," and on looking about to find the young bird, discovers that the noise comes from birds in the shell. Whether or not they are fed at this age is not known. Sometimes they live as long as two days in the shell with only the beak protruding. At this stage in their development they make no response to the warning cry of the adults as they do later on. They go on " peeping " lustily after the adults have flown. The peculiar protective attitude of the young birds has been mentioned already, that is, the ability to lie outstretched and perfectly motionless. If left for a time in this attitude, they begin to " peep " as soon as the sun's rays become oppressive. This means of protection persists until locomotion makes possible a more effective method. When the protective attitude disappears and locomotion becomes possible, the birds run to cover when disturbed. Hiding is never in any sense complete; indeed, the reaction seems to be almost thygmotactic. The moment the young bird can put its head in the crotch of a limb or get its body in contact with some solid object, locomotion ceases.

First day.—The young birds which were captured showed apparent signs of fear. Moving the hand quite rapidly near them, as in offering a piece of fish, caused them to dodge quite noticeably. The instinctive cry is a lusty " peep-peep." They are well developed but clumsy. The wings droop and the birds have difficulty in standing; co-ordinated sitting positions are likewise almost impossible. The birds are somewhat hard to feed during the first day, but after this age the process is easier with them than is the case with the noddies of a corresponding age. In the case of the sooties, as was not the case with the noddies, the mere sight of the food will cause the bird to open its beak. Light contact will likewise cause the beak to open. Once the food gets into the mouth the rhythmical movements of swallowing follow perfectly. Some locomotion is possible. They take a few wobbly steps with wings down and legs wide apart. Fairly well coördinated swimming movements are present, but the heavy down with which they are covered soon causes the birds to become waterlogged and they sink. As the salt water begins to enter the mouth the bird raises its beak higher and higher and shakes out the water vigorously, crying lustily the while. One of the young birds taken on that day had not emerged from its shell; only its beak and the base of the beak protruded (the eyes being covered by a membrane). Almost any call from the observer would cause this bird to " peep." Small minnows were offered and swallowed. The contact of the minnows caused the beak to open. The shell was removed; the bird made adaptive movements as if completing the process itself. After removal the bird was very insecure in its movements.

Second day.—The difference in growth is remarkable. Birds can waddle around rapidly and maintain upright position fairly well. They follow moving objects with the head and eyes quite easily. Will dodge very quickly if hand is suddenly extended towards them. Some tendency present to nestle under one another, under hands and under folds of the cloth. They are beginning to peck at one another, the bare wings being the spot usually attacked. Feeding is quite easy. Moving the finger, fish, or bits of straw rapidly across the beak will cause the beak to open wide. Whole minnows are swallowed with ease. The birds sleep a great deal of the time. The adult birds flying over the experimental cage and crying are invariably answered by a " peep " from the young ones. Even on the second day feeding is an active process with them. A fish dangled in front of them will cause them to strike at it. If the beak fastens upon the fish in the center of the body the young bird, by a peculiar twist of the head, will suddenly right the fish and swallow it head first. It is safe to say that at the end of the second day the young sooty is sufficiently developed to take any fish from the beak of the parent which is likely to be found there. Even at this early age the birds are found pecking at one another's mouths or at a piece of food which another is swallowing. Pecking at one another in a way forceful enough to suggest the beginning of the enormously important fighting instinct was, however, not noticed up to this time. Any signs of fear which might have been present the first day have entirely disappeared by the end of the second.

Third day.—The birds have begun to run towards the observer when he approaches them and calls. They will lustily answer his " peep " at any hour of the day or night. The fighting instinct appeared today in almost complete form. Two of the young birds faced each other and began striking simultaneously. A firm hold is taken on the body and maintained, the victor all the time shaking his opponent as does the adult. Not the slightest sign of play has yet manifested itself. The birds as yet show no discrimination as regards what objects they peck at: they are as likely to attempt to swallow the finger as the fish. Very minute objects, however, such as specks of dirt and hairs, are not noticed by them.

Fourth day.—The birds are healthier and larger than those in the field. Three birds, 4 days of age, were taken from the field to compare with the birds reared in captivity. These birds were exceedingly wild. They were kept in captivity for 2 or 3 weeks, but while showing improvement in this respect, they never wholly lost their fear of the observer. The sleeping and lounging attitudes of the first lot captured are very striking. In most cases, after a full meal is taken, they go to sleep. When lying down one leg (at times both legs) is stuck out so as to give the ventral surface of the body contact with the ground; head is completely outstretched and laid on one side; eyes are closed. At other times the bird rests its rump on the ground, using the legs as a prop, and dozes in this position. As it dozes its head falls to the right or to the left or vertically downward between the legs. When the beak strikes the ground the eyes are partially opened, the head is raised again, and the process is repeated.

Seventh day.—The bird's feeding movements are wonderfully fast. The extremely rapid movements of the (live) fish are not more rapid than the movements of their beaks. There is little improvement in discrimination to be noticed. Today, while feeding some of the birds, a tug was felt by the observer from behind, and on turning around it was found that one of the birds had swallowed about 3 inches of his handkerchief and was straining every muscle to force the rest down! The young birds were offered lemon peel today: it was snapped up by all of them greedily. They continued to snap and swallow the lemon rind for 3 to 4 trials, and refused thereafter to open the beak for it. Fighting is furious and prolonged. The young birds are exact replicas of the old in this respect. All that is necessary to start a fight is for one bird to come within striking distance of another.

Eighth day.—The young birds began to dig holes in the sand, using exactly the same movements which are employed by the adults in digging the nest, except that the young birds do not shape the hole with the breast as the adults do the nest. By digging such a hole the bird secures a surface which is damp and cool. The holes are usually dug near some solid object, whether because of greater coolness there (temperature reaction), or through some thygmotactic tendency (tactual reaction) we are not able to state. A new instinctive reaction was observed today which is continued from this time on. A bird standing still will suddenly hop an inch or two in the air and come down in the same spot (first step in flying?). Detailed records of the development of these birds were kept until they were 30 days of age, but on account of the great similarity of these later records to the above, we shall not cite them in detail. Experiments on learning to respond adaptively to the common objects in the environment were made from day to day, but all such tests gave results very similar to those which have already been described. After the birds had learned to pick up fish from a dish, it was possible to put seaweed, grass, bits of coral, etc., in with the fish. At first these were taken eagerly, but after a few trials the birds learned to take the fish and leave the debris. Such habits, however, never became very accurate. When very hungry the birds would attack objects other than the fish. It may be found of interest in this connection to say a few words about the way the young birds in captivity and those in the field spend the greater part of their time. We have already remarked upon the fact that there are no signs of play. This was as nearly true of the birds in the field as of those observed in captivity. The only reaction which it is at all possible to consider a playful one is the one already mentioned, viz., the frequent hopping up and flapping of the wings. It is a question whether Gross' theory of play after all fits the facts in any genus of animals except that of mammals. Certainly the facts which we could gather both with reference to the noddy and sooty terns do not lend support to this theory. These birds certainly lead an instinctively complex life. Surely the picking up of a live fish darting over the surface of the water is as complex an act as the catching of a mouse. And yet it is impossible to practise this act in play. Probably the instinct is perfectly and completely called out the first time the birds see a minnow darting over the surface of the water. The birds spend the greater part of their time in doing *absolutely nothing*. They will lie outstretched in their sand holes, getting up at times to stand stock still for an hour or more, or to doze with head bent down. At intervals they peck at their feet and occasionally preen their feathers. In the field the routine is broken by the call from the parents which have returned to feed the young. At other times the young birds get hungry. At such times they begin to cry lustily and go up to the parent (which is likewise standing or fighting in the neighborhood) and beg for food by " peeping " and by striking at the parent's beak. Getting nothing, the young birds will wander off for 10 or 15 feet and lie down again in the shade. Frequently they engage in fighting with other young birds. Occasionally they will attack adult noddies which drop down to gather sticks. The young sooty never attacks an adult sooty. As the birds get older they begin to fly short distances. At the end of 35 days they can cover 30 to 40 feet very rapidly by a series of flying hops.

III. Quantitative study of improvement of instinctive function.—Under I we considered the initial performance of several instinctive acts. Much has been said and written about the degree of perfectness of such acts and about the rapidity of their rate of improvement when exercised. Within recent years efforts have been made to obtain a quantitative report on the initial accuracy of such acts and their rate of improvement.

Breed has presented an interesting investigation of the pecking reaction of the chick. For purposes of study he divides the act into (1) missing, (2) striking, (3) seizing, and (4) swallowing. The curves showing the rate of improvement in swallowing (4) are the most instructive and interesting in this connection, since under the term swallowing he includes the whole reaction, i.e., successful striking, seizing, and swallowing in any errorless chain of movements. On the second day the chick is presented with small grains at which it begins to peck. The number of correct reactions the chick makes in 50 attempts to take up the grains is noted. The same routine is repeated each day for 25 days. Thus it was found that the average number of correct (complete) responses obtainable on the second day in one group was 10.3; on the third day, 28.3; on the seventh day, 38.3; on the sixteenth day, 43.2. Initial accuracy of the whole act is thus low, but the increase during the first few days of practice is enormous. Fig. 29, curve IV-E, portrays the result Breed obtained from a group of 6 chicks. (In the same figure, curve IV-F, is shown a similar set of records of chicks, which had been allowed to watch the pecking of older birds. This curve will be discussed on p. 141.)

Granting that we can measure the degree of accuracy and general perfectness of an instinctive act, the question of interpretation still arises. Lacking experimental evidence, it is easily possible for one to affirm that the increase of the perfectness of the act comes not by virtue of the exercise or practice of the function, but rather by maturation of the sensory motor arcs (including here developmental or growth processes in receptor, system of conductors, and the effector). The obvious way to control these factors is to prevent those arcs from functioning until maturation in them has partially advanced. We can

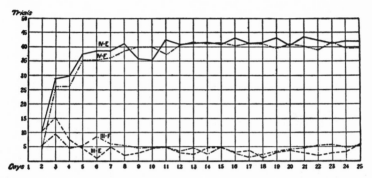

FIG. 29. A Comparison of Curves of Development of the Pecking Instinct to Show the Possible Effect of Social Influence

Distances along axis of abscissæ represent days of age; distances along axis of ordinates, the number of a given type of reaction in a daily series of fifty pecking reactions. Curves III-E and III-F show respectively the rate of decrease in the number of reaction 3 for groups E and F; curves IV-E and IV-F show the improvement in accuracy of reaction 4 for the same groups. (After Breed, *Behavior Monograph*, Ser. No. 1, p. 31.)

then test the accuracy of the function under the two conditions of practice and non-practice. The comparison of the two sets of records ought to enable us to separate the increment due to practice from that due to maturation. Some experiments have been made with this object in view: Fig. 30 shows the development of the normal pecking reaction in chicks and the development where pecking has been artificially prevented for 3, 4, and 5 days previous to the first tests. The curves were obtained in a way similar to the ones just discussed. The number of perfect, complete reactions were recorded in each daily set of 50 trials. It will be seen that the standard curve (S), beginning on the second day, shows that the average number of correct responses on that day was 8.7; on the seventh day, 36.7; on the twentieth day, 40.8. This standard curve is based on the average of 21 chicks. Curve I shows what happens when pecking is prevented for 3 days; curve III likewise for 3 days; curve IV, for 4 days; and curve V, for 5 days. During the days in which pecking

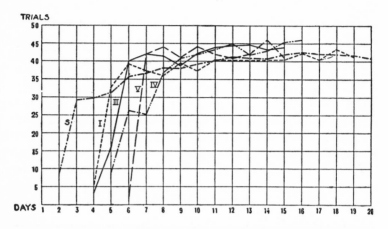

FIG. 30. CURVES SHOWING THE COURSE OF DEVELOPMENT OF THE
PECKING INSTINCT AFTER ARTIFICIAL DELAY

S, standard curve, representing rate of improvement in accuracy under natural conditions. I, III, IV, and V, curves for corresponding groups of chicks in which the action of the instinct has been artificially prevented for three, three, four, and five days, respectively, previous to the first tests. (After Breed and Shepard, *Jour. Animal Behav.*, 1912, p. 278.)

was prevented, the animals were watered and fed artificially and confined to the dark room. In general it may be seen from these curves that the initial efficiency is low in every case, no matter what length of time is allowed for maturation. The number of normal responses on the first day (i.e., when the chicks were 2 days of age) was 8.7 out of a possible 50. The average number of perfect responses in the group in which pecking was prevented for 1 day was 5.5; for 2 days, 3.1; for 4 days, 8.7; and for 5 days, 2. No one could have predicted that a 5-day-old chick, prevented from previous pecking, would start in with an accuracy no greater than that found in chicks 24 hours of age. The next interesting point in the tests on the chicks which were prevented from pecking appears when it is seen that the curves showing their rate of improvement very quickly advance to the level of the standard (S), only 2 days of practice as a rule being necessary to effect this.[4] From these experiments it seems safe to conclude that the enormous increase in the accuracy of pecking during the first three or four days, which is always observable in chicks which are brought up under normal conditions, is due to the effect of practice as we ordinarily understand the term.

IV. Modification of instinct through social influences.—Several interesting experiments have been carried out on young birds to show the types of song and call notes which they exhibit when reared in isolation from adults of their own species, and to show the effects of the song and call notes of a given species upon the young of another species. It is admitted by all that the various birds, such as the robin, the bobolink, and the oriole, when reared

---

[4] These writers hold that a given amount of practice is necessary to smooth the way for the operation of a native capacity whose efficiency is largely a function of the age of the animal. They hold that such a curve has two parts—the early state (2 days of practice) showing effects of practice; the latter stage (from this point on, where a slow but steady increase in accuracy is shown) showing the slow process of maturation. This conclusion is surely questionable and certainly confusing. The curve exhibits what every habit curve in animals shows, i.e., a rapid initial increase in efficiency and then a slow increase until the level of no further improvement is reached. Unless the writers are willing to admit that the latter part of every habit curve is illustrative of *maturation*, it seems useless to use such a terminology here. They may intend to imply this; but what such " maturation " would mean in the case of habit formation in the adult is not clear. The authors are not quite consistent in the use of the term anyway. In the beginning of the article one gets the idea that they mean what one commonly would mean by it, i.e., actual growth, increase in size and length of conductors, possible increase in the number of connections, increase in size and efficiency of the effector, etc., and possibly certain structural growth of the receptors. In the latter part of the article, they use it without giving the reader a clear idea of how they would define it. These growth processes may influence the rate of improvement in the function whose accuracy they measured, but the writers offer no real evidence of it, since exactly the same results are obtained whenever habit curves are recorded.

in the field by the parents, possess songs which are characteristic. Until recent years it was supposed that the
characteristic songs of birds were inherited, like instincts.
Apparently this is not wholly true. It would seem from
the work of Scott and Conradi that what the birds inherit
is a strong tendency to sing, but that no characteristic
song develops without training. What are inherited are
throat formation and vocal apparatus suitable to produce
the song of the race if the bird is thrown under the proper
influences (habit). Scott isolated Baltimore orioles before
they had heard any of the songs of their species. He observed the birds for a number of years. They became very
gentle in their artificial environment. The early vocal
reflexes were quite similar to those of the wild birds, e.g.,
the single call note, the peculiar rattling chatter, etc. The
birds finally became good singers. During certain seasons
of the year song was incessant. " It was now a loud clear
series of notes of great brilliancy, poured forth in such
rapid succession as to be like that of the house wren
(*T. aëdon*) in the intervals, and lasting about as long as
the warble of that bird. Except for the rattle, which was
now and then a part of the repertoire, this song had nothing in it that reminded one of the song of the Baltimore
oriole as heard in New York, Massachusetts, or at any
other point where the birds occur." The birds dwelling
thus in isolation developed a song of their own. The experimenter next put a young brood of Baltimore orioles
6 days of age to live with 2 adult birds that had
been brought up in isolation. This young brood began
to sing at the proper age, but to sing the song of their
2 adult associates. This same author found very great
modification in the songs of the various species of birds
when some 15 to 16 different species were brought up together and within hearing of one another's songs and the
songs and call notes of their neighbors on the outside of
the aviary. Some of the birds were more resistant to such
influences than others. The robin had what Scott called
an invented song. The wood-thrush's song, while varying
much from the normal, was not original. All of the cat-

birds showed mimicry of the songs of other birds. In particular he found a yellow-breasted chat learning to imitate the postman's whistle with such a degree of accuracy that the experimenter was often deceived. One of the red-wing blackbirds crowed constantly for two months in the year. The crow was in imitation of the crow of a bantam rooster. Conradi reared a young English sparrow in the same room with canaries. The regular sparrow chirp developed at the proper time, although the bird had never heard this chirp from the outside. Probably under the influence of his canary-bird environment, he lost the chirp and took on the peep similar to the peep of the young canaries. When the bird was about three and a half months old '' he constantly chimed in with the canaries in his own fashion, giving a low note followed by a few high notes, with now and then some slurring from a high to a low note, similar to the notes the canaries have in their overtures. He joined the canaries freely for a few days, when he became ill and was silent for a week.'' Two weeks later he again joined the canary chorus. In general Conradi says that the sparrow's efforts resembled the confusion of notes which occurred when all three of his adult canaries were singing at their best. These experiments were repeated upon other sparrows, in some cases even with more marked success. The sparrows so trained by the canaries were then removed to a place where they would be away from the canaries and under the influence of a group of sparrows which frequented that part of the building. They rapidly lost their canary notes and readopted a considerable part of the sparrow chirp. Nevertheless, their voices remained more musical than those of the untrained sparrows. When again placed under the influence of the canaries they rapidly regained what they had lost.

Breed carried out some experiments upon the chick to determine the effect of social influence upon the development of the pecking instinct. In the one case the chick was allowed to develop its pecking instinct in isolation; in another, the chick was allowed to develop the pecking reaction where it could watch the pecking of older birds. In general it was found that the effect of social influence was practically *nil* in increasing the rate of improvement in accuracy of the pecking reaction. Curve IV-F, Fig. 29, p. 139, shows the growth of the reaction where tuition is allowed; curve IV-E where tuition is denied. In general the two curves are closely similar. Apparently both the dove and the chick are influenced to some extent by their mates, so far as the initiation of the drinking and pecking instincts is concerned, i.e., when two or three chicks out of a brood begin to either peck or drink, the act serves as a stimulus and causes the others to engage in the same activity.

V. Hereditary character of certain instinctive acts and traits.—Yerkes has so far made the only contribution bearing directly upon the heredity of instinctive acts and traits. He has recently tested the heritability of savageness, wildness, and timidity in certain strains of rats. He first tested the rats and graded them with respect to the presence of these traits. On regrading after an interval of several days he found that the judgment as to the grades of savageness or wildness remained almost constant.

Savageness was indicated by (1) biting; (2) exposing or gnashing the teeth; (3) jumping at hand or forceps; (4) squeaking. *Wildness* by (1) attempts to hide from view in cage or in hand; (2) random or excited running about in the cage or excited attempts to escape from the hand or forceps; (3) squeaking; (4) urination and defecation. *Timidity* by (1) attempts to avoid the experimenter; (2) by a kind of chattering or gnashing of the teeth; (3) by cowering and what looks like trembling; (4) urination and defecation. Timidity is possibly not sharply enough marked off from the other traits to measure it quantitatively.

The wild rats possessing these traits were then mated with strains of tame rats which had been bred in the Harvard laboratory for at least 10 years. The offspring (F_1) from these crosses were tested, as likewise the progeny (F_2) obtained by mating the individuals of F_1 among themselves. Yerkes holds that his tests show conclusively that savageness, wildness, and timidity are heritable behavior complexes.[5] This same author tested the heritability of the mode of whirling in the dancing mouse. The dancers may be classified into right, left, and mixed whirlers. In one line of descent (No. 400) he found the tendency to whirl to the left was heritable.

In view of observations of Franz that certain monkeys are left-handed and certain others right-handed, it would be interesting to test the heritability of the preferential use of right or left hand.

VI. Waning of instinct: loss through disuse, etc.—In the case of mammals one instinct common to many species exhibits the process of waning very clearly. This instinct in question is that of carrying the young from place to place in the mouth. The following quotation is taken from one of the author's early observations upon the white rat:

"Within the last two days (when young were from 12 to 14 days of age) a change has come over the mother. When the rats were 10 days old the mother would become frantic if one of them were taken beyond her grasp. At 14 days of age she was not at all worried when I took one of them out for an experiment. Indeed for two days past she has not received the young rats in her mouth when they entered the cage, but has allowed them to scramble through the straw to her as best they could."

While this instinct wanes as the general cycle of instincts changes, it reappears with all its vigor on the birth of the next litter of young. The process of weaning in nearly every case is a gradual one. We have under observation a young monkey (*M. rhesus*) nearly 18 months of age which is still nursing. There is no actual necessity for nursing longer than 18 weeks (even less).

There are no reliable observations which have been experimentally controlled on the loss of instinct through disuse. The case of the Scotch terrier attempting to bury food in the carpet and then finally giving over the attempt on all subsequent occasions has often been cited.[6] The

[5] Yerkes' complete report has not yet appeared.

[6] An interesting case of elaboration of this instinct to bury food appears in an observation made by Frost (*Journal of Animal Be-*

observation comes from William James. The observation, so far as it goes, is unquestionably true, but there is no evidence that the instinct is lost. Given the proper environment and the proper conditions of hunger, and we should expect to see the instinct reappear in all its pristine vigor. In the further case cited by Mr. James, viz., that of the young goslings kept away from water, a similar lack of control in the experiment is apparent. Spalding, who made the test, states that when the goslings were reared in a kitchen away from water until they were several months old and then taken to a pond, they not only refused to go into the water but scrambled back to the bank the moment they were thrown into it. It is quite possible that if Spalding had taken goslings that had been reared in the water and tossed them in in this way, they would have done exactly the same thing. There is room for interesting work upon this question. That instincts are overlapped and obscured by later habits is unquestionable. Whether this process of obscuration results finally in the complete elimination of the instinct is certainly not proven by any observation we have in the field at the present time.

BIBLIOGRAPHY

ALLEN, J., "The Associative Processes of the Guinea Pig," *Jour. Comp. Neu. and Psych.*, 1904, XIV, 293.

BERRY, C. S., "An Experimental Study of Imitation in Cats," *Jour. Comp. Neu. and Psych.*, 1908, XVIII, 1.

BREED, FRED S., "The Development of Certain Instincts and Habits in Chicks," *Behavior Monographs*, Ser. No. 1.

BREED, FRED S., and SHEPARD, J. F., "Maturation and Use in the Development of an Instinct," *Jour. Animal Beh.*, 1913, III, 274.

CONRADI, E., "Song and Call Notes of English Sparrows When Reared by Canaries," *Am. Jour. Psych.*, 1905, XVI, 190.

CRAIG, WALLACE, "Behavior of Young Birds in Breaking Out of the Egg," *Jour. Animal Beh.*, 1913, II, 296.

——————— "Observations on Doves Learning to Drink," *Jour. Animal Beh.*, 1913, II, 273.

havior, 1913, p. 145). The squirrel at times buries nuts in separate caches, and on later occasions revisits these separate caches and assembles all in one hiding place. This was observed while snow completely covered the ground. The finding of the separate hiding places seems to be almost instantaneous with the squirrel.

FRANZ, S. I., "Observations on the Preferential Use of the Right and Left Hand by Monkeys," *Jour. Animal Beh.*, 1913, III, 140.

JAMES, WILLIAM, *Principles of Psychology.* New York, Henry Holt, 1890.

LASHLEY, K. S., and WATSON, J. B., "Notes on the Development of a Young Monkey," *Jour. Animal Beh.*, 1913, III, 114.

NEWMAN, H. H., "The Habits of Certain Tortoises," *Jour. Comp. Neu. and Psych.*, 1906, XVI, 126.

PECKHAM, G. W. and E. G., *Wasps, Social and Solitary.* Boston, 1905.

REIGHARD, JACOB, "The Natural History of Amia Calva Linnæus," *Mark Anniversary Volume*, 1903.

SCOTT, W. E. D., "Song in Birds," *Science*, 1901, XIV, 522.

———————— "Data on Song in Birds," *Science*, 1902, XV, 178.

———————— "The Inheritance of Song," *Science*, 1904, XIX, 154, 957.

———————— "Rearing Wild Finches," *Science*, 1904, XIX, 551.

SHERRINGTON, C. S., *The Integrative Action of the Nervous System.* New York, Scribner's, 1906.

SMALL, W. S., "Notes on the Psychic Development of the Young White Rat," *Am. Jour. Psych.*, 1899, XI, 80.

SUMNER, F. B., "The Adjustment of Flatfish to Various Backgrounds," *Jour. Exp. Zool.*, X, 409.

WATSON, J. B., "The Behavior of Noddy and Sooty Terns," *Carnegie Pub.*, No. 103.

WHEELER, WILLIAM MORTON, "Ants, Their Structure, Development and Behavior." New York, Columbia Univ. Press, 1910.

YERKES, R. M., *The Dancing Mouse.* New York, Macmillan, 1907.

———————— "The Heredity of Savageness and Wildness in Rats," *Jour. Animal Beh.*, 1913, III, 286.

YERKES, R. M., and BLOOMFIELD, DANIEL, "Do Kittens Instinctively Kill Mice?" *Psych. Bull.*, 1910, VII, 253.

CHAPTER V

CONCERNING THE ORIGIN OF INSTINCTS

Introduction.—In the preceding chapter we dealt with certain activities on the part of the animal which do not have to be learned. We intimated there that such activities or instincts appear because of the fact that the animal is born with certain systems of arcs ready to function in serial order the moment the appropriate stimulus appears (as has been brought out, many such systems are not ready to function until definite intervals after birth). We wish now to consider especially the origin of such structures. It can readily be seen, since instincts are but the functioning of certain preformed structures, that any consideration of the origin of the special structures underlying them must inevitably involve a consideration of the origin of the whole organism. It is not our purpose to enter the field of experimental evolution except for the purpose of bringing out certain facts which appear to be helpful in envisaging our own problems. One such group of facts which especially concerns the behaviorist comes from embryology.

Early differentiation of parts.—Embryology teaches us but little of the early differentiation and growth of particular reflex arcs. In regard to the larger divisions of the nervous system the case is different. The investigations of Harrison, Lewis, Spemann, Hooker, and others show that the gross development of neural structure is

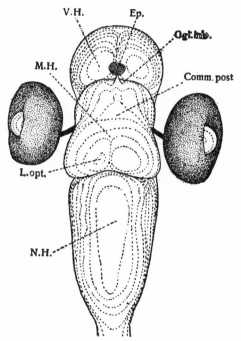

FIG. 31.   NORMAL BRAIN OF FROG EMBYRO

V.H., fore brain; M.H., midbrain; Comm. post., posterior commissure; Ep., epiphysis.

determined early in the course of embryonic development and progresses to a large extent independently of the changes which occur in other organs. Spemann's experiments bring this out with great clearness. He cut out small pieces from the floor of the medullary plate of the frog embryo and replaced them in a reversed position so that the end which before had been anterior was now posterior. The embryos continued to develop; the neural grooves closed, and eventually brains were formed. But these brains showed marked abnormalities. In many cases two sets of optic cups were produced and the normal relation of parts within the brain was much disturbed. The structures produced were those which the reversed tissue

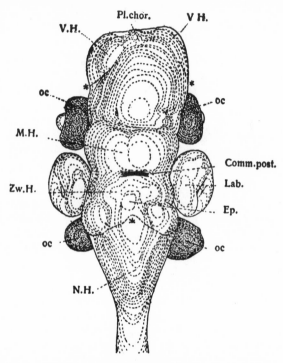

FIG. 32.   BRAIN FORMED AFTER THE INCISION OF A PORTION OF THE FLOOR OF THE MEDULLARY PLATE

The dotted line -------- indicates the boundary of the disturbed area. The chief relations of these areas are reversed; a second pair of optic cups has been produced behind the labyrinth, and the thalamus, Zw. H., lies behind the posterior commissure. (Both cuts after Spemann, *Zool. Jahrb.*, 1912, Taf. 1.)

would have produced if undisturbed, but their positions were now reversed.

"The gross form relations of the grafted pieces naturally undergo a certain amount of modification at their boundaries but the recognizable portions retain even here their peculiar tendencies to development. The finer differentiation proceeds, not only in the middle of the reversed piece but even at the borders where the cells have been brought into new and abnormal relations. For some time there is a distinct boundary along which the different tissues may be distinguished by their appearance. Thus it follows that both the gross relationships and the finer differentiation of individual parts of the brain are already determined in the open medullary plate."

Fig. 32 shows such a brain. For comparison a normal brain is also given.

Not only have the various parts of the nervous system this early independence of development but the extraneural structures as well. Goldfarb destroyed the spinal cord of the newt in the lumbo-sacral region together with the sensory ganglia of the nerves of this region, thus cutting off entirely the nerve supply of the hind legs. Regeneration occurred in such animals just as in normal ones, growth and differentiation of the regenerating foot taking place in some cases after the complete degeneration of all nerve elements of the leg. Growth of neural and extraneural structures thus seems to be relatively independent. It is thus clear that one result of a great part of the work in experimental embryology has been the establishment of the fact that many of the final details of the structure of the adult are already determined in the early cleavage stages of the egg before any differentiation can be recognized. It would seem from this that we can safely assume that what is true of the gross anatomical structure of the brain and nerves is also true of the microscopic structures, of the position, number, and possible interconnections of the neurones, i.e., of the reflex arcs. If this is true it means that the special systems of arcs underlying instinctive activity are predetermined in some way in the egg. It is probable, furthermore, that at the birth of the animal or soon afterwards all possible nervous connections are already established and that all later development—all adjustments of the animal to changes in its environment by habit formation involve only changes in resistance through various inherited arcs. Thus the possible habits which an organism may acquire are limited by its nervous structures.

I. Heredity: the Concept of Unit Characters

Unit characters.—These embryological studies from the standpoint of our very special interests teach us little more than that the structure which must later develop into the anatomical mechanism of instinct is already present in the fertilized egg of the given species. They teach us little about the process by means of which one egg will produce a mammal, another a bird, or of the manner in which one chick forms white feathers and another barred. Or put in another way, how it comes about that one mammalian egg will develop into a form which will possess the structures involved in catching and killing mice, and another egg will develop into a form which will gnaw down trees and construct a dam. Nevertheless, in spite of our ignorance of the way in which such differences are produced, it has been found possible to determine beforehand, from a consideration of the characters of the parents, many characters which will appear in the new-born animal. This may be illustrated by numerous examples. Possibly an illustration of the inheritance of combs in the domestic fowl will be best for our purpose. Three types of combs are commonly met with. The most common type is the single comb, which is high, relatively narrow, and deeply toothed (Fig. 33—A). The second type, the pea comb, is smaller, less notched, and is ridged lengthwise (Fig. 33—B and C). The third type is the rose comb, flat, broad, triangular, and covered with numerous papillæ (Fig. 33—D). When fowls bearing pea combs are crossed with others bearing single ones their progeny all have pea combs. In the next generation obtained by interbreeding these hybrids the single comb appears again in one-fourth of the birds. The remaining three-fourths have pea combs. The same thing occurs when rose and single combed birds are crossed. Their progeny will have rose combs and when interbred will produce rose and single combed birds in the proportions of three to one. When rose and pea combed birds are crossed the results are, in the first generation, quite different. The progeny have neither rose nor pea combs, but an entirely new type which consists of an irregular fleshy knob at the front of the head, the back of the head being rather bare, the so-called walnut comb (Fig 33—E). When walnut combed fowls are interbred they give walnut, pea, rose, and single combed progeny in the proportions of 9 : 3 : 3 : 1. There are some irregularities in the proportions, and the mechanism by which they are brought about is too

FIG. 33. VARIOUS TYPES OF COMBS IN FOWLS

A, single comb; B, pea comb: cock; C, pea comb: hen; D, rose comb (bantam) cock; E, walnut comb in young cock. (After Bateson: Mendel's *Principles of Heredity*, Cambridge, 1909. Permission to use this cut was kindly granted by the press of Gustav Fischer.)

complicated to be entered into here. The important fact for our present purpose is that when the progeny of any cross are interbred among themselves, they produce in their progeny not only their own type, but also that of both their parents, and in quite definite proportions. The characters do not lose their identity in hybrids but reappear unchanged in later generations and appear, moreover, in definite proportions which may be determined empirically. The example of the fowls illustrates Mendel's law of segregation and heredity, the principle of which may best be shown by a brief summary of some of its discoverer's own experiments.

MENDEL'S EXPERIMENTS: Mendel bred different varieties of common garden peas and studied, among other characters, the form and coloration of the seeds. When he bred plants from varieties bearing smooth seeds with others from varieties bearing wrinkled seeds, he found that all the seeds produced from this cross mating were smooth. The character of wrinkledness seemed to have been lost entirely. But the next generation, grown from these seeds, when interbred among themselves gave 7,324 seeds, of which 5,474 were round and 1,850 were wrinkled; a proportion of about 3 to 1. The character of wrinkledness had not been lost completely but had only withdrawn from observation. Each of the two characters retained its own individuality in the cross. In the next generation from these plants Mendel found that wrinkled seeds produced only wrinkled ones; the smooth seeds gave rise to plants of two sorts. One-third of them gave plants which produced only smooth seeds even after several generations of close inbreeding; the remaining two-thirds produced both smooth and wrinkled seeds and again in the proportion of 3 to 1. They were in all respects like the first generation hybrids.

If we suppose that the two characters are absolutely independent of each other, that either one or both may be present potentially in the organism, and that the presence of one, roundness, hides the presence of the other, these proportions may be explained. The first generation hybrids receive from one parent the capacity to be round, from the other the capacity to be wrinkled. The roundness prevails in this generation, but the thing which causes wrinkledness, the *determiner,* persists unchanged though hidden. When the adults of this generation produce new germ cells, these germ cells may receive either determiner for roundness or that for wrinkledness, not for both. Since all the hybrids produce both egg cells and pollen grains containing both determiners in equal numbers, all possible pairing of the determiners may occur in the fertilized eggs, i.e., individuals may be formed having either two determiners for roundness; one determiner for roundness and one for wrinkledness; or two for wrinkledness. Those which contain any determiner for roundness will be round, so that only one in every four pairings will be wrinkled. These relations can best be shown by the consideration of a simple diagram.

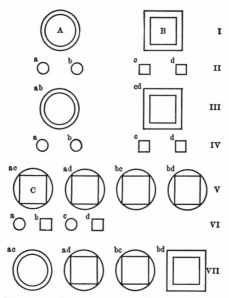

FIG. 34. DIAGRAM ILLUSTRATING MENDELIAN INHERITANCE

The above diagram illustrates the explanation which has been advanced to account for the proportions obtained when individuals differing with respect to a single character are crossed, as in the case of the peas. The circles may be considered as smoothness and the squares as wrinkledness. The first three lines, I, II, and III, show the condition of reproduction in lines breeding true to type. A and B represent the two types, each of which can give off germ cells of its own type only (II, ab and cd). So long as the individuals of each line are bred separately they can produce only the combinations *ab* and *cd*. But when the two lines are crossed, every germ cell of A unites with a germ cell of B to produce an individual having determiners for both smoothness and wrinkleness (C). All the individuals of this first hybrid generation will have the same make-up and all will be alike in appearance. Although both characters are present in this hybrid generation, one is hidden by the other, as the square is enclosed by the circle, so that, in external form, the individuals of type C are not to be distinguished from type A. When individuals of type C produce germ cells, they produce equal numbers containing the determiners for each of their characters, as is indicated in VI, a, b, c, d. When equal numbers of the two kinds of germ cells unite by chance, the result will be as indicated in VII. The possible combinations are ac, ad, bc, bd, which produce one of type A, two of type C, and one of type B, the proportions of 3 to 1, which Mendel obtained with peas, since types *A* and *C* are not distinguishable from their external form. When two or more pairs of characters are involved, as greenness *versus* yellowness, roundness *versus* wrinkledness, each pair is found to be inherited, as in the above example, but the two pairs are found to be independent of each other, so that they occur in all possible combinations: green-wrinkled, green-smooth, yellow-wrinkled, and yellow-smooth. In such a case the proportions obtained are 9 yellow-smooth, 3 yellow-wrinkled, 3 green-smooth, and 1 green-wrinkled. These are the proportions already mentioned in connection with the walnut combs of fowls and the proportions to be expected from the laws of chance.

Further details of the process, blending inheritance (as in the walnut comb), linkage of characters, and the structural basis of the process of inheritance need not be entered into here. Certain important features may be emphasized. First: the parts, organs, or characters of the plant or animal are to a great extent independent in inheritance (hair color may be inherited from one parent and hair form from the other). Second: the characters are not altered in their passage from one generation to the next; they may blend together in the hybrid, as the rose and pea combs blend to form the walnut comb, but they will separate eventually into the component parts.

Some attempts have been made to apply these laws to behavior complexes, but as yet psychology has provided little foundation for such studies. The most thoroughgoing attempts have been made with human mental traits and some evidence has been collected here in favor of the view that differences in the instinctive behavior of individuals are inherited according to Mendelian ratios. But in the field of human psychology too little is known of the genesis of character, of the distinction between native and acquired behavior, to provide a very firm foundation for the work of the geneticist. A few studies of the inheritance of some more readily determined characters have been made upon animals. On p. 144 we presented the work of Yerkes on the direction of whirling in the dancer and upon the inheritance of the instinctive traits of boldness, timidity, etc., in the rat. Certain studies have also been made upon the inheritance of wildness in ducks. Kammerer has found that certain variations in the brooding instincts of the obstetrical toad are inherited in Mendelian ratios. None of the other studies has been carried far enough to show that the traits studied reappear in the offspring in Mendelian ratios.

II. Origin of Diversities in Organisms

Introduction.—The laws of heredity thus far considered apply only to the transmission of characters already present in the organism. They say nothing as to the origin of these characters, yet the wide diversity of instincts with which the behaviorist is constantly confronted suggests, perhaps first of all, the question: how could such diverse forms of behavior have come into existence? This is a part of the problem of evolution, of which Bateson says, summing up the work bearing upon the question:

" The many converging lines of evidence point so clearly to the central fact of the origin of the forms of life by an evolutionary process that we are compelled to accept this deduction, but as to almost all the essential features, whether of cause or mode, by which specific diversity has become what we perceive it to be, we have to confess an ignorance nearly total."

While the origin of a new race or type of animals has been observed in but few cases (and some writers are inclined to believe that even these are not truly new, but merely the reappearance of something already present but hidden), the indirect evidence obtained from comparative anatomy, embryology, and historical geology is so complete as to leave no room for doubt that new forms are constantly arising from the old, by some process the details of which are not yet clear.

In the present incomplete stage of the problem it will be impossible to reach any final conclusion as to the manner in which evolution has taken place. At best we can but point out the paths of investigation which promise to yield the solution of the problem, and summarize (very incompletely) the evidence which has been collected in support of the various theories as to how new characters arise. The first students of evolution sought to find the method of origin of new species, of groups of animals differing rather markedly from other groups, usually with respect to several characters. The results of Mendelian experiments have changed this point of view in great measure. The student of evolution is now concerned chiefly with the origin of single new characters, of " unit characters," such as the wrinkledness of the pea or the single comb of the fowl. Davenport says of this:

" The fact that most characteristics are not necessarily associated— that they may occur in various combinations—certainly accounts for the multiplicity of 'varieties' in domesticated species; and for much of the variation in feral species. Moreover, it probably accounts for the presence of many 'species' in a genus."

In order to recognize the origin of a new character, it is necessary that the experimenter be thoroughly familiar with the normal conditions in a small group of related organisms. Not only must he know what characters are present visibly in the bodies or *soma* of his material, but he must know also what characters are *potentially present* in their germ cells, as *recessives* in the Mendelian sense. Students of variations have accomplished this in investigations of many morphological characters, such as hair color in mice; but students of behavior have been lax in analyzing and recording the many individual differences in instinctive behavior which have come to their attention. The few studies of variation in instinct which have thus far been completed have given results of considerable importance for theories of evolution. Practically all of the work has been done by students of the inheritance of acquired characters and will be considered with the evidence bearing upon this problem. Owing to the lack of material in the field of behavior, it will be necessary to base our discussion of the method of the origin of variations upon morphological studies of extra-neural structure, disregarding, for the moment, the difference between structure and behavior; or rather, assuming that there is no fundamental difference between the two, since, ultimately, all behavior must be looked upon as the functioning of structure.

Darwin's conception of variations.—Recent studies of variation, with advancing knowledge of the mechanism of heredity, have shown clearly that not all diversities (variations) are of the same nature either with respect to causation or heritability. This fact was perceived vaguely by the early investigators, but they did not understand its full significance. Darwin distinguished at least two kinds of variations: the so-called *continuous* ones, constantly exhibited by all organisms, slight differences of size, proportion, depth of pigmentation, etc., in which continuous series may be recognized; and *discontinuous* variations, sports or monsters which appear suddenly, differ rather widely from the racial type, and show no intermediate stages. He considered this latter class as of little significance in evolution, as mere accidents of nature, of too rare occurrence or of too extreme a form to affect the course of development of species. The former class, he believed, furnished the differences, which, preserved and fixed by natural selection, formed the basis for new varieties. Concerning the cause of these variations he was uncertain, but inclined to ascribe them to some fundamental property of living matter, of equal rank with irritability or with the power of reproduction itself.

Continuous variation due to the direct action of environment upon the developing organism.—It is now generally admitted that continuous variation is due to the direct action of the environment upon the body or soma of the developing organisms. If large numbers of individuals of any pure race of animals or plants are considered, it will be found that the greatest number of them are nearly alike, forming the racial average, while the variants in the two directions from the racial average grow proportionately fewer, with an increasing degree of variation. This condition may be illustrated by a group of measurements of the size of bean seeds descended from a single individual (a pure line)—taken from the measurements of Johannsen.

Class distribution; weight in centigramms.	10	15	20	25	30	35	40	45	50	55	60	65
Number of seeds of each weight in the group of related seeds.	8	18	71	156	172	127	35	15	3	6		

As was first shown by Quetelet, the distribution of such variations around the racial average follows the law of chance distribution. The effect of environment upon the production of variation in the soma can be seen quite clearly in the following investigations of Stockard, Fuld, and Cunningham. Stockard has shown that while the eggs of the fish (*Fundulus*) under ordinary conditions produce normal two-eyed fish, the addition of magnesium salts to the water causes them to develop into Cyclopean monsters. Some of the changes are apparently of such a nature as to make the animal better fitted to meet the demands of its environment. Thus, Fuld found that dogs which had their forelegs removed during the first year of life later showed changes in the proportion of the femur and tibia of the hind-legs which mimicked the normal conditions in leaping animals of the type of the hare. Cunningham illuminated the ventral surface of young flounders, which are normally unpigmented there, and induced the formation of pigment.

The non-inheritance of continuous variation.—The belief that continuous variations of the type considered are inherited was shared by all investigators up to recent times. The whole Darwinian theory of evolution is based upon this concept. In 1903 the heritability of continuous variations was put to a crucial test by W. Johannsen. He studied a population of beans and found that it was made up of a number of races which differed from each other in the average size of their seeds and in other characters. The descendants of one plant gave seeds of small size, varying, it is true, from small to medium, yet maintaining for generation after generation an *average* size considerably lower than that of the population. The variations within this race were not inherited at all; the smallest and largest seeds, if only they had the same ancestry, gave progeny of the same average size. The descendants of other plants taken from the mixed population had larger seeds and the difference between the races persisted for as many generations as they were studied. By selecting large and small individuals from the mixed population it was possible to isolate large or small races, but after the race was once isolated a selection of variations occurring within it did not lead to any change in the average size of the race.

Since the publication of this result the experiments of Jennings, De Vries, Pearl, Shull, Woltereck, and many others have confirmed it and extended it to many other classes of organisms. The results of this experimental work dealing with the constancy of heritable characters and the effects of selection of slight differences in these characters prove conclusively that the vast majority of the variations of organisms are not inherited. Just what is the cause of all such variations is not yet certain, but it is probable that all are the responses of the organism to changes in its environment and that these changes affect only the body of the individual and not the germ cells.[1] Fig. 35 (3) indicates this condition. The body of the organism is changed as an effect of environmental action, but its germ cells (represented in lighter color in the abdomen of the diagrammatic moth) and hence the characters of the progeny remain unchanged.

Discrete variation or mutations.—We have considered the lack of influence of continuous variations (fluctuating variations of Darwin) upon heredity. Darwin himself, as has already been noted, had observed another type of variation which he failed to consider because he believed that its occurrence was too rare to influence the course of evolution. He called such variations " sports " or monsters. The first investigator to lay great stress upon the importance of discontinuous variation of this type was De Vries, influenced by his work on the evening primrose (*Œnothera lamarckiana*). For over twenty years he bred this plant under conditions of scientific accuracy. His first culture gave a wholly new sport or mutation and in the continued cultivation of the plant many other mutants were obtained, some

---

[1] There is, however, accumulating a considerable body of evidence that indicates that *some* somatic variations, perhaps of a special kind, are inherited. This will be considered in the discussion of the inheritance of acquired characters.

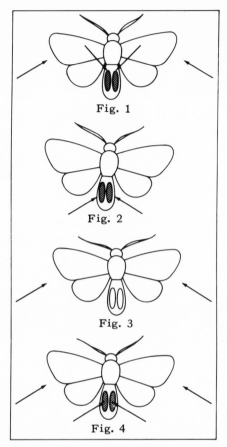

FIG. 35.   POSSIBLE MODES OF INHERITANCE OF NEW CHARACTERS

1. Somatic induction, the transmission of the effects of the environment upon the soma to the germ cells.   2. The direct action of the
environment of the organism upon the germ cells without effect upon
the body (ordinary mutations).   3. Somatic variation, changes in the
body which do not affect the germ cells.   4. Parallel induction, the
same changes produced by the independent action of the environment
upon the body and the germ cells.   From Kammerer, "Die Abstam-
mungslehre," Gustav Fischer, Jena, 1911 (after Ziegler).

of which, such as the giant and dwarf varieties, are very
striking.   Some fifteen types of mutants in the evening
primrose have been described, which for the most part breed

true, i.e., retain their individuality in later generations
when hybridized or inbred. De Vries obtained similar results with other plants and assumed that such discontinuous mutations furnish the differences which make the basis
for evolution.

The rediscovery of Mendel's laws of segregation and
heredity have made possible a different interpretation of
much of De Vries' material. In the light of these dis-
coveries it has been shown that his original strain of
O. lamarckiana was a poly-hybrid, and that most of the
mutants from it, if not all, were, in reality, but the reappearance of combinations of characters already present,
although hidden, in the original stock. But although the
greater part of the original mutations do not seem to have
produced anything new in the race, the impetus given to
the study of mutations by De Vries' work has led to the
discovery of other " sports " which seem really to have
produced something new. The number of such mutations
so far discovered in laboratory experiments which may be
truly said to add something not present in the parent stock,
i.e., to be progressive, is small. Many recorded mutants
seem rather to be due to the *loss* of some character. Thus
albinism, which has appeared more than once in a pure
strain, is due apparently, not to the addition of any factor
which will cause albinism, but rather to the loss of whatever substances in the germ cells cause the production of
pigment. In some cases progressive changes have appeared. Many such are recorded as occurring suddenly
among wild organisms, but the true nature of these is
usually uncertain. Several mutations have been experimentally produced by Standfuss, Fischer, Tower, Morgan,
and McDougall. Tower subjected various species of the
potato beetle at the time of the ripening of the germ cells
to extremes of temperature and moisture. The result was
the formation of many new types of beetles, differing most
conspicuously in pigmentation. These new beetles showed
no tendency to revert to the parent form but *bred true* for
generation after generation. Thus races having lighter
color, darker color, differences in the arrangement of the

markings on the wing covers, etc., were produced, races which were in all respects " good " species. Furthermore, it is asserted that these races differed in their instinctive equipment. Some, e.g., were far more rapacious than others.

Frequency of mutations.—Thus the sudden appearance of new, discontinuous, and heritable diversities in organisms may be looked upon as established. But there is little agreement as to the extent and frequency of such mutations. There seems to be a growing tendency among biologists to hold that they may be, in many cases, of very slight extent and of very great number, so as to form what is almost a continuous series. Davenport brings out this point of view clearly in the following:

"Sometimes a prominent character is represented by a single determiner like (perhaps) roseness of the comb of the fowl; but in most cases there is a multiplicity of factors, as in human hair and skin pigments, in the yellow of mice, in shank feathering of fowls, and in seed coats of oats. In consequence of the fact of this multiplicity of factors and of the fact that a variable number may be present in different cases, the adult character appears in numerous grades of development.

Indeed, the gradation of characters is, in these cases, such that one has to recognize that discontinuous variation passes over into continuous variation, in the sense that 40, 41, 42 form a continuous series, if not in the sense that X, $X + dX$, $X + 2dX$, etc., do. If a desire for uniformity leads us to conclude that all variations in the germ-plasm are discontinuous, at least we see in many of these variations sufficient justification for the continuity hypothesis of the old-fashioned selectionist."

Cause of mutation.—When we come to ask the cause of mutation we find very little certain evidence. Various theories have been advanced and must be considered in some detail. A possibility which has received great emphasis in the past, chiefly in the works of Weismann, is to be found in the union of diverse elements in the two germ cells at the time of fertilization. We have seen that such union does sometimes produce new forms by combination of Mendelian unit characters, as in the production of the walnut comb of the fowl. But in such cases the new character does not seem to be permanent, but breaks up in later generations into its component parts. Whether new and fixed forms may be produced in this way is not yet decided. The results of Morgan upon linkage of characters suggest that this is quite possible if a rearrangement of the constituents of the chromosomes takes place in such a way that characters which originally segregated freely can no longer do so. The greater amount of evidence points to the direct action of the environment upon the *germ cells* as the cause of mutation. McDougall injected various chemicals into the immature ovaries of *Œnothera biennis* with the result that new heritable forms were produced. Similar results were obtained with other plants. Standfuss and Fischer have produced new forms of the butterflies *Vanessa* and *Arctia* by subjecting the pupæ to low temperatures, and similar results have been obtained with other lepidopterous insects. Tower, as we saw on p. 163, has obtained mutations by subjecting the pupæ of the potato beetle (*Leptinotarsa*) to abnormal conditions of temperature and moisture during the period when the germ cells are ripening. This type of evidence, of which a considerable amount has been collected, goes far towards proving the dependence of mutations upon changes in the germ cells caused by direct environmental action. Whether or not this is the only cause of progressive mutation cannot be decided from the evidence at hand. Whatever be the cause, it is certain· that many differences in organisms do arise suddenly as " sports " and are transmitted unchanged to the descendants of the individuals first showing them.

Mutations not swamped by cross-breeding.—In so far as the transmission of the new characters produced by mutation has been studied it appears to follow the laws of Mendelian heredity (p. 154). The new characters retain their individuality and are not swamped by cross-breeding with the race from which the mutant sprang. This fact is of extreme importance for evolution, since new characters produced by mutation are thus fixed immediately and give rise to new races which are in no danger of being swamped by interbreeding with the great mass of the population.

Frequent repetition of the same mutation.—Another fact of importance is that when a group of organisms has once produced a mutation, the probability is that the same mutation will occur again and again. De Vries was the first to point out this condition. He obtained the same mutant many times from his cultures of *Œnothera*. The same condition has been observed in other organisms. This interesting fact may be explained either upon the assumption that the environmental action was the same in the various cases, or that some factor within the plant determined the form of the mutation, without regard to the nature of the environmental stimulus. The latter seems to be the true one. MacDougall obtained the same type of mutants from plants whose ovaries had been injected with different chemicals and treated with radium. He also obtained different mutants from different plants injected with the same chemical.

Such results suggest that the type of the mutation is determined by something already present in the organism and that the unusual conditions in the environment serve to start the change. The abnormal environment sets off the mutation, but it appears that the character of the latter is determined by the nature of the organism in which it occurs. This fact leads to another important conclusion, that there is no adaptive relation between the mutation and the environment. So far as can be determined from the evidence at hand, the application of excessive heat to growing rats might, conceivably, produce either extra toes or sparse hair in the next generation.

The Darwinian conception of natural selection.—The fact last brought out, viz., that mutations need not be adaptive and often have *no conceivable relationship to the demands made by the environment upon the animal,* leads to a consideration of the influence of selection upon mutations. On the Darwinian hypothesis natural selection is looked upon as an actual causative agent. As has been brought out, he supposed that, given fluctuating variations, natural selection would shape the direction of evolution in such a way that, given time, the organism would become perfectly adapted to its habitat. On such an hypothesis every instinctive act observable in an organism must be looked upon as having adaptive value. Two quotations from Darwin seem clearly to bring this out.

" But the mere existence of individual variability and of some well-marked varieties, though necessary as the foundation for the work, helps us but little in understanding how species arise in nature. How have all those exquisite adaptations of one part of the organism to another part, and to the conditions of life and of one organic being to another being, been perfected? We see these beautiful co-adaptations most plainly in the woodpecker and in the mistletoe; and only a little less plainly in the humblest parasite which clings to the hairs of the quadruped or the feathers of the bird; in the structure of the beetle which dives through the water; in the plumed seed which is wafted by the gentlest breeze; in short, we see beautiful adaptations everywhere and in every part of the organic world."

"Again it may be asked how is it that varieties which I call incipient species become ultimately converted into good and distinct species, which in most cases obviously differ from each other far more than do the varieties of the same species? How do those groups of species which constitute what are called distinct genera and which differ from each other more than do species of the same genus, arise? All these results . . . follow from the struggle for life. Owing to this struggle, variations, however slight and from whatever cause proceeding, if they be in any degree profitable to the individuals of a species in their infinitely complex relations to other organic beings and to their physical conditions of life, will tend to the preservation of such individuals and will generally be inherited by the offspring. The offspring, also, will thus have a better chance of surviving, for, of the many individuals of any species which are periodically born, but a small number can survive. I have called this principle, by which each slight variation, if useful, is preserved, by the term natural selection, in order to mark its relation to man's power of selection."

Changes in the concept of natural selection.—With the discovery, on the one hand, that Darwinian fluctuations are not inherited, and, on the other, that new characters appear suddenly, due possibly to the direct action of the environment upon the germ cells, there has come about necessarily a marked change in our conception of the function of natural selection. In the first place, the mutation hypothesis has relieved the investigator of the burden of attempting to find adaptive value in the various activities of animals, and has allowed him to examine such behavior without preconceived notions. It is now admitted that adaptation, the fitness of the organism for the conditions of its life, is by no means so perfect as has been sup-

posed: more and more characters, studied in natural surroundings, are found to be quite indifferent, to offer no
discoverable advantage or disadvantage to the organism
possessing them. What does it matter whether the snail's
shell be twisted to the right or to the left; whether the
pigment of the elytra of the beetle be arranged in continuous or broken lines; whether the young noddy is gray or
white? The answer of the extreme selectionist has always been: '' I do not know the value of the character,
but it must have some worth. Otherwise it could not
exist.'' But the discovery that in a species of butterflies
two distinct types of females, widely different in color,
may live side by side, each breeding true in Mendelian
ratios, quickly raises the question whether the coloration
of these insects has any protective or selective value. Such
cases of seemingly indifferent characters might be multiplied indefinitely. On p. 113 are cited certain specific examples of non-adaptive types of *activity*. Parker has recently argued in similar vein and has extended the conception of indifferent characters to the whole range of animal reactions. He says:

"It is my opinion, at least, that many animal reactions which we
have been accustomed to call adaptations should not be thus designated, and that the difficulties that we often meet in attempting to
account for such reactions are due to our consideration of them
from the standpoint of adaptations when in reality they are far
from being such."
"The majority of animal reactions are, in all probability, neither
conspicuously advantageous nor disadvantageous to the life of the
individual. They are dependent chiefly upon the material composition
of the given organism, and, so long as they are relatively indifferent
to the continuance of life, they pass without special consequence."

Effect of natural selection upon mutations.—To accept
the mutation hypothesis as at least *one* of the ways in
which diversified structure arises, does not necessitate
throwing overboard the concept of natural selection. A
moment's consideration shows that many animals and
plants do thrive in the environment in which they are
found, i.e., that they are adapted to meet environmental
demands: furthermore, that there is often an almost

perfect correlation in the functioning of the different parts of the animal. The growing conception is that while natural selection has no part in shaping such adaptations and such correlations, it nevertheless *still retains the function of killing off those organisms unfitted to live in the environment in which they are placed.* A simpler way now to express what is meant is to avoid the use of the term selection and to state specifically what probably happens to new races. It is clear, in the first place, that a mutant when it is thrown off, must bring with it organs of reproduction. Furthermore, it must possess certain instinctive modes of procuring food and a mechanism for the digestion of food and for the excretion of waste products. Depending also upon the environment where it first appears it must bear essential mechanisms of attack and defense or else of flight. If the mutant falls by chance where, with its equipment, it can live and reproduce its kind, it thrives. On the other hand, if this same mutant comes into existence in a locality where its equipment is not adequate, it perishes. If these simple (or complex) structural and functional demands are satisfied, the animal may possess—and often does possess—a host of structural and functional characteristics which have no necessary rôle in its daily life (this is inconceivable on the Darwinian concept of evolution). Unquestionably the reason there are so many " adaptive instincts " on record and so few " unadaptive " ones is due to the fact that the naturalist has generally found what he sought.

Ability to form habits enables the animal to supplement a faulty inheritance.—When we examine the higher vertebrates, especially the mammals, shortly after birth, we find, as was brought out in the preceding chapter, that they are not born adapted, and furthermore, that when their instincts do appear they are oftentimes by no means perfect in their action. It is here that habit reveals itself as being a positive factor in evolution. On the basis of what we now know to be true of habits, it seems possible to modify the demands we made above upon a mutant (if it is to survive) by saying that it either must appear adapted to the environment, or else it must appear with sufficient plasticity to enable it readily to form habits. This appears most clearly in the work of Breed, already cited. The chick is born with the pecking instinct sufficiently developed to keep the organism alive. Adaptation becomes perfect through habit.

Some special forms of asserted adaptations.—Throughout the literature of the Darwinist one finds voluminous reference to (a) protective resemblance; (b) warning coloration; and (c) sexual dimorphism. It is claimed by them that these phenomena may be explained by natural selection. Since such phenomena, however produced, are of especial interest to the students of behavior in view of the fact that the sense organs of animals are involved in their discussion, it seems worth while to consider them for a moment (although they offer no great difficulty, so far as explanation goes, on the hypothesis of mutation and selection already considered).

(a) *Protective resemblance.*—We have touched upon the facts included under this heading on p. 124. Protective resemblance includes all the structural modifications of animals which tend to make them less conspicuous to their enemies or to make them resemble other animals which are not preyed upon by those enemies (mimicry). Many animals seem to resemble in color or pattern the backgrounds against which they normally live. Some slight evidence has been collected showing that mimicry is "protective." E. B. Poulton and C. B. Saunders noted the survivals among a large number of the pupæ of the butterfly (*Vanessa urtica*) in different localities and found that those placed most conspicuously for the human eye were most readily found and devoured by birds. Cesnola fastened green and brown Mantis to plants of similar and contrasting color with the result that birds found the conspicuously placed ones, the ones upon plants of contrasting color, most readily. (It might be noted here that vision in birds seems closely comparable with that of man, in so far as it has been tested, and hence the field studies are supported by those of the laboratory.) Pearl has shown that while self-colored chickens (those which are of a uniform color all over the body) are more conspicuous for man than are barred or speckled birds, there is no larger percentage of the former killed by natural enemies than of the latter. Inconspicuousness for man does not, in this case, guarantee protection from other enemies. Doubt has been raised as to the reality of many of the more perfect cases of protective coloration, and only careful field studies can establish the adaptive character of the doubtful cases.

(b) *Warning coloration.*—The theory of warning coloration supposes that brilliant and conspicuous colors in animals are associated with effective defensive weapons. Such conspicuous characters serve as " danger " or " warning " signals to protect animals so equipped from attack. The theory has little factual support. Przibram has collected a large amount of evidence to show that warningly colored insects and their mimics are eaten readily by many other animals, yet this evidence shows only that the protection afforded by the defensive organs is not perfect, not that the insects are not at all protected by their conspicuousness. Reighard has shown conclusively that the brilliantly colored coral reef fishes do not possess " that combination of conspicuousness with unpleasant attributes necessary to the theory of warning coloration." The ordinary gray snappers which frequent the docks around juxtatropical ports feed greedily upon the gaudily colored coral reef fishes when opportunity is offered under experimental conditions. The delicate coral reef fishes escape annihilation because of the protection offered by the reefs and because of their agility.

(c) *Sexual dimorphism.*—To the theory of sexual selection Darwin attached great importance. In its extreme form the theory supposes not only a highly developed sensory acuity upon the part of the selecting animal but it assumes that animals have also definite color, form, and size " preferences," i.e., a highly developed æsthetic sense. There is as yet no evidence that this is the case nor can such evidence be gathered until it has been proved that the animals in question have a sensory equipment sufficiently delicate to form a basis for such a selection.   The problem is still complicated, even when such anthropomorphic conceptions are ruled out.   The phenomena which one seeks to explain by the theory of sexual selection are chiefly those of sexual dimorphism, differences in structure and behavior of the two sexes, although there are other characters which may be subject to the same selective agents.

Many cases of sexual dimorphism do not demand any active selection by a member of one sex between two members of the opposite sex.   The vigorous struggle between males for the possession of the females, mutual fitness for mating, the care of the young, all such activities would lead naturally to the production of sexual dimorphism by a selection which involved no sensory discrimination by members of either sex.   In any given case of dimorphism it is extremely difficult to determine what part may have been played by this impersonal struggle and what part by a true preference for some earlier mutants.   Certainly the truth or falseness of the theory can be demonstrated only by experimental methods and as yet but little evidence has been obtained by their use.

The experimental evidence of sexual selection.—Andrews, Chidester, Holmes, and others have shown that smell and taste are the chief sensory agents in the mating of arthropods.   Mayer experimented with a moth (*Callosamia promethea*), in which the males and females are different in color, in order to test the preferences and selective activities of the females.

"In order to test this hypothesis I cut off the wings of a number of females, leaving only short stumps, from which all the scales were carefully brushed.   Male wings were then neatly glued to the stumps, and thus the female presented the appearance of the male.   Under these conditions the males mated with the females quite as readily as they would have done under normal conditions."

"I tried the experiment of gluing female wings upon the male.   Here again the mating seemed to occur with normal frequency, and I was unable to detect that the females displayed any unusual aversion towards their effeminate-looking consorts."

"It is also interesting to note that normal males pay no attention to males with female wings."

"In another series of experiments the wings were cut entirely off the males and females and the scales brushed off their bodies;

and yet these shabby males were readily accepted by normal females, nor could I see that normal males displayed any aversion to mating with wingless females."

" We are therefore forced to conclude that the melanic coloration of the male has not been brought about through the agency of sexual selection on the part of the female."

More recently Mayer and Soule have repeated these experiments with another species and verified the results in all respects save one: wingless males were selected against by normal females but mated successfully with blind ones. Sturtevant has taken up the same question with the fruit-fly and has found that vigor is the chief factor in determining the matings. Since certain eye colors of Drosophila are associated with greater or less vigor, there results a quite definite selection of eye color, but such a selection could not be the determining agent in producing a sexual dimorphism. From this and other less direct evidence Morgan is inclined to rule out sexual selection as a factor in evolution, ascribing sexual dimorphism rather to the persistence of indifferent mutations which have arisen in the sex chromosomes. In contradiction to this view a certain amount of evidence may be cited in favor of sexual selection, which, although not conclusive, still keeps the problem open. Sturtevant (reported by Morgan, 1913) removed the wings from male fruit-flies and offered females a choice between normal and wingless males. Neither was preferred, mating with wingless and normal males occurring in equal numbers. But when the males were placed separately with the females the average interval before mating was for the normal males 18 minutes, for wingless males, 40 minutes. This is interpreted as meaning that the female is more readily excited by the normal males. It was not a determining factor for selection of confined individuals, but it should be pointed out that among unconfined individuals where courtship is subject to interruption the quicker excitement of the female by any male would lead to an effective selection of that male. In a recent paper Davenport has stated that he finds a selection against certain brilliant colors in the cock, and evidence for color vision in the fowl at least offers a basis for such selection.

Moreover, the behavior of animals in experiments where attempts are made to hybridize certain species should not be overlooked. The zebra can with difficulty be induced to mate with the horse, while crosses between the zebra and ass are made without difficulty (Rommel). In a very suggestive paper Pearl has called attention to the fact that the jacks kept by mule breeders acquire reactions that are somewhat comparable to those called out by sexual symbols or fetishes in man. The problem of sexual selection has never been approached in a systematic manner and there is really no evidence at present upon which any general conclusions may be based. Cases such as those cited above indicate that, in higher mammals at least, the problem may be seriously complicated by the habits of the animals, and accordingly that sexual selection is not a general or a racial problem, but one which more narrowly concerns the individual.

III. Inheritance of Acquired Characters

Lamarck's laws.—In a note on p. 161 we expressed the view that there is a growing body of evidence to show that certain types of somatic variations are heritable. We wish now briefly to consider this evidence. As the individual develops it becomes better fitted to its environment through the perfection of instinctive mechanisms and the formation of habits. Early in the history of evolution the possibility that such ontogenetically acquired adaptations might be transmitted to the offspring suggested itself. Lamarck gave the most thorough formulation to this view in his two well known laws:

" *First law.*—In every animal which has not reached the limits of development the frequent and sustained use of any organ strengthens that organ little by little, it develops, enlarges and assumes a strength proportional to the amount of use; on the contrary, the failure to use any organ constantly causes it to grow weaker, it deteriorates, loses its function and finally disappears.

" *Second law.*—All that nature has forced the individual to acquire or lose by the influence of circumstances to which its race has long been exposed, hence all that has been acquired or lost by the predominating use or disuse of any organ, has been preserved in later reproduction to later individuals by inheritance, provided that the modifications have been acquired by the two sexes in common or by those individuals which have given birth to the new race."

The followers of Lamarck carried this theory to still further extremes, assuming that all characters acquired by the individual as the result of the action of environment were inherited. Darwin accepted Lamarck's view of the value of *use* and *disuse* in evolution, calling upon this principle whenever his own theory of natural selection seemed inadequate to account for the facts observed. As soon as an attempt was made to verify the theory by experimental evidence, the strongest possible objection to it appeared—the theory did not seem to work—the tails might be cut from mice for many generations without reducing the size of the tails of the progeny; the strong arm of the blacksmith was not transmitted to his son. Then came Weismann's theory of the continuity of the germ-plasm which showed the difficulties in the way of the transmission of bodily characters to the germ cells. Lamarck's theory was practically dropped for many years.

Recent experiments on the inheritance of acquired characters.—During the past few years the theory has been revived by several investigators who seemingly have obtained experimental evidence of the existence of the inheritance of certain types of somatic variations. The method which has secured this evidence was first indicated by the experiments of Marie V. Chauvin upon the Mexican Axolotl. Under favorable conditions this salamander retains the aquatic habit throughout life, breathing with external gills and never forming functional lungs. Unfavorable conditions in nature will, however, lead to the loss of the gills, to the formation of functional lungs, and to the assumption of a terrestrial mode of life. In the laboratory the metamorphosis may be brought about by various means, such as the reduction of the oxygen in the water. The eggs of animals which had been forced in the laboratory to assume a terrestrial mode of life were deposited and hatched under normal conditions. The larvæ were kept under conditions where the progeny of untreated parents had never

been known to desert the water.   But at the end of a year
these larvæ showed a reduction in the size of the gills and,
when offered an opportunity to go on land, went through
the metamorphosis in a shorter time than had ever been observed among normal animals.   From this it seems that the
induced tendency to metamorphosis was inherited.   Yet
the experiments were too limited and too lacking in controls to do more than indicate the direction which further
work should take.

The same may be said of the work of Schroeder upon the
willow-leaf beetle.   The eggs of this insect are deposited
and the larvæ fed upon the smooth leaves of a willow
(*Salix fragilis*).   Schroeder transferred the eggs and larvæ
to a downy-leafed willow where the larvæ learned to push
away the down with their heads before feeding upon the
tissues of the leaves.   After metamorphosis the adults were
offered a choice between the smooth and the downy willows,
and a small percentage deposited their eggs upon the downy
leaves.   This '' training '' of the larvæ was repeated for
four generations with a gradual increase in the percentage
of adults which chose the downy leaves until, in the fourth
generation, all of the adults deposited their eggs upon
the downy willow, avoiding the natural food plant.   The
results are open to the criticism that no adults fed on
smooth-leafed willows were given a choice of the two
plants as a control, and that the plants used differed greatly
in size, so that no accurate judgment of the results to be
expected from chance can be formed.

The larva of the moth (*Gracillaria stigmatella*) eats the
leaves of a willow, bending over and fastening the tips of
the leaves on which it is feeding so as to form a sort of tent
in which it lives.   Schroeder cut off the tips of the leaves,
whereupon the larvæ made their houses by bending over the
edges of the mutilated leaves, adapting themselves to the
new conditions.   The next generation was again brought
up upon leaves without tips, and all formed their tents by
rolling in the edges of the leaves.   The third generation was
restored to normal conditions.   Nineteen larvæ were obtained.   Fifteen of them rolled up the leaf tips, just as

the wild insects do, but 4 made their tents from the edges of the leaves. The final numbers are too small to be conclusive, particularly so since no accurate data respecting the occurrence of this habit in nature were obtained; but the experiment is suggestive of promising work in the same field.

The experiments of Kammerer.—The same objections cannot be urged against the experiments of Kammerer, which are very extensive and, save for the remote possibility of faulty technique, seem to establish the inheritance of certain somatic adaptations. The experiments have been carried out in great detail upon several amphibia and reptiles and the results are far too extensive to be reviewed here. Certain observations upon the obstetrical toad (*Alytes obstetricans*) have, however, a direct bearing upon the origin of instincts and may be summarized briefly. The obstetrical toad is ordinarily exceptional in its mode of reproduction. It has acquired an almost exclusive land habit, going to water only at rare intervals to moisten the skin. Copulation takes place on land and the eggs, which are relatively few and large, are carried by the male, wrapped around his thighs. The embryos mature in their gelatinous capsules while attached to the male and escape only when he goes to the water. By subjecting the toads at the breeding season to high temperature in a terrarium provided with a water basin, the toads were forced to spend much of their time in the water and the eggs were deposited there. When the egg chains were laid in the water their gelatinous envelops would not adhere to the thighs of the male and consequently the eggs were left to develop in the water. After this was repeated during several breeding periods the toads acquired the " habit " of going to the water to lay their eggs, and this habit persisted when they were restored to normal conditions. The eggs laid at the different breeding periods during the formation of the aquatic habit were kept under normal conditions of temperature until they reached maturity and the behavior of this second generation of toads was noted.

First brood.—The eggs which formed this brood were

laid when the parents were first driven to the water by heat and before they had gained the aquatic habit. The members of this brood all laid their eggs in the normal manner.

Second brood.—The members of this brood, formed after the parents had begun to acquire the habit of laying in the water, were abnormal to a slight extent. At their first breeding period the eggs were laid upon the land but the males did not take them up. All later broods produced by members of this second brood were carried normally by the males.

Third brood.—This brood, like the second, laid their eggs upon land, but in their first and second broods the eggs were not taken up by the males. In their third brood the eggs were partly taken up, and in their fourth brood the behavior became normal.

Fourth and later broods.—The eggs which formed this brood were laid after the habit of laying in the water had become thoroughly established in the parents. Their first brood was laid in the water, the second upon land, but without being taken up by the males. The third brood was normal.

Some of the adults from these broods were subjected again to the high temperature and forced to breed repeatedly in the water, and this was repeated for several generations. Many structural changes appeared and increased from generation to generation. One of these was the appearance of a horny pad upon the thumb of the males of the fourth generation, a pad which closely resembled that found ordinarily upon the thumbs of frogs breeding normally in the water. In the third generation the pad appeared as a slight thickening of the skin, so its acquirement, like that of the instinct to lay the eggs in water, seemed to have been gradual. These experiments indicate an actual inheritance of adaptive somatic characters in which the degree of inheritance of the character is proportional to the length of time during which the parent was subject to the influence of the abnormal environment. A large number of other experiments by Kammerer upon other characters in salamanders and reptiles have given similar results.

Some evidence negative in character.—Experiments of this type, considered alone, are enough to convince one that acquired characters are inherited, but zoölogists are inclined to regard such results with more than usual suspicion and this attitude is certainly justified by the mass of contradictory evidence. The evidence from selection has already been considered and is entirely negative. Many attempts to get an inheritance of characters forced, as it were, upon the soma have all failed. Thus Bogdanow cut off the wings of the house-fly for ten generations without causing any change in the wings of the progeny, and Galton transfused the blood of differently colored rabbits without affecting the color of their descendants. The more weighty evidence comes, however, from transplantation experiments. Harrison was able to graft together parts of the larvæ of two species of frogs which later developed into a chimæra with a head of one species and a body of the other, neither part being influenced by its close association with the other. The results of several investigators in transplanting ovaries from one variety of animals to another have been negative. In rabbits, fowls, and in ascidians the transplantations were without effect, the eggs were quite uninfluenced by their new surroundings. In only one case is there definite evidence to the contrary. Kammerer has found a marked influence of the soma upon transplanted germ cells of the fire salamander. In this case transplantation of the ovaries to ordinary individuals had no effect, but transplantation to a new race, which Kammerer holds to have been produced by the inheritance of acquired characters, gave positive results.

The direct adaptation theory of evolution.—Although, as yet, the evidence in favor of the inheritance of acquired characters is inconclusive, it is of sufficient importance to make it impossible to disregard entirely the possibility that such inheritance has played a large rôle in adaptive evolution. Various theories have been advanced to explain the mechanism by which characters might be impressed upon the race by the action of environment. Fig. 35 illustrates the chief two divisions into which these theories fall. First the change may be brought about by the action of the environmental agent upon both the soma and the germ cell, the *parallel induction theory,* producing in each changes of the same nature. The experiment of Sitowski, although not showing a true inheritance of an acquired character, may serve to illustrate this point. He fed the larvæ of a moth with a dye (Sudan red III.) and found that the dye was carried over through the eggs to the next generation of caterpillars. The dye affected both the *body* and *germ cells* of the larvæ, i.e., stained them, in the same way. However, the mass of evidence seems to be against this view, since it was shown earlier (p. 167) that the direct action of the environment upon the germ cell in those cases which have been studied carefully has the effect of causing variations which are not adaptive—not in line with the habits which are acquired during the life of the individual.

The second possibility is that of indirect action of the environment through the soma (Fig. 35). The changes which take place in the body are supposed in some way to react upon the germ cells, inducing a corresponding change in them. Darwin's theory of pangenesis is probably the most widely known of such theories, although it has been completely abandoned. He assumed that every cell in the body was constantly giving off minute replicas of itself which were carried in the blood and finally got into the germ cells, where they provided the material for the reproduction of similar structures in the next generation. A more recent view to account for the indirect effect of environment upon the germ cells is known as the *hormone theory.*

The hormone theory.—Cunningham, basing his argument chiefly upon the observational and experimental evidence on the production of secondary sexual characters, has evolved a chemical theory to explain the inheritance of acquired characters, known as the hormone theory. The connection between gonad (sexual cells) development and the formation of the secondary sex characters is now well established. The hen, after ovariotomy, assumes the spurs and plumage of the male. The crab, castrated by the parasites, Sacculina, assumes the proportions and many of the characteristics of the female. Cunningham supposes that such observations prove that the development of the secondary sexual characters follows upon the production of some secretion of the reproductive cells or gonads. He then assumes that a reversal of the process is possible, i.e., that a developing structure, a callus, e.g., can produce a secretion or hormone, which, carried in the blood, may reach the reproductive cells and induce in them a change corresponding to the somatic change. Since Cunningham published the theory (1908), a considerable body of favorable evidence has been collected. (As examples, see the works of Gudernatsch, Todd, Rörig.[2])

Summary.—Since, finally, the activities of organisms must be considered as the functioning of definite structural elements, the problem of the origin of new reflexes, of new instincts, and of new possibilities of habit formation become one with the problem of the evolution of morphological characters in general. In the instinct, as in the structural arrangements, two orders of phenomena are apparent— diversity and fitness. The diversity is accounted for by the interaction of developmental processes within the organism, and environmental factors. Most of the variations in the individual are quite undirected and without adaptive relation to the agents producing them, but some, like the new characters acquired in habit formation, are made adaptive by a process of learning in the individual. The inheritance of such adaptive characters, if demonstrated, would form a ready method of evolution which would account for all diversity and fitness; but as yet the inheritance of somatic adaptation is not established. The only new characters whose heritability has been demonstrated are mutations, and these are never directly adaptive. The problem as to why

---

[2] The "Mneme" of Semon in which an attempt is made to explain the inheritance of acquired characters can scarcely be interpreted in terms of a physiological mechanism and is of little help in the *envisagement* of our problems.

they seem to be adaptive is answered—how completely it is as yet uncertain—by assuming that natural selection eliminates individuals (mutants) which are not endowed with characters enabling it to exist in the locality in which it first appears. The application of either the selection or the direct adaptation theory to behavior complexes is as yet impossible, owing to the lack of any very definite concepts of the structural basis of behavior.

BIBLIOGRAPHY

BATESON, W., *Mendel's Principles of Heredity.* Cambridge, 1909.
——————— *Problems of Genetics.* New York, 1913.
CESNOLA, A. P., "Preliminary Note on the Protective Value of Color in Mantis Religiosa," *Biometrica*, 1904, 3.
CHAUVIN, MARIE V., "Ueber die Verwandlung der mexicanischen Axolotl in Amblystoma," *Zeit. f. wiss. Zool.*, 1876, XXVII, 522.
CUNNINGHAM, J. T., "An Experiment Concerning the Absence of Color from the Lower Sides of Flat-Fishes," *Zool. Anz.*, 1891, XIV, 27-32.
——————— "The Heredity of Secondary Sexual Characters in Relation to Hormones, a Theory of the Heredity of Somatogenic Characters," *Arch. f. Entw.*, 1908, 26.
DARWIN, CHAS., *Origin of Species.* London, 1875, sixth edition.
DAVENPORT, C. B., "Light Thrown by the Experimental Study of Heredity upon the Factors and Methods of Evolution," *Amer. Nat.*, 1912, 46.
DE VRIES, HUGO, *Species and Varieties; Their Origin by Mutation.* Chicago, 1905.
FULD, E., "Ueber Veränderungen der Hinterbeinknochen von Hunden," *Arch. f. Entw.*, 1901.
GOLDFARB, A. J., "The Influence of the Nervous System in Regeneration," *Jour. Exp. Zool.*, 1909, 7.
GUDERNATSCH, J. F., "Feeding Experiments on Tadpoles," *Arch. f. Entw.*, 1913, 35.
JOHANNSEN, W., *Ueber Erblichkeit in Populationen und in reinen Linien.* Jena, 1903.
KAMMERER, PAUL, "Experimentelle Fortpflanzungsveränderung bei Geburtshelferkröte (*Alytes obstetricans*) u. Laubfrosch (*Hyla arborea*)," *Arch. f. Entw.*, 1906, 22.
——————— "Vererbung erzwungener Fortpflanzungsanpassungen. III, Die Nachkommen der nicht brutpflegenden Alytes obstetricans," *ibid.*, 1909, 28.
——————— "Das Farbkleid des Feuersalamanders (*Salamandra maculosa Laurenti*) in seiner Abhängigkeit von der Umwelt," *ibid.*, 1913, 36.
LAMARCK, *Philosophie Zoologique.* Paris, edition of Charles Martin, 1873.
MACDOUGAL, D. T., "Alterations in Heredity Produced by Ovarial Treatment," *Bot. Gazette*, 1911, 51.

MAYER, A. G., " Mating Instincts in Moths," *Ann. Mag. Nat. Hist.*, 1900, V.

MAYER, A. G., and SOULE, C. G., " Some Reactions of Caterpillars and Moths," *Jour. Exp. Zool.*, 1906, 3.

MENDEL, G. J., *Versuche über Pflanzen-Hybriden*, (English translation reprinted in Bateson's *Principles of Heredity*).

MORGAN, T. H., *Heredity and Sex*. New York, 1913.

PARKER, G. H., " Adaptation in Animal Reactions," *Amer. Nat.*, 1913, 47.

PEARL, RAYMOND, " Data on the Relative Conspicuousness of Barred and Self-Colored Fowls," *Amer. Nat.*, 1911, 45.

———————— " Notes on the Sex Behavior of the Poitou Jacks," *Jour. Animal Beh.*, 1913, 3.

POULTON, E. B., and SAUNDERS, C. B., *An Experimental Inquiry into the Struggle for Existence in Certain Common Insects*, Bristol, Report, British Asso., 1898.

PRZIBRAM, HANS, *Phylogenese*. Leipzig, 1910.

REIGHARD, JACOB, " An Experimental Study of Warning Coloration in Coral-Reef Fishes." Washington, Papers from Tortugas Lab. of Carnegie Inst., 1908, 2.

ROMMEL, G. M., " The Grevy Zebra as a Domestic Animal," *Amer. Breeders' Mag.*, 1913, IV, 3.

SCHROEDER, C., " Ueber experimentell erzielte Instinktvariationen," *Verh. d. Deutsch Zool. Ges.*, 1903.

SEMON, R. N., *Die Mneme als erhaltendes Prinzip im Wechsel des organischen Geschehens*. Leipzig, 1908.

SPEMANN, H., " Ueber die Entwicklung umgedrehter Hirnteile bei Amphibienembryonen," *Zool. Jahrb.*, 1912, 3 (Supp. 15).

STOCKARD, C. R., " The Artificial Production of a Single Median Cyclopean Eye in the Fish Embryo," *Arch. f. Entw.*, 1907, 23.

TODD, CHAS., " On the Recognition of the Individual by Hæmolytic Methods," *Jour. Genetics*, 1913, 3.

TOWER, W. L., *Evolution in Chrysomelid Beetles of the Genus Leptinotarsa*. Washington, Carnegie Pub., 1906.

YERKES, R. M., *The Dancing Mouse*. New York, 1907.

———————— " The Heredity of Savageness and Wildness in Rats," *Jour. Animal Beh.*, 1913, III, 286.

CHAPTER VI

THE EXPERIMENTAL STUDY OF HABIT FORMATION

I. Content of the term habit.—In Chapter IV it was shown that instinct is analyzable into simple congenital reflexes. It was suggested there that habit also might, so far as analysis goes, be found to consist of congenital reflexes. Experimental studies upon habit formation lend support to this view. Instinct and habit differ so far as concerns the origin of the *pattern* (number and localization of simple reflex arcs involved) and the *order* (temporal relations) of the unfolding of the elements composing that pattern. In instinct both pattern and order are inherited: in habit both are acquired. We do not hesitate to define habit as we do instinct—as a complex system of reflexes which function in a serial order when the organism is confronted by certain stimuli, provided we add the clause which marks off habit from instinct, viz., that in habit the order and pattern are acquired during the life of the individual animal. After habits are perfected they function in all particulars as do instincts. No mere examination of adult animals will enable us to differentiate between the respective rôles of habit and instinct, since the one observable difference between the two types of acts is that of origin. Since habits are thus seen to be individual acquisitions of particular animals, it is necessary to describe the process by means of which certain reflexes are selected out from among a very large number of possible reflexes. Such a description of the factors involved in selection can be more adequately presented after we have looked more carefully into some of the general features of habit. Accordingly we shall take up the process of selection in the following chapter.[1] It may be inferred from the above statements

[1] We must emphasize the fact that all organized responses which can be called forth from both man and animal fall under the one or the other of these heads, instincts (including here the simplest form of reflexes), and habits. In Chapter I we tried to show that what are called " images " (and the thought processes generally) are really nothing more than the implicit habits which are formed principally in the laryngeal muscles, and we would further state now that those functions which we have hitherto called " affective " really belong in the realm of instincts. It will be remembered that James made the following distinction between the motor processes of emotions and those of instincts: those underlying emotions consist of bodily reverberations, movements of breathing, circulation, glands, etc., the loci of which are confined to the subject's own body; whereas those underlying instincts consist largely of movements of the striated muscles. As we understand James he seemingly would make emotions objects of introspection, whereas instincts are the legitimate prey of the behaviorist. Since we do not admit any such distinction, it follows that from our point of view both emotions and instincts belong in one and the same class. It follows further that the so-called affective processes must be grouped under what has hitherto been called emotions, and hence under our general class of instinctive modes of response. Behavior regards all three groups from the same point of view. A given stimulus may, through inherited systems of reflexes, produce a response of a certain kind in the striped musculature which we may name *flight*. On the other hand a stimulus may produce its effect largely through the sympathetic system (dilation of vessels in the face, etc.) which psychology would call *embarrassment*, finally (as a special form of

that the organism is dependent upon heredity for unit acts. The number of these apparently can never be increased or decreased, but large numbers of them can be shaped so as to form different types of habit, depending upon the kind of environment into which the organism is thrown. The organism is so constructed that when certain stimuli are presented certain types of random movements are set free. Individuals certainly differ enormously in the number and kinds of random activity which they may display upon the presentation of given stimuli.[2] If appropriate random acts do not appear upon the incidence of the given stimulus, it is fruitless to attempt to establish habits respecting that stimulus, e.g., if the child fails to respond adequately to colors, pencils, chalk, and to the form and size of objects (when intensity and combination are sufficiently varied) it is useless to try to instil artistic habits. On the other hand, this same child may show a rich display of random activity, suitable to the formation of habit, when presented with the objects belonging to what are called the mechanical arts or trades; habits under such conditions are formed quickly and readily. It seems safe to conclude that all of the vocations are probably at bottom dependent upon particular hereditary types of organization, i.e., dependent upon the presence of random activity of proper kinds. The same thing appears in the case of the animals. It has long been recognized that in order to get the animal to form habits one must set problems for him which will call only for the random type of activity of which he is capable. One does not usually set the same type of problem for a bird that one sets for a monkey. We scrutinize pretty carefully in the young animal the reper-

emotion) another stimulus, through inherited or acquired connections, may produce an effect of one or another kind upon the errogenous zones, which psychology would class as the one or the other affective element (process?).

[2] It would be interesting to test habit formation under conditions such that instead of increasing the stimulating value of an object (complex stimuli) we should heighten the state of irritability of the organism by the administration of strychnine, etc. The effect of drugs on behavior can be more easily attacked in the animal than in the human world.

toire of random activity, and so shape the problems that their solution calls for no unit acts not in his repertoire.

Restatement.—What we emphasize in brief may be stated again: when an animal is presented with a stimulus which calls forth random movements (e.g., food inside of a problem box), the reflex repertoire is set free. Now in this repertoire is a combination of reflexes which will enable the animal to get food. In some way (by a purely mechanical process, to be later described) this combination gets selected and in time comes to be the only system which responds when that particular object is presented to the animal. It should be. clear from our description that to use the term " habit " to cover all observable adjustment in animals is most confusing. The literature is full of such titles as the " habits and natural history " of a given species. Such titles cover both the instincts and the habits of the animals under consideration, and no effort is made to separate the two forms of adjustment. A still more violent strain upon the meaning which the term habit should connote comes from experimental zoölogy. They speak there of the habits of growth of certain tissues. In such cases it is preferable to speak of temporally spaced systems of growth, or to adopt some wholly new phrase. The term habit should be confined strictly to *new forms of adjustment acquired during the lifetime of the individual animal.*[3]

II.   Types of habit.—The human experimenter in the laboratory forces certain types of habit upon particular animals. Where the object is to bring into relief the various action systems, he forces the animals to form what are called *motor habits.* In studying them the experimenter may be primarily interested in the rapidity of the formation of such habits; the stages in their formation, such as the initial accuracy of the first performance, when considered from the standpoint of the amount of excess time and excess effort; the rate of elimination of these excess

[3] It is just possible that owing to the growing body of evidence that certain habits are transmitted by parent to offspring, we shall have to speak of ontogenetic habits and phylogenetic habits.

factors in early stages and in later stages; the number and complexity of the habits which may be formed; whether such habit systems mutually influence one another as regards reënforcement or the reverse. He may wish to consider, after having determined the normal course of the formation of a habit, ways in which the so-called normal process may be altered, e.g., the effect of " putting the animal through " the act, allowing the trained animals to perform within the sensory range of the untrained animals, etc. We shall reserve the discussion of these latter factors until Chapter VIII is reached.

Examination of the work which has been done on motor habits shows that such habits fall usually under two subheads: (1) *motor habits* in the narrow sense, e.g., as those formed in the maze and in box I; and (2) *habits of manipulation*, e.g., the opening of latches, the pulling of strings, turning buttons, pulling out plugs, etc. Such acts may be very simple or, through combination, very complex. In the discussion which follows we use the term motor habit in its restricted sense.

In contrast to the motor stand the *sensory habits* (called by Yerkes discrimination habits). Here emphasis is laid upon the functioning of the receptor (or upon defining the stimulus to which response is made, p. 61) rather than upon that of the muscle. The act which the animal has to perform may be already in its repertoire, e.g., he may have only to walk to the right or to the left, depending on which side the stimulus is administered. The experimenter's object is to bring out the whole range of stimuli to which the animal can respond, the amount of stimulation necessary for response, etc. His criterion, however, as to whether the stimulus lies within the sensory range of the animal is afforded by the fact that a definite habit can be formed, viz., that of reacting positively or negatively to the stimulus. The results presented in the chapters on sensory responses have been largely obtained by forcing the formation of such habits. On p. 220 we shall undertake the analysis of a group of sensory habits (the response of rodents to monochromatic lights).

A third type of habit of very great interest has been studied at the University of Chicago, mainly under the influence of H. A. Carr. This type of habit, called the *delayed response*,[4] falls under neither of the above heads, yet it seems to involve very complex motor processes as well as sensory. The essential object in establishing the delayed reaction is (1) to see within what limits reaction to a given stimulus may be delayed. In a rough way we might illustrate the type of delayed reaction by citing those cases of hunting animals which prey upon smaller species living in holes or coverts. The hunter is stimulated visually only momentarily by his prey; nevertheless, he goes to the place into which it has vanished. He is reacting during the final stages of the response just as though the specific visual stimulus were present.[5] This response has been brought under laboratory control by training the animal to go for food to a light which may appear in any one of three boxes, left, in front, or to the right (for apparatus see p. 105). After training, the light is turned on in any one of the boxes. While the light is on the animal is stimulated by it but he is restrained from reacting to it. The light is then turned off. The experimenter waits for a definite interval and then releases the animal. The correct response on the animal's part calls for a positive movement towards the box in which the light has appeared. (2) Another object of the experimenter is to determine the factors by means of which correct response is attained (i.e., the behavior during the period of delay, maintenance of bodily attitude, etc.).

Motor habits: mammals.—One can very easily watch the

---

[4] The element of delay is present probably in every habit. It is possible to consider this form of response under the heading of kinæsthetic and organic responses (p. 421). On the whole, however, it seems more appropriate to treat it under the general head of habit.

[5] Those familiar with the work on the lower organisms will recognize at once the fact that in this type of habit one meets the old question in somewhat different form as to whether the stimulus to orientation must exert its directive influence constantly as is assumed by Loeb for the tropism, or discretely and momentarily as is maintained by Jennings and Mast.

formation of a motor habit by allowing the white rat to obtain food from a simple problem box, such as that shown in box I on p. 94. We have reason to believe, through our knowledge of the rat's motor organization, before we start, that the acts by means of which he will get the food all lie within his repertoire. After sawdust has been banked around the box for a height of 2 or 3 inches the food is placed inside. Since there is no instinctive mechanism which will immediately enable the animal to get the food, several separate reflexes must be chained together. These, when perfectly concatenated, will function just as surely and just as perfectly as an instinct. This fact must be emphasized—the physiological condition of the animal is such (state of hunger) that food stimuli (it will be seen that we cannot tell what receptors are involved, smell, sight, etc., except by experimental analysis) will release the native reflexes. In this case they are, in brief, as follows: Running rapidly and walking slowly from place to place; sniffing, sneezing, washing the face or body; touching constantly the sides of the restraining cage and the box with vibrissæ or the bare snout, feet, etc.; clinging to all of the objects, sometimes with head up and sometimes with head down; crawling on the ceiling of the restraining cage; butting the nose into the crevices of the wire; gnawing at the wire and at all of the wooden parts; pushing with great force against the box; stopping every few minutes to clean the paws of bits of sawdust; sitting up on haunches and chewing these bits; scratching at the sawdust with a group of characteristic movements which not only produce a hole but throw out the sawdust as well (this of course when the animal has had no experience with the sawdust); squeezing through holes so made; moving vibrissæ and nose across the bottom of the cage; mounting up through the hole; seizing the food; dragging it out to the nest, in case the latter is allowed, etc. This list is not by any means complete. These movements are repeated over and over again with ever varying order. Finally, however, the order is such that the food is obtained. The animal walks to a definite place, scratches and pushes out the sawdust

to make a hole sufficiently large to squeeze through, enters
and reaches the food. The total time of success will vary
(7.04 min.—17.65 min.). On the second trial, which may
be given immediately after the first (but the time of success of the second trial will vary with the method) we find,
as a rule, an enormous decrease in the number of reflexes.
The activity is more confined, i.e., the area covered by the
animal is less and what area is covered is covered less
intensively (time, 1.69 min.—7.20 min.). On the third
trial the time is still further decreased (.48 min.). At
the fourteenth trial the time is reduced to .11 min.

Motor habits: birds.—A similar motor habit in birds
follows: When a wire box with a suitable door
has been inverted over the nest of a sooty tern and
left there until the bird has become completely accustomed
to it, and the opening is then banked up with sand, we
observe somewhat similar movements to those just described in the case of the rat. On the first test the bird
alighted from the air near the nest. It did not seem
frightened by the change in conditions. It walked immediately to the nest, but finding the sand, walked around
and around the box trying to force its way in through the
meshes of the wire. It tried to get into the door again, but
would not scratch at the sand. It divided its time between
the east side of the box where the eggs could be plainly
seen, and the west side where it had formerly gained admission. The types of movement displayed were, on the
whole, rather simple: they consisted mainly of walking;
pushing the beak through the meshes of the wire, striking
the wings against the cage, flying away for a short distance and then coming back to the old alighting place,
only to repeat the endless movements just described. It
is rather interesting to note that the bird did not use the
scratching reflex, although this particular species digs a
hole in the sand in which to deposit its eggs. This reflex
seems to be tied up with a very definite period of the nesting
cycle, viz., such holes are dug only before the egg is laid.
Nevertheless it is possible to exaggerate the inflexibility
of this reflex, since even the young birds will dig holes in

the sand in hot weather (p. 136). Thinking that the egg might be destroyed, the experimenter scraped away the sand covering the entrance so as to expose an inch of the opening. The bird alighted, passing by the door again and again. Two inches of the opening were then exposed. Under these circumstances the bird mounted the sand pile again and again and attempted to push its way through the meshes of the wire above the opening. Finally by accident it poked its head through the opening and squeezed the rest of the body through, making no effort to scratch. The time required for this whole trial was 1 hour. After allowing the bird 5 minutes on the nest it was driven away, and the sand piled up against the door to the height at which it had previously been successful. Most of the useless movements disappeared. The time required was only 1.16 minutes. On the third trial the sand was piled so as to completely cover the entrance. After 20 minutes of random movements with no success an inch of the opening was exposed. The bird came up and squeezed through the hole, making violent efforts, in 0.25 minute. On the following day no further tests were made, since the mate of this bird was on the nest. On the second day afterwards the sand was piled up to within 1 inch of the top of the door. The time for entrance was 2 minutes. On the next trial, once again the sand was piled so as to completely cover the entrance. After 38 minutes of random movements, while attempting to poke its head through the wire meshes above the opening, it accidentally poked its bill and head through the sand pile, withdrew the head, walked around and around the cage, as it came back to the hole poking its head into it 6 or 8 times. Success was attained at the end of 40 minutes from the beginning of the test. On the next test this animal required 7 minutes to effect this response. On succeeding tests it dived at once for the opening, made a small hole, pulled the head out, ran half way round the box, returned and squeezed through the opening. Time, 0.66 minute.

Motor habits: fish.—Thorndike has described in very general terms the labyrinth habit of a fish *(Fundulus)*. His plan was to confine the animal in the sunlight in a tank by means of glass partitions which had holes in them placed at different distances from the ends, thus converting the tank as a whole into a simple labyrinth. The animal first, e.g., has to swim up and to the left to cross the first partition; up and near the center to cross the second; and up and to the right to cross the third. The animal when confined in the sunlight tries to get back to the opposite end of the tank which is shaded. He reacts to the situation at first by swimming against the screen, and bumping against it here and there along the bottom. He may stop and remain still for a while, but he will occasionally rise up towards the top of the water. When he happens to rise up to the top at the left-hand side, he has a clear pathway in front of him, and thus can cross the first partition. We have few detailed studies of motor habits in fishes. Triplett has given an example of the formation of an interesting habit in the perch *(Perca Americana)*. A glass tank was constructed $4 \times 2 \times 1\frac{1}{2}$ feet in size. The study was begun upon two of the perch. They were fed for several months upon live minnows 2 or 3 inches in length. At the beginning of the experiment in question a glass partition was placed in the tank and the food of the perch changed to angle worms. Three times a week, Mondays, Wednesdays, and Fridays, for nearly a month, between the hours of 4 and 5 in the afternoon the perch were fed, and after that on every day at that hour. In making the test the minnows were put into their side of the tank for 30 minutes, during which time the behavior of the perch was observed. At the end of 30 minutes the minnows were removed until the next trial. Triplett's note on their behavior follows:

"Two minnows were placed in the tank at 4:30 P.M. The perch immediately began ramming the glass to get at them. Their actions became very violent as the minnows approached the partition. They ceased their butting and swam away from the glass for a few seconds after 7 minutes of continuous effort. A second trial lasting only 1 minute followed, and this was followed in turn by still shorter periods. The greater energy was shown always when the minnows turned their heads towards the perch, as it is only when they are 'head on' that the latter strike. At 4:55 the female was showing what seemed to be signs of anger and was striking the glass hard. . . . By 5 o'clock both perch had left the glass and seemed to have given up the attempt completely."

On the second day their efforts were not so long continued nor so violent as on the first day. There was a gradual lessening of the time and energy spent in striking at the minnows. This depended, though, somewhat upon the state of hunger. By the end of a month the perch had ceased to strike at the minnows when the latter were put into the cage. The second step in the experiment then followed. The glass partition was raised and the minnows allowed to swim into the compartment containing the perch. The male perch paid not the slightest attention to the minnows. The female moved towards them several times but did not harm them. On succeeding days the minnows were admitted in the same way. Several times the perch started to stalk the minnows, but within a short distance of their heads they turned aside. In the early trials before admitting the minnows the appetites of the perch had been dulled a little by feeding them with worms. In the later trials, however, this was not done. The third step in the experiment was to leave the minnows in the tank continuously for a week, separated from the perch only by the glass partition. The perch soon ceased entirely to touch the glass. They would frequently take up a position near the glass and watch the minnows playing on the other side within 2 or 3 inches of them. When the partition was removed they did not attack them any more than in the case just mentioned.

The most interesting feature of Triplett's experiment and the one which bears most plainly upon the motor side of habit formation comes out in his discussion of Bateson's statements concerning the lack of habit-forming powers in fish. Bateson says:

"None of the fish seemed to get any lasting appreciation of the nature of the plate-glass walls of the tank. The same fish will again and again knock its head and try to seize the objects moving on the other side. After repeated attempts to take food on the other side of the glass, they will desist, but some of the oldest inhabitants (*plaice, pollock,* and *bream*) which have been living in the aquarium for about a year will perseveringly try again the next time."

Triplett entirely disagrees with this. He says:

" While these fish did not entirely cease striking the glass during the time when the trials were about 30 minutes long, their attempts grew very much more infrequent and their blows feebler. Later, in the changed form of the experiment, becoming accustomed to the sight of the minnows, they gave up striking the glass, merely continuing to watch them. This, in connection with their conduct towards the minnows when the glass was removed, suggested that they have at least a strong temporary appreciation of the obstacle."

The strongest proof of the formation of a habit shows in their conduct after the partition itself had been removed. On reaching the place where the partition had formerly rested they stopped and turned back, advanced again, made little jumps towards it as if expecting to strike the usual obstruction and were plainly at a loss. They then turned and swam down as if following the glass. Ten days later, with the same conditions, they swam out to the mark several times and then turned and swam back. On a later occasion, when the glass was taken out, they turned 3 times at the mark, but finally crossed it in a hesitating manner.

Motor habits: reptiles.—The turtle has been studied in the laboratory by Yerkes. It is extremely sluggish in its movements. The impulse or incentive to get the animal to work was that of escape. Instinctively the animal attempts to hide in some dark secluded place and will try to escape from confinement and go towards such a place. This combination serves very well for a motive. Hunger could not be used for a motive since the reptile does not eat well in confinement and its time of eating is very irregular and hard to control. The maze consisted of a simple box 3 feet long, 2 feet wide, and 10 inches deep. It was divided into 4 portions by partitions also 10 inches deep. At different points in the partitions a hole 4 inches long and 2 inches deep was cut. This permitted the passage of the animal. After passing through the last partition the animal could get to its darkened nest of damp grass. A small speckled turtle learned this simple maze as follows: After wandering about constantly for 35 minutes, it chanced to find the nest, into which it immediately crawled and remained there until taken out 2 hours later. Experiments were made every 2 hours. On the second trial the nest was reached in 15 minutes. There was much less wandering. The time for the third trial was 5 minutes; for the fourth, 3 minutes and 30 seconds. During the first three trials the course taken was so tortuous that records of it were hard to obtain. There was aimless wandering from point to point within each space, and from space to space. After the third trial the routes became more direct. The tenth trial was made in 3 minutes and 5 seconds, with only 2 mistakes in turning. The time of the twentieth trial was 45 seconds; that of the thirtieth, 40 seconds. In the last experiment the course was direct, as was also true in the case of the fiftieth trip, which was made in 35 seconds.

Habits of manipulation: mammals.—An interesting example of the manipulation of a complicated piece of apparatus appears in the tests on the rhesus monkey. This example illustrates the general features of habits of manipulation as well as the complexity of such habits. The animal was first allowed to learn a series of simple problem boxes similar to those shown on p. 94 ff. After it had mastered a number of the boxes with simple fastenings a box was constructed which could not be opened until a combination of fastenings (made up from the earlier learned simple fastenings) had been released in serial order. In the particular case mentioned the monkey was required to bear down on a lever at the left of the box; to push in a bar at the right, and to pull out a string behind. These were all so arranged that when once moved they locked and could not be shaken back, and thus prevent the moving of the next part of the combination. The cut for this particular box is shown on p. 99. The monkey in attacking a box of this kind uses his hands incessantly. He tries first one and then the other in quick succession. One part worked, he tries all the others, though he may labor on one at a time and try often to move parts that have already been moved. A complete record of these movements is very instructive. In order to bring success these locks must be manipulated in the order **1, 2, 3, 4**. The numbers are printed in bold-faced type whenever the movement was successfully accomplished. It will be seen that the animal tried each separate combination many times before successfully working it. The list here given is for a second trial. 1, 3, 2, 4, 3, 2, 3, 2, 4, 2, 1, 2, 3, 1, 3, 2, 1, 3, 4, 1, 3, 2, 4, 1, 4, 2, 3, 3, 2, 3, 1, 4, 2, 1, 3, 2, 4, 1, 3, 3, 2, 4, 1, 3, 2, 3, 1, 4, 2, 1, 4, 2, 1, 4, 2, 3, 2, 1, 4, 1, 3, 4, 2, 4, 1, 3, 4, 4, 3, 4, 3, 2, 4, 1, 3, **2, 1, 3, 4**. It will be seen from these figures that latch **2** was tried 19 times before it was really moved. The twentieth trial reads as follows: 2, 4, 2, 3, **1**, 3, 4, **2**, 3, 4, **3, 4**. The eighty-sixth trial reads: 2, **1, 2**, 4, **3, 4** (Kinnaman). The raccoon and porcupine when tested on similar combinations show a remarkable degree of manual dexterity. They are capable of learning combinations fully as difficult as the one under discussion.

Habits of manipulation: birds.—Porter describes formation of the habit in the English sparrow of opening a small food cage, the door to which was held in place by a latch. To the latch was attached a string which led out over the box in such a way that the bird, in crawling over the box, would press the string in, and thus raise the latch. The door would spring open of its own accord (p. 98). The behavior of one English sparrow, B, is described somewhat in the following manner: B succeeded in opening the door first by pushing in the string with his claws. On the first trial he hopped up to the left of the door, on the far end covered with wire, and climbed down over the sides from the top. He next walked along the front side with one foot on the floor and one on the side of the box. Finally he accidentally struck the right place and the box opened. The records show that the unnecessary reactions get fewer in number with each successive experiment. In the tenth test he had left off all of them. At about this time he began to use his bill on the string. Instead of pushing it with his claws he struck it with his bill. On the twenty-seventh test he no longer clung to the sides of the box while striking the string with his bill, but pulled the string while standing on the floor. The time of the first trial was 10 minutes and 50 seconds; of the fifth trial, 3 minutes; of the twelfth, 1 minute; of the twentieth, 15 seconds; and of the thirty-fifth trial, 6 seconds. It will be seen that the above manipulation device is extremely simple in character. The structural relations and methods of living of reptiles, amphibia, and fish make it difficult to test their ability to form habits of manipulation. Up to the present time no such habits have been reported.

Sensory habits.—It would take us entirely too far afield to discuss sensory habits in detail as we have the two types of motor habits. Reference to p. 61, where methods of forming such habits are discussed, and to pp. 220 and 222, where the learning curves and the analyses of sensory habits, respectively, are treated, will give a fairly definite idea of how such habits are formed. For similar reason the delayed reaction is not treated separately here. Reference should be made to p. 224.

III. Curves of learning: motor habits.—Enough examples at least of motor habits have been given to show their common characteristics. The first few trials always require a large amount of excess time; succeeding trials require less and less time. If the total distance the animal traverses in reaching the food in successive trials is recorded instead of the time, the same situation appears. In the maze, e.g., the rat, on its first trial, may run 400 meters (when the distance from entrance to food box is 4.48 meters) before finally reaching the food. On his fiftieth trial he may not take a useless step. Investigators usually plot curves of learning in terms of time or distance and number of trials. Below is presented the curve for the learning of the maze by white rats (27). The number of trials is marked off along the abscissæ and the units of time and distance along the ordinates. The average of the time and of the total distance is recorded at each successive trial. In general it may be seen that there is an enormous drop in both the time and the distance curves on the first 8 or 9 trials. All succeeding trials show a slow and steady decrease in time and distance, until at the

seventieth trial the animal reaches the normal physiological
limit of training.   The habit is perfected.   Individual
animals differ somewhat as might be expected in the abso-

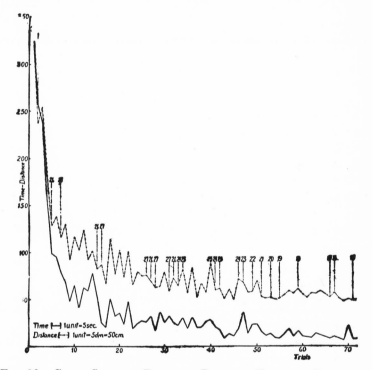

FIG. 36.   CURVE SHOWING RELATION BETWEEN TIME AND DISTANCE.

Solid line shows total average time (seconds) on each trial of
27 rats in maze: dotted line the average total distance run (centi-
meters).   (After Hubbert, *Jr. Animal Beh.*, 1914, IV, p. 60.)

lute time required to run the necessary distance (4.48
meters).

The peculiar shape of the learning curve, the initial
abrupt slope, has led to much speculation. We cannot
enter very profitably into a discussion of this subject because at the present time our knowledge of learning curves
is limited to a very few of those illustrating the simple
sensory and motor acquisitions. It is probable that the
curve of learning of very complicated acts would not have

this initial abrupt slope. Many other factors enter in to determine the contour of the learning curve: the number of trials necessary to learn the act as a whole; the absolute and relative rates of elimination of excess time and excess distance at each trial; the number of trials allowed each

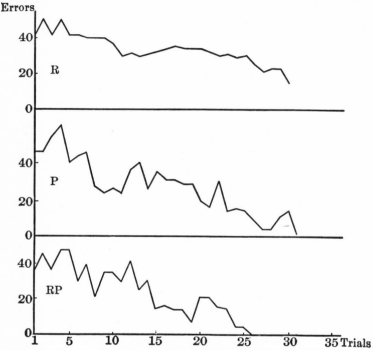

FIG. 37. CURVES ILLUSTRATING RISE OF SENSORY HABITS [6]

R = with reward alone
P = " punishment alone
RP = " " and reward.

The figures along the base line give the number of the series of trials necessary to form the habit. A series consisted of 20 trials.

day; the age of the animal; its sex, etc. Some of these factors will be considered in part on p. 235.

Curves of learning: sensory habits.—Even a superficial examination of the curve illustrating the acquisition of a sensory habit will show that the fall of the curve (i.e., the curve of error) is a very gradual one. In acquiring such

[6] These curves are further discussed on p. 206.

habits where no initial preference is noted the number of wrong responses and the number of right responses ought to be approximately equal on the first few trials. Fig. 37 shows the growth of such habits (Hoge and Stocking). Gradually,[7] and usually very gradually, the number of right responses exceeds the number of wrong responses until finally all the responses are right and the habit is formed. Here again, the method of conducting the test alters the character of the curve, e.g., the number of tests made on a given day; whether punishment is given alone for wrong choice and food alone for right; or whether food is given for right response and punishment for wrong, etc. Many other factors are at hand which alter the general character of the learning curve, such as the amount and kinds of previous practice the animal may have had; differences in instinctive traits, such as boldness, fear; the amount and kinds of distraction, etc.; the general method of attacking the problems; and finally the method of plotting the actual data may alter greatly the general appearance of the curve—telescoping of trials and time, etc. When one considers all of the factors which actually modify learning, and the different methods of treating the data on learning, it is not to be wondered at that there is no such thing as a characteristic and typical curve of learning. In conducting experiments, though, the various factors can be controlled; at least we can make the conditions of learning comparable for all the animals being experimented upon, and we can vary any one factor at will so as to bring out differences in the learning ability of young animals and old, male and female, normal and defective, etc.

Motor habits in the human being.—Tests upon the acquisition of simple motor habits have been made upon human beings, e.g., learning to typewrite; to toss and catch balls, to shoot with the long bow, etc. The general features

---

[7] Some exceptions to this rule are to be noted even here. In Shepherd's work on the discrimination of colored foodstuffs by monkeys where wrong response was punished with a bitter taste, quinine, the habit arose very quickly (p. 347).

of these curves of learning are quite similar to those of the animals. Usually there is an abrupt drop and then a somewhat gradual decline until the physiological limit is reached. Even here, though, the contour of the curve is dependent upon the complexity of the act, the method of treating the data, etc. The curves of Book, Swift and Bryan and Harter exhibit usually an abrupt descent. In the curve of archery which we have obtained the slope is very gradual. Improvement is slow at first and continues slow throughout. In an individual case there was no improvement even at the end of the three hundredth trial. Some of these curves seem to exhibit what are called plateaux and breathing places, although not all of them do. These places—where the curve remains horizontal, showing neither gain nor loss—need explanation. It is probable that their explanation is to be found in the failure to control the incentives (p. 204). No such plateaux or resting places are to be found in the curves illustrating the motor acquisitions of animals. When an animal has to work or remain hungry; to make a correct response at an alley or be punished, etc., the incentive may be said to remain at a maximum. The situation is clearly different when human beings are forced to learn to typewrite. The act is a very complex one and the stimuli leading to action are not compelling. If a man's food (reactions to sex stimuli, shelter, etc.) were dependent upon acquiring skill in a certain line—conditions which we can now control in the animals—such resting places and plateaux would in all probability disappear from his learning curves.

Comparative learning ability of different animals.— We have little accurate comparative data at present upon the differences in the learning ability of the different phyla. The statement is often made and is probably true that the monkey, with his superb eye-hand coördinations, can form habits of manipulation much more quickly than any of the other animals. From the work that has been presented by several investigators it is probable that the raccoon stands next to the monkey, and after him the porcupine and then the cat. Probably the dog should appear next, yet the rat is extremely apt in forming simple habits of manipulation. On the other hand, mammals like the guinea pig and the rabbit are clumsy in forming such habits. The bird class as a whole is notoriously poor in acquiring acts of skill.

On the other hand, the rat stands preëminent among the animals in his ability to thread a complicated maze, and the gray squirrel probably stands next to him in this ability. The monkey, however, acquires the maze habit readily. Birds, fish, reptiles, and amphibia form maze habits with very great slowness. Birds can, with great difficulty, learn complex mazes, but the amphibia, fishes, and reptiles have so far been known to form only very simple habits of this kind. Some experiments have been made for the purpose of comparing the relative learning ability of blindfolded human adults, children, and blind white rats to learn a maze under approximately comparable conditions. While the conditions for rat and man differed sufficiently to make comparison difficult, it would seem that the absolute number of trials was less for the rats than for the human subjects. When one compares the rapidity of the elimination of excess time and distance (i.e., time over and above that required to traverse the maze when the habit is learned, and distance over that of the length of the true pathway from entrance to food) one finds that the human subjects make such eliminations much more slowly than do the animals. On the other hand, the animals start with a much larger number of excess factors and show a very much greater variability all through their learning curves than do human subjects (Hicks and Carr). We have little comparative data on the relative ability of different varieties of animals to form sensory habits. Since the motor and instinctive equipments of the different animal groups differ so enormously it is doubtful if we shall ever have any accurate means of grading animals with regard to the rapidity with which they can form motor habits. On the other hand, there seems to be no real reason why birds and monkeys, e.g., may not be accurately compared with respect to the rapidity with which they form, visual sensory habits, etc. The interpretation of such differences in learning ability (were such found to exist) would be as difficult as in the case of motor habits. Differences in learning might be due to differences in sensitivity to the stimuli rather than to differences in the rapidity with which the arcs are established (assuming that the response demanded is on a par in the two cases). Until our determinations of the range of effective stimuli, the relative stimulating effect of stimuli, etc., have been carried much farther, observed differences in learning among the different phyla do not mean very much.

IV. The rise of habits when incentives are controlled.—It can hardly be said that behavior has yet developed any very complete methods of controlling incentives. Punishment in one form or another for wrong reactions and food for right response have been used as controls since animals have been trained. In training for circus work the two incentives have usually been combined. In such work the whip has been largely employed and still is the mainstay of the professional trainer. With them, however, the whip serves the double purpose,—that of punishing when wrong response is made and that of giving the signals or cues to which the animals respond.

Apparently Elmer Gates [8] was the first person to employ the method of induction shocks. Since his experiment is not very well known and has not been largely quoted, we give a brief abstract of his experiment upon the dog. On the floor of a hall were placed colored metal squares. All of the squares, except those of a given color, were connected with an induction coil. The dog, in passing down the hall, had to jump from one square to another. By jumping only upon same colored squares he could pass safely through the hall without receiving punishment.

Yerkes has very greatly extended the use of Gates' method (p. 59). His work on behavior, coupled with that of Martin on the standardization of the Porter inductorium, gives us our first approach to a real control of incentives. Some of the difficulties in the use of the

[8] *The Monist,* 1895, p. 584.

method have already been discussed. As we have pointed out, no scientific control of the other incentives seems possible, and yet certain steps in that direction may be taken with food (p. 58). A good practical method, as we have already remarked, in regard to the use of food, is that of allowing the animal to eat sparingly of mixed necessary food after each trial, and then either to satiety at the end of the daily routine of tests or else for a specified length of time. In the discussion of the experiments which follows some such method of food control, either during the tests or after them, is always used. Even when punishment is used alone, the control of food is a necessary factor.

Habits formed without the use of punishment.—Since the punishment method has come into favor very slowly and has some serious limitations, we find that much of the work upon both sensory and motor habits mentioned in the literature on behavior has been carried on in the absence of punishment. Certain other incentives, of which we cannot make separate mention, have been used, such as escape from narrow quarters, escape from cold, from bright light, etc. Examples of habit formation under such conditions have been given on p. 193 and p. 195.

With punishment as the sole incentive.—It would seem to be established by experimentation upon sensory habits (1) that when the difference between the two directive stimuli is great, the rapidity of learning increases as the strength of the electric stimulus (punishment) increases from the threshold of stimulation up to the point where the current becomes dangerous to the tissue. This law may be looked upon as holding for what we may call *easy habits*. (2) Where the habit arises with some difficulty, i.e., where the intensity difference between the two stimuli is less, there seems to be at present no clear relationship between the number of trials necessary to learn the habit and the strength of the punishment. In general it will probably be found that there is an optimal strength of stimulus for every difference in intensity between the two stimuli upon the basis of which a habit is to be established. Suppose, e.g., we are working with two lights.

The difference in intensity maintained may be 10 c.p., 5 c.p., or 1 c.p. Only experimentation could decide what strength of stimulus should be used with any one of these differences in intensity. Yerkes has stated the general law as follows: " As difficultness of visual discrimination increases, that strength of electrical stimulus which is most favorable to habit formation approaches the threshold. The easier the habit the stronger that stimulus which most quickly forces its acquisition; the more difficult the habit the weaker the stimulus which most quickly forces its acquisition."

With punishment for wrong response and food for right.—So far only one set of results has been obtained upon this subject. It would seem from work upon the white rat, where a habit of responding positively to the brighter of two lights (2 c.p. and 16 c.p.) was desired, that punishment for failure and food for right response give the most advantageous situation for the rise of the habit. Fig. 37, p. 200, shows these results.[9] This work needs confirming by the use of a much larger number of animals than was employed.

V. Analysis of reflexes involved in habit.—So far in our discussion we have spoken of habits as though they consisted of only a few well-directed and definite muscular movements; as though the complex stimulus (problem box, maze, etc.) called forth on first presentation a large number of random acts, among which acts were to be found those necessary to obtain food (to escape punishment, etc.), and on later presentations fewer and fewer excess movements. Finally the stimulus arouses the few necessary acts in serial order. Such an illustration fits very well those cases of habit where the movements are simple and definite in character, such as pulling a string, knocking up a latch, etc. But certain habits are enormously complex. Consider, e.g., the learning of the Hampton

[9] A reference to this figure shows that where no punishment was used (R) the habit was not perfected within the time limits of the experiment; where punishment alone was used 610 trials were required (P); where reward and punishment were combined only 530 trials were necessary (RP).

Court maze, with its many possibilities of false turns. It is evident that in order to thread this maze as a whole it is necessary for the animal to have a series of simple habits (i.e., one wherever an error of turn is possible) of the character we have just considered. It becomes necessary in the prediction and control of behavior to make an analysis both of the simple types of habits and of the most complex. We should like to be able to state, were such possibilities of analysis ideal, (1) the number, location, and serial order of functioning of the reflex arcs from the initial response until food is reached; and (2) the stimulus which releases each arc. Furthermore there is some evidence that these systems of arcs change somewhat as the habit passes from the initial stage to the final or automatic stage. We may possibly make this latter point clearer by saying that in the early stages visual, auditory, tactual, etc., stimuli are all functioning (necessary for the release of the appropriate motor impulse), whereas in the later stage only the kinæsthetic [10] are functional. There is less and less resistance in the synapses of the kinæsthetic arcs and probable actual blockage in the synapses of the arcs of the distance receptors. The movement of muscle 1 (it will be remembered that such muscles contain sensory neurons as well as motor) sets up a sensory stimulus which, upon entrance into the proper place in the central nervous system, releases a motor impulse which brings about movement 2. This routine continues until the whole train of movements has been run off. It is thus seen that the muscle is at one and the same time the *effector* of the arc in operation and the *receptor* of the arc which is next to function. The notion that every habit is of this character is more or less current. That this need not be true may easily be understood when we consider that the stimulus to movement 1 may be olfactory, visual, etc., but movement 1, however released, may set up an auditory stimulus

[10] By kinæsthetic we mean the sensory impulse aroused by the contraction of the muscle. When the muscle contracts the muscle spindles (sensory nerve endings in muscles) are chemically stimulated. The endings in the tendons are aroused at the same time.

(the animal may run over a trap which causes a door to drop,—auditory but no visual stimulus). The succeeding movement, movement 2, may be released now through at least two avenues: (*a*) the sensory impulse coming from the muscles used in springing the trap; (*b*) through auditory impulse aroused by the impact of the falling door. As we watch the behavior of a normal animal while executing a customary act we find ourselves wholly unable to state what impulses are functioning. Special types of experimentation are necessary for analysis and for tracing the history of a habit. Suppose (to take a very simple case) we train an animal to open box III, p. 95, with all sense organs intact. After training we may begin analysis: the auditory impulse may be blocked by eliminating the sense organ (operative method), or it may not be aroused at all, which may be effected by padding the door (normal method). We may find that the animal can still execute movement 2, i.e., run to the door, enter it, etc. On the other hand, we may begin our analysis in the learning stage by forcing the animal to learn with certain stimuli absent. Actual tests show that learning may proceed with the auditory stimulus absent, or in an animal with auditory organ destroyed; but the character of the learning curve may or may not be altered, depending upon the animal used. In the laboratory in order to evaluate results we have proceeded upon the assumptions (1) if the *trained* animal can as quickly and with as little excess effort execute the habit under consideration after the auditory stimulus has been removed through normal or operative methods, we are justified in concluding that movement 1 gives the impulse which releases movement 2. On the other hand, (2), if, after the loss of the auditory stimulus, there is a serious break in the habit, we must conclude that the auditory stimulus functioned at least along with the kinæsthetic. If, (3) after the loss of the auditory stimulus, the animal can relearn the problem, we conclude that the kinæsthetic impulse may come to function alone, i.e., be completely substituted for the auditory. If the animal (4) deprived of the auditory stimulus, by whatever means, can *learn* the problem in as short a time and with as little excess effort as the animal not deprived of the auditory stimulus, we can conclude that the stimulus of movement 2 is kinæsthetic; whereas (5) if learning is more difficult, we assume that the auditory stimulus is functioning in normal learning. The right of making such conclusions from the premises stated has been questioned somewhat in the literature. Some authors would have us believe that the animals have a nervous system so delicately constructed that there can be an immediate shift in the arcs; e.g., if in cases where distance receptors are functioning in a well-established habit we block impulses over those avenues, they maintain that there may be an immediate shift to kinæsthetic impulses with no break in the habit. Such a view must have some factual support before it need be seriously considered. This simple illustration makes it obvious that habit analysis forces us to resort to methods of elimination of stimuli. This may be considered under two heads; normal methods and operative methods.

Normal and operative methods of eliminating sensory impulses.—Since many investigators object to removing the sense organs in animals, various normal methods have been devised. The simplest way of excluding visual impulses, e.g., is to work in a dark room; to exclude auditory impulses, to work with noiseless instruments; to exclude olfactory impulses, thoroughly to cleanse and wash the apparatus after each experiment. Animals may be trained with these stimuli present until the habit becomes automatic. These stimuli may then be removed and the effect noted upon the execution of the act. On the other hand, we may force the animal to *learn* with several of such stimuli excluded. The objections to the use of normal methods are many and serious. We have proceeded usually upon the assumption that the sensitivity of the receptor of a given animal to a particular form of stimulation is the same as our own.

The error of such a procedure appears clearly when we consider the olfactory sensitivity of many animals. Washing and even boiling the maze may not conclusively eliminate the olfactory stimulation, i.e., such as trails, etc., for certain animal forms. On the other hand, if we wish to exclude visual stimulation by working in a dark room, we eliminate, *pari-passu,* the experimenter's possibility of observing the behavior of the animal.

The safest method, in the case of distance receptors, is to remove the organ. When this is done under proper operative condition, most animals are abnormal only with respect to those functions for which we desire abnormality.[11] The normal method can give us only indications of the data, and can never be said to furnish scientific proof of their existence.[12] It must be obvious that while we are principally concerned with the analysis of motor arcs, methods of eliminating undesirable sensory stimuli must be constantly employed in the establishment of sensory habits, and habits of the delayed reaction type. On p. 63 we mention the necessity for control of this kind. Were it possible, in work upon certain aspects of vision, to use animals in which only the visual receptors with the necessary effectors were functioning, our results could be obtained with far greater accuracy than at present.

Some results of experimental analysis of motor habits in mammals.—The simple case of habit analysis discussed on p. 208 enables us to examine in detail a much more complicated case—that which the rat forms in the Hampton Court maze (p. 103). One is struck immediately by the peculiar rapidity and neatness with which the rat learns to thread this maze. Fig. 38 gives the learning curve of 4 normal rats. It will be seen that on the average 29 minutes are required for a first successful trip and that by the end of the thirtieth trial this time has been reduced to approximately 30 seconds. As we see the rat threading this complicated maze with never a false step, we get no

[11] Birds offer an exception to this observation in so far as visual receptors are concerned.

[12] For obvious reasons we cannot enter into a complete treatment of the operative methods and technique. The reader is referred to the author's paper, *Psychological Monograph No. 33,* and to that of Florence Richardson, *Psychological Monograph No. 48.* In order to avoid all criticisms it is best to have such operations made under medical supervision, and where possible by physicians themselves.

indication of the system of arcs involved in the execution of the act as a whole.   The sensory avenues may be very numerous.   On early trials the animals cover every square inch of space, passing in and out of the *culs de sac,* coming back to the entrance, advancing, returning again, etc.   Soon the animal passes by the openings into the *culs de sac* at A

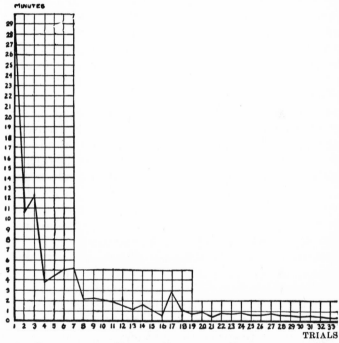

FIG. 38.   SHOWING THE NORMAL PROCESS OF LEARNING THE MAZE

Based upon four normal male rats, about one year of age.   In all of the following curves one division of the ordinate represents one minute, while one division of the abscissa represents one trial.

and B (Fig. 25).   Gradually those further along are safely passed and finally the whole run is made without error. It is obvious that learning to avoid any one of these *culs de sac* may be looked upon, for convenience, as involving the formation of a habit.   Since there are several *culs de sac* it is clear that we have several unit habits " chained " together.   After all these units are formed and concatenated, learning is said to be complete.[13] Two questions arise: (1) What process is involved in forming any one of these unit habits? We have the same condition at each *cul de sac* that we have in the simple habit considered above, random movements giving place finally to the right movement, i.e., making the proper turn or keeping straight ahead. We have already spoken of deferring this discussion to Chapter VII. The answer to these questions does not involve an analysis of the arcs employed. It gives a reason in mechanical terms for the more or less complete elimination of all random movements. (2) What systems of receptors are involved in the various parts of the maze—the straight-aways as opposed to the turns, the *culs de sac*, etc.? We can conceive of the animal, deprived of all its distance receptors, walking or running from the entrance to the food box. Each movement executed would arouse new contact and kinæsthetic impulses which in turn would release the succeeding movement. It is difficult to conceive of such a defective animal learning the maze *de novo*. When an animal, after leaving O, arrives at A, the first *cul de sac*, the sensory situation becomes more complex than in the alleys. There are differences in the optical stimulation offered, differences in the olfactory, and differences in contact, since the vibrissæ on the left are in contact with the walls of the maze, while those on the right are not in contact. Furthermore, there are differences in the direction and intensity of the air currents and in temperature. Likewise the auditory stimulation is different—there are differences in the reflection of the sound of the animal's own footsteps, etc.—and finally kinæsthetic impulses change. The possibility of a change in the form of stimulation at the entrance of the *cul de sac* as contrasted with that in the alleys is very great. The question arises: are all of these impulses necessary for the release of the movement which carries the animal safely past the *cul de sac*? If all are not necessary, which ones are? Furthermore, all (or many) may be necessary in the early

---

[13] On p. 261 we show that concatenation is not a part of the process; it appears *ipso facto* when errors are eliminated.

stages of the habit, but only the kinæsthetic in the automatic stage. These questions we have attempted to answer by experimental methods. (1) We first trained several animals in daylight and then tested them in darkness. The appended table shows that the animals executed the habit in the dark in as short a time as in the light. This is

MAZE IN LIGHT

Rats	I	II	III	IV	V
Trials	Min.	Min.	Min.	Min.	Min.
1	.40	.36	.29	.30	.36
2	.41	.25	.50	.24	.24
3	.46	.33	.25	.24	.24
4	.53	.60	.24	.30	.28
5	.70	.40	.25	.66	.70

MAZE IN DARK

1	.50	.40	.31	.31	.25
2	.33	.25	.50	.26	.30
3	.41	.25	.25	.24	.33
4	.56	.35	.24	.25	.24
5	.41	.45	.24	.29	.30

AVERAGES FOR THE FIVE TRIALS IN THE LIGHT AND THE FIVE IN DARKNESS—EACH RAT SEPARATELY

In light.	.500	.388	.306	.348	.364
In dark.	.442	.340	.308	.270	.302

merely indicative of the fact that after the habit is learned it can be executed automatically without the use of the visual receptors. (2) We then forced several rats to *learn* the maze in the dark. They likewise learned in normal time. (Fig. 39.) Could we be sure that vision was completely excluded in this learning process, we should have good evidence that vision is not necessary to the formation of this habit. In order completely to control our work, we eliminated vision by removing the sense organs in two groups of animals, one (3) wholly untrained in the maze and (4) the other trained to it. When brought to test the untrained animals learned the maze as rapidly as did the normal animals. (Fig. 40.) The trained group of blind

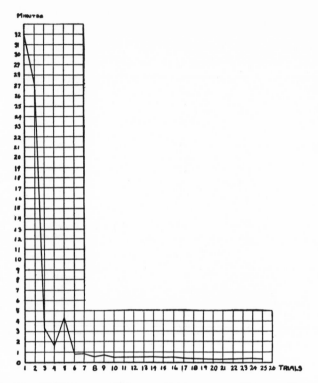

FIG. 39.   LEARNING OF MAZE IN DARKNESS BY NORMAL RATS

animals ran the maze with only a slight loss in efficiency
which might have been predicted when we recall the fact

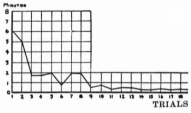

FIG. 40.   LEARNING OF MAZE BY BLIND RATS

that after the animals had been operated on, they were not
again tested in the maze until 40 days had elapsed; consequently there was a slight loss in retention.   (Fig. 41.)

It would seem that visual receptors are not involved in the formation of the maze habit at any stage.

We made no attempt to control the factor of smell by normal methods, but (5) removed the olfactory bulb in

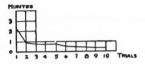

FIG. 41. SHOWING THE EFFECT OF THE LOSS OF VISION UPON RATS TRAINED TO THE MAZE WITH SENSE ORGANS INTACT

several rats and forced them to learn the maze in the light. The learning time was normal in every sense and the learning curve was identical with that of the normal group. (Fig. 42.) The anosmic animals were then (6) forced

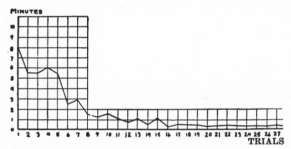

FIG. 42. LEARNING OF MAZE BY ANOSMIC RATS

to run the maze in darkness. No disturbance of the habit was noticeable. (7) Animals with defective auditory receptors (drum membrane and auditory ossicles removed) were next tried. The learning was normal. (Fig. 43.) (8) Trained normal and defective animals with vibrissæ removed were next tried. No disturbance was noted if the animals were kept in the cage for a few days after the removal of the vibrissæ. (9) The maze is learned by animals without vibrissæ as readily as by those with them. (Fig. 44.) The effect on trained animals of (10) altering the direction and intensity of air currents and (11) of the temperature of the air at the *culs de sac* was without effect.

(12) The effect of producing local anæsthesis (ethylchloride) of the soles of the feet, snout, etc., was likewise *nil*.

We seem forced to conclude that in the rat kinæsthetic

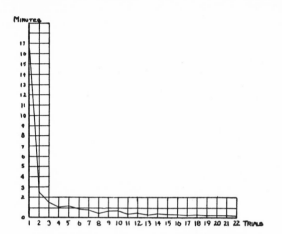

FIG. 43. LEARNING IN PARTIALLY DEAF RATS

arcs are the only ones necessary at any stage of the formation of this habit. This does not mean that the distance receptors and the tactual are not being stimulated while

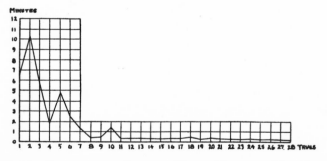

FIG. 44. LEARNING IN ANIMALS WHOSE VIBRISSÆ HAD BEEN REMOVED

the animal passes through the entrance point to the food. It has later been shown that conditions can be so arranged in the maze that arcs other than kinæsthetic are necessary to the formation of the habit. It may be objected that the evidence so far advanced is purely negative, obtained by the exclusion of data other than kinæsthetic, consequently that we have no real proof of a positive character to show that the kinæsthetic arcs really function in the way in which we maintain. Very definite and positive proof that our main thesis is right has been furnished by taking a maze that could be shortened or lengthened without altering the relations of the turns. Fig. 26, p. 104, shows this form. Two groups of animals were trained upon this maze, one group in its shortened and the other in its lengthened form. Animals that had been trained with the lengthened form were tried with the shortened form. Q in the diagram is thus made to take the position Q′. Under this change the animals released at O gathered speed as they made the various turns and then ran with full strength into the wall at 1. With the kinæsthetic arcs functioning, the extra-organically aroused impulses (visual stimulation of walls, etc.) were unable to inhibit the customary movements. When the animals that had learned the shortened form were tested in the lengthened form, they tried to turn in at the places where formerly they had turned in. Again the evidence is conclusive. The turns had been made hitherto solely on the basis of proprio-ceptive impulses. Changing to the lengthened form brought no immediate change in these impulses, so the animal tried to turn into the solid wall. As soon, however, as the failure occurred, the old chain broke and the new habit was formed—i.e., of going forward several inches and then turning. Many other experiments furnished the needed positive proof that was lacking in the elimination method.

One objection has been raised to the resolving of the maze habit process into the functioning of a serially chained kinæsthetic arc system. It may be stated as follows: in man and in animals kinæsthetic arcs function in perfect habits until some disturbance occurs, i.e., until rival impulses coming in over other receptors become sufficiently strong to produce inhibition of the customary movements. It is held that a similar situation exists in the case of the rat in the maze. The animal may be automatically

traversing the maze at a high rate of speed when suddenly
a loud noise, a strange odor, or an intense itching occurs.
The chain of movements is broken. How now does automaticity become reëstablished? The human being under
similar circumstances—when momentarily lost while executing a purely automatic habit—remains unoriented until
supplementary distance sense data are at hand; e.g., he
glances at the score if playing a piece of music. These relations at hand, the reign of the kinæsthetic arcs is reëstablished and the automatic character of the acts again becomes
apparent. But in the case of the rat do distance sense
data function in this way? We conclude, on the basis of a
large amount of experimental work, that automaticity is
reëstablished for the rat solely from the distinctive
kinæsthetic impulses which function exactly as do the
visual impulses in the case just stated for man. If the
trained rat is put down in a part of the maze other than
the entrance, he runs at first randomly. He may wander
about, turn round and round in the alleys, but suddenly
he darts off and traverses the remainder of the maze in the
usual automatic way. We hold that during the period of
random activity the animal passed over what we may call
a "kinæsthetic unit," thereby arousing a certain sequence
of the kinæsthetic impulses which could not be aroused in
any other part of the maze. This distinctive group of
impulses is sufficient to reëstablish automaticity. Examination of any maze shows that there are several ways in
which kinæsthetic impulses become grouped: (a) two run-
ways are unequal in length; (b) they may be of equal length
but occur in different positions of the total series, i.e., they
are preceded by different conditions; (c) they may be alike
in every respect except that one may be entered by a turn
to the right and the other by a turn to the left; (d) the
runs may be of the same length and be entered from the
same direction but present possible differences in their
stimulating effect by reason of the fact that they extend in
different directions (180°, etc., rotation of the maze, which
changes only the absolute direction of the run-ways, produces marked disturbance in habit). When the unori-

ented animal passes over any distinctive part of the maze, the kinæsthetic impulses arise, releasing the old movements.

We are far from maintaining that we have a complete analysis of the maze habit even in the case of the rat.[14] Some experiments in the maze showed quite clearly that there still are unanalyzed factors. If the Hampton Court maze is rotated 180°, normal, blind, and anosmic animals are disturbed, i.e., a breakdown occurs in the execution of the habit. What this disturbance is due to is not clear. It may depend upon the disturbance of sensory impulses which are already known (i.e., no new systems of receptors are required for its explanation).

Analysis of motor habits in birds.—The bird stands in marked contrast to the rat with respect to its behavior in the maze. In the first place it is very difficult to get the bird to learn a maze as complicated as that which the rat learns with ease. Consequently experiments have been carried out upon birds with much simpler mazes. While experimental analysis is not so complete as in the case of the rat, it is quite evident that distance receptors play a very large rôle if not a preponderating one in the formation and execution of this habit. The bird is so constructed physiologically that visual impulses are necessary for motor activity of any kind. Hence it is impossible to exclude light, either by normal methods or operative methods, and get the animal to learn at all. This makes it extremely difficult to test the actual rôle of vision. On the other hand, birds show almost no trace of sensitivity to olfactory impressions (p. 403). Hence it is highly improbable that olfactory arcs function in this habit. In general it seems safe to conclude that analysis will show that visual arcs, auditory arcs, and kinæsthetic arcs are all functional. It is perfectly clear from all the work upon the formation of maze habits that birds never become the automata that rats become.[15]

[14] In the more recent work of Bogardus and Henke it is claimed that the number of contacts (touches with snout) made at the corners by untrained rats whose vibrissæ were removed is directly in proportion to the number of errors made in learning the maze.

[15] It is interesting to note that birds apparently never dash into partitions in work on the shortened and lengthened forms of the

Analysis of sensory habits in mammals.—For purposes of analysis we will take some sensory habits which the rat forms when confronted with monochromatic lights. The method of conducting such tests is given on p. 61, the apparatus on p. 71. When this animal was stimulated simultaneously by the lights *red*, 655 $\mu\mu$, and *green*, 505 $\mu\mu$, a habit developed. In this case the animal responded positively to red and negatively to green. Ten to twenty trials per day were given. After 555 trials the animal became automatic in his responses. He was then considered ready for control tests. In the training series the energy of the two monochromatic bands was not known. As the results of the experiment stand we are not able to *define the stimulus* which led to response. The results might be interpreted in three ways: (1) the animal may have been responding on the basis of wave-length difference; (2) upon the basis of intensity difference; (3) only one stimulus was effective—the other stimulus lying wholly outside the sensory range of the animal. If the latter supposition were true, it remained to find out which light was stimulating the animal.[16] Control tests to decide among these suppositions

maze, or when obstacles are placed in the way. Some experiments were made in the Hopkins Laboratory (by Dr. Ulrich) to test whether pigeons, after hopping (and "half flying") to a food box 1 meter away, would hop short or over the food, depending upon whether the box had been brought nearer to the starting point or moved farther away. As is well shown by Richardson, rats, when trained to jump, e.g., 20 inches for food, are unable to adjust for new distances without training. If, e.g., they are trained to jump 20 inches and the box is brought 12 inches forward, the animal jumps to the old distance, 20 inches. He jumps short if the food box is moved farther away, e.g., to 28 inches. The pigeon, on the other hand, makes these adjustments with equal readiness regardless of the distance. Tests were made within the limits of .75 meter on either side of the mid position. All of the work so far carried out on the rat's motor habits show the almost complete dominance of the proprioceptive impulses over the skeletal muscles. In contrast to this it appears that the skeletal muscles in the pigeon are dominated by the impulses from the visual receptors.

[16] It should be made clear that sensory habits may arise where two stimuli are present when only one stimulus is effective. Furthermore, the non-effective stimulus may be either positive or negative.

were begun with rather striking results. A diary record of the control tests follows:

1911.
March 7th. *Red* (positive) full intensity. *Green* cut to 11% of full intensity. 15 trials. 93% correct.
March 8th. *Green* full intensity. *Red* cut to 11% of full intensity. 15 trials. 100% correct.
March 9th. *Red* full intensity. *Green* cut to 2.7% of full intensity. 11 trials. 40% correct. Complete loss of habit. Then immediately afterwards 9 trials were given with both stimuli full intensity. 100% of correct choices.
March 10th. Conditions as beginning of test on previous day. 15 trials. 53% correct. Complete loss of habit. 5 trials were then given with both stimuli at full intensity. 100% correct. From March 11th to March 16th certain experiments were tried to determine the effect of external illumination upon the discrimination. These experiments were so unsatisfactory that mention of the results is omitted. By June 5th the animals were again trained to react perfectly to *red* and *green*. Further control experiments to determine the nature of the effective stimulus were then undertaken.
June 5th. 8 normal trials were first given. 100% correct. Then *red* beam was cut out. *Green* left at full intensity. Went to *red side* (darkness) on every trial (10 trials).
June 6th. 8 normal trials. 100% correct. *Green* was cut out and *red* left at full intensity. *Right position habit developed immediately.* Discrimination lost. Then 4 normal trials were given. 100% correct.
June 7th. 8 normal trials. 100% correct. *Green* out, *red* at full intensity. 14 trials given. *Right position habit developed immediately.* 4 normal trials were then given. 100% correct.
June 10th. 8 normal trials were given. 100% correct. *Red* cut out, *green* full intensity. Went to *red side* (darkness) on all 15 trials. 2 normal trials were next given. Both correct.
June 11th. 6 normal trials given. 100% correct. *Green* out, *red* full intensity. *Left position habit developed immediately.* (9 trials.) Then 10 normal trials were given. 90% correct.
June 12th. 6 normal trials given. 100% correct. *Both* lights cut out for 15 trials. *Right position habit developed.* 4 normal trials were given. 100% correct.[17]

These results seem to show perfectly that the *green* was the effective stimulus and that the *red* had no stimulating value whatsoever. *The animal was reacting against a lighted compartment.* One might decrease the intensity of the *green* light enormously and eliminate the *red* altogether,

[17] In all of the control tests food might be had regardless of the stimulus reacted to. Food was always kept in both compartments even during the training series.

without changing the accuracy of the responses. When, however, the intensity of the *green* approached the threshold, as on March 9th, a disturbance immediately manifested itself. Whenever the *green* was cut out the animal behaved exactly as though no light stimulus were present (contrast tests of June 11th with those of June 12th). These results seem to show that we are dealing with a defect in the receptor. Summarizing the results we find: (1) that the *green* was the effective stimulus; (2) that the *red* had no stimulating effect. The results harmonize with the hypothesis that the *red* chosen lay outside of the animal's spectrum.

It follows from this experiment that supposition (3) was correct. But from our results we are still unable to define the nature of the stimulus—we do not know from them whether the animal was reacting on the basis merely of its intensity or whether its wave-length was a factor also. We might easily have carried the experiment farther and tested whether the animal would have responded as readily to a white light as to the green. Instead, however, we began experiments upon two other rats, using stimuli both of which lay in the sensory range of the animal, viz., *yellow*, $595\mu\mu$, and *blue*, $478\mu\mu$. In this case No. I responded positively to blue and No. II, positively to yellow. One interesting fact was brought out very clearly: when both stimuli were in the field the animal failed to form the habit within the time limits of the test. In order to hasten the growth of the habit only one stimulus (the positive in each case) was used. As might have been predicted from our tests on red and green, the habit arose readily. Then (with energy of both stimuli known) we introduced the negative stimulus. As fast as possible, without breaking down the habit, the intensity of the negative stimulus was increased. The following table shows the results of this test. Column 1 gives the number of days the test endured, and column 2 shows the angular opening of the sector. An opening of 10° admits a beam of very low intensity. At 360° the full intensity of the beam was utilized (i.e., the two stimuli possessed equal energy, but did not contain

equal stimulating value). Column 3 gives the percentages
of correct responses (in 10—20 trials).

TABLE SHOWING EFFECT ON HABIT OF LEAVING POSITIVE COLOR AT
FULL INTENSITY AND GRADUALLY INTRODUCING COLOR REACTED
AGAINST

	RAT I (Reacting positively to *blue*)			RAT II (Reacting positively to *yellow*)	
Days	Angular opening on *yellow*	% correct	Days	Angular opening on *blue*	% correct
1	10	90	1	10	80
2	10	83	2	10	80
3	10	93	3	10	80
4	20	93	4	10	90
5	30	100	5	20	80
6	40	93	6	20	75
7	50	100	7	20	90
8	60	93	8	30	80
9	70	90	9	30	77
10	80	95	10	30	50
11	90	100	11	30	60
12	100	100	12	—	94
13	110	85	13	10	100
14	110	100	14	20	80
15	120	100	15	20	75
16	130	93	16	20	80
17	140	93	17	20	60
18	180	93	18		
19	200	93	19		
20	200	100	20		
21	240	93	21		
22	360	96			
23	360	100			

This shows almost perfect
habit at equal energy.

Could not be brought to
full intensity. Shows that
animal was reacting to intensity and that *blue* at
20°-30° had the same
stimulating effect as the
yellow at full intensity.

A difference in the behavior of the two animals becomes at
once apparent. No. I persisted in the habit when both
lights possessed considerable intensity. No. II lost
the habit when the angular opening on the stimulus was
set at 20—30° (when the energy of the blue was 1/18—
1/12 that of the yellow). The fact that the habit disappeared when the negative color bore 1/18—1/12 the

energy of the yellow furnishes almost conclusive evidence that supposition 2 above is correct: This animal was responding on the basis of the difference in intensity, i.e., when both stimuli were present, positively to the more intense; as soon, however, as the negative stimulus possessed the same stimulating effect, the basis for response disappeared. The results of the experiments on No. I cannot be interpreted except by the use of control tests. Without entering into the details of these it was found that the stimulating value of blue for this animal was very high and that in order to get an equal stimulating effect from the yellow one must make its energy many times greater than that of the blue. When the stimuli were so manipulated that both possessed equal stimulating value, the habit disappeared for animal No. II just as it did for No. I. It was further shown that when the negative color was made to possess higher stimulating value than the positive, the response was reversed, i.e., the animal then reacted positively to the light which it had formerly reacted against. The same condition obtained when a strong white light was presented in place of the color reacted against—the animal responded positively to the white light. Furthermore the animals responded positively to the negative stimulus when it was given alone. The conclusion that the stimulus to which the animals were responding was an intensity difference, and that a difference in wave-length possessed no stimulating value, seems valid (at least so far as concerns the responses to yellow-blue).

Analysis of the delayed reaction.—On p. 105 we discussed the method by means of which the delayed response is obtained. The situation in brief is as follows: while the animal is held in restraint its visual receptors are stimulated by a light which may appear in any one of three boxes, left, in front, or at the right. The animal has previously been trained to go to the lighted compartment for food. After training the animal is not released until after the light has been turned out. Upon release it must go to the box in which the light last appeared. The experimenter may, at will, allow an appreciable time to elapse between turning out the light and releasing the animal. Let us glance at first at the maximum delay which can be obtained in different types of animals. Hunter has tested rats, dogs, raccoons, and children. We may observe his results more conveniently in the form of a table.

Subject	Maximum delay
Rats	10 seconds
Dogs	5 minutes
Raccoons	25 seconds
Children	25 minutes

The problem here seemingly is to determine the mechanism by means of which correct response may be made to a stimulus which is no longer present. We shall see later that this problem may be restated so as to bring it in line with the other types of response which can be explained in terms of the immediate functioning of neural arcs. Prior to experimental analysis there appear to be several possibilities of sensory stimulation which might lead to successful response after the period of delay: (1) the experimenter himself might give the stimulus in one of several ways, such as shifting his position, changing the breathing, etc.; (2) the order in the tests might not have been sufficiently varied; (3) the box in which the light last appeared might have risen in temperature; (4) the increase in the temperature of the light box might have increased the diffusion of the gaseous particles which arouse the olfactory receptors;[18] (5) the after-glow of the recently lighted lamp might have been responded to; (6) the after-images of the light might lead to response. These possibilities of sensory stimulation are not exhaustive. They are merely illustrative of the many which must be considered. We cannot take up in detail the various methods by means of which such possible stimuli were eliminated. In general they were found to be inoperative and the only extra-organic factor was the presence of the light in the box. Normal methods of elimination were used in reaching these results.

On what basis, then, is it possible to react to the position

[18] Neither (3) nor (4) was sufficiently controlled by Hunter.

of a stimulus which was present for a time and then disappeared? Obviously one possibility of explanation lies in the fact that the light when present releases a definite set of arcs which function the one after the other, as in every habit. It is easy to see that the light itself forces into action a definite set of arcs, which result in bodily orientation, such as turning the head and body to the light, crouching, maintaining that attitude, and the inhibition of other movements. The movements initiated by the light in turn arouse kinæsthetic and organic impulses which in turn inhibit movement, etc. The auditory and visual stimuli offered by releasing the animal immediately initiate the walking and the running movement. Since the animal is already oriented, naturally the movements take him to the box which was last lighted. Once there the habit of entering the box, eating the food, etc., is re-aroused. We might call this the first method by means of which the light could exert a determining effect although absent (i.e., through initiating the reflex arcs which function continuously and serially from the moment the light is presented until the animal arrives at the food).

In more highly organized subjects in which speech habits are adequate for all ordinary situations, the light may arouse a group of throat movements long since correlated with definite modes of response (e.g., the words " go to the box in front when door opens "). With such a highly complex system of habits there is no need for the arc originally aroused continuously to exert its function as in the first case considered. The animal with speech habits may begin to play or engage in any number of activities without producing a breakdown in the response when the door is opened. At the moment of release the visual stimulus of the opening door re-arouses the vocal impulses which lead to their natural sequences, viz., movements straight forward to the box in front. We will call this method two.

In the less highly organized animals the periods of delay are wholly determined by the length of time it can retain bodily orientation. This will depend upon its organization (i.e., sensitivity to forms of stimulus other than kinæsthetic) and to the actual intensity of the sensory stimuli present (noises, changes in the light, bites of insects, etc.).

Observation of the various animals seems to show that the rat, in order to respond correctly, must maintain actual gross bodily orientation. It cannot move about after the light is turned out. If this overt orientation is lost for a moment any one of the three boxes may be entered. This statement holds true for all of the correct responses of the rat and the dog, and for most of those of the raccoon. On the other hand, several of the responses of the raccoons and all of the responses of the children offered a mode of behavior which cannot be explained in the terms of maintained bodily attitude. It is possible for the raccoons and the children to lose all bodily orientation and then to respond correctly when the door is opened. It is possible, also, in the case of the raccoons, to introduce loud noises, etc., without disturbing the response. The case of the long delays of the children may be explained by the use of the language habit (p. 328). The behavior of the raccoons cannot be explained in this way since language habits are not present.[19] There is no known mechanism of response which might account for this. It thus seems best to reserve our attempt at explanation.

Summary.—A habit is thus seen to involve always a series of definite arcs beginning in a receptor and ending in an effecter. In sensory habits we isolate and define the stimulus which will initiate the impulses in these arcs. In motor habits by the interposing of certain conditions (setting of certain problems) we force upon the animal certain

---

[19] Both Carr and Hunter would insist that there are other possibilities of explanation, i.e., that certain other proprio- and entero-ceptive processes might function in the same way that we have assumed that language habits function (i.e., so that continuous bodily orientation is not necessary). Were Hunter a less careful investigator, we might think that there was an actual error in observation. Most of the raccoons were admittedly making the correct reaction upon the basis of maintained bodily orientation. What more simple than to suppose that those animals which were not disturbed by loss of bodily orientation had learned to make correct response upon the basis of olfactory stimuli which were not sufficiently controlled in Hunter's work?

types of synthesis of action of the effectors, temporally space their action, note the rapidity of growth of the combination, etc. It must not be forgotten, though, that even in motor habits the receptors are equally involved. If we examine such habits from this standpoint we find that: (1) all receptors may be involved in a given habit at every stage, i.e., there may never be any complete reduction to kinæsthesis; (2) in some animals the learning of certain habits requires the coöperation of all receptors, but the execution of these habits after learning requires the functioning mainly of the proprio-ceptors; (3) in other animals, both the learning and the final execution may be mediated by the proprio-ceptive system.

VI. Efficiency of training methods: motor habits.—In the animal world we have a better opportunity for testing the various methods of training than we have in the schools, for the human child. The subject of efficiency as a whole has not yet received the attention which it deserves. Our records are fairly complete at least for one species of animal—the white rat—so far as his motor habits are concerned. The various questions to which we can return answers may be stated as follows: (1) what number of trials per day should be given an animal while it is acquiring one motor habit at a time, if our object is to secure a perfect habit with a minimum number of trials? (2) What is the effect upon the retention of the habit of this method as compared with a method which requires a larger number of trials? (3) Will the same method which has happened to serve the purpose of (1) serve equally as well when the animal is acquiring simultaneously more than one motor habit, e.g., three such habits?

In order to test these questions, Ulrich (whose report is as yet unpublished) has made a three-years' study upon the white rat. He allowed several groups of animals to learn box II, each group being given a different number of trials per day,[20] all other conditions except the one

[20] By trial is meant the complete reaction from time of release in the confining cage until the animal has solved the problem and eaten the food. If more than one trial is given the animal is allowed to

specified being kept constant. The groups and the trials given are as follows:

One-in-one method.	Group I.	One trial per day.
Three-in-one method.	" II.	Three trials per day.
Five-in-one method.	" III.	Five trials per day.
One-in-two method.	" IV.	One trial every other day.
One-in-three method.	" V.	One trial in three days.

In Figs. 45 and 46 are given the distribution curves of the learning of these separate groups, both from the stand-

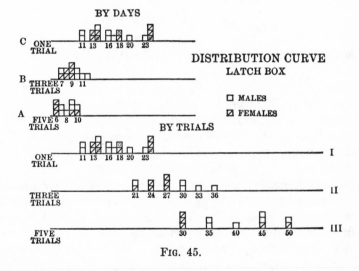

FIG. 45.

point of the number of trials given, and from that of the number of days required to learn the problem. These curves may be easily understood, e.g., the distribution curve for Group I is shown in Fig. 45, I. It shows that 2 animals learned the problem after 11 trials; 2 after 13 trials, 3 after 14, etc. All 16 of the animals had learned the problems by the end of the twenty-fourth trial. If now we pass to Group II (Fig. 45, II) we see that the first animal learning the problem required 21 trials, while the last

eat but sparingly. Food is then immediately given on the second and succeeding trials. At the end of the daily allotment of trials, the animal is allowed to eat its full ration of food in the box.

animal required 36 trials. Similarly, in Group III (Fig.
45, III) the first animal to learn the problem required 30
trials; the last animal 50 trials. Group IV (Fig. 46, IV)
gives 9 trials for the first animal to learn, and 22 for the

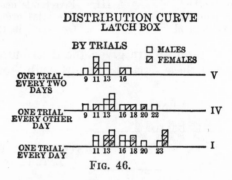

DISTRIBUTION CURVE
LATCH BOX

FIG. 46.

last. Group V (Fig. 46, V) showed that the first animal
learned in 9 trials and the last in 17.

We find in this experiment the answer to question (1)
raised above. Within certain limits, which have not been
determined yet, it is far more economical, so far as the
number of trials is concerned, to give a few rather than a
large number of trials per day. From the distribution
curves it would seem that the one-in-three method is certainly far more economical than the three-in-one or the
five-in-one; indeed, it seems the most advantageous method
of all. As regards our second question, i.e., the effect of
a different method on the retention of the habit, the results seem to show that no one method has any distinct
advantage over the others. The five-in-one method and
the one-in-two method gave the poorest results. After
each animal had been trained to the problem it was not
tested again until after 60 days had elapsed. During the
non-training period the animals were forced to run daily
to the end of a long straight-away to obtain food. They
were allowed to eat the same amount of food as during the
training period. This method kept them in training (prevented the laying on of fat, the onset of sluggishness,
wildness, etc.). At the end of 60 days each animal was tried

for 2 days on the original problem. For convenience are given the average of each group on the last trial of the training series, and the average of the first trial of the retention series.

No. animals		AVERAGE TIME OF LAST TRIAL ON REGULAR PRACTICE Minutes		AVERAGE TIME ON FIRST TRIAL IN RETENTION TEST Minutes	
		Av.	Av. M. V.	Av.	Av. M. V.
(17)	Group I.	.014	.006	.082	.074 (1-in-1)
(11)	" II.	.016	.007	.022	.008 (3-in-1)
(11)	" III.	.011	.005	.117	.144 (5-in-1)
(13)	" IV.	.014	.004	.205	.205 (1-in-2)
(9)	" V.	.012	.004	.056	.040 (1-in-3)

When we consider the number of days required to form the habit, we find an entirely different situation. The distribution curves by days are given on p. 229, Fig. 45. The curve of Group I is repeated (Fig. 45, C) for the sake of convenience. In plotting these curves the number of days required to learn the problem replaced the number of trials in the early curves, e.g., in the graph showing the five-in-one method (Fig. 45, A) it will be seen that 3 animals required 6 days; 2, 7 days; 1, 8 days; 3, 9 days; 2, 10 days. When all the curves have been considered it appears that within the limits of this experiment the larger number of trials given per day, the less the number of days required for learning.

The third question raised above can be answered only by experimentation. Which of the above methods is most advantageous when three problems are learned abreast? Three groups of animals entirely different from those just discussed were allowed to learn simultaneously boxes II and III and maze I (pp. 95 and 100).

Group I. 1 trial on box II, then immediately 1 trial on maze I, then 1 trial on box III.
  "   II. 3 trials on box II, then immediately 3 trials on maze I, then 3 trials on box III.
  "   III. 5 trials on box II, then immediately 5 trials on maze I, then 5 trials on box III.

For our purpose we need to examine only the distribution curves of the learning of box II. These curves are to

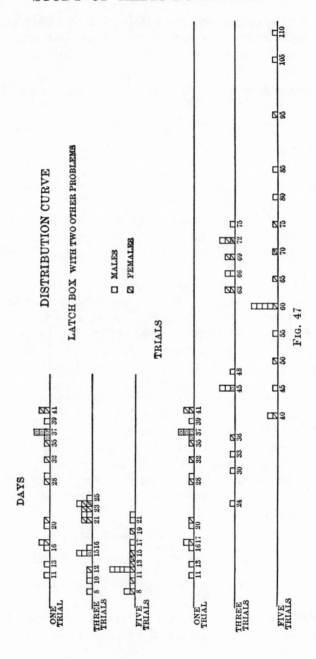

DISTRIBUTION CURVE

LATCH BOX WITH TWO OTHER PROBLEMS

FIG. 47

be compared with those on p. 229. Looking first at the number of trials required to learn the problem we see (1) that by any of the methods the absolute number of trials required to learn box II, when 2 other problems are learned simultaneously, is far greater than when box II is learned alone; (2) that the one-in-one method shows the greatest economy so far as the necessary trials are concerned when contrasted with the three-in-one and the five-in-one methods.

	AVERAGE TIME OF LAST TRIAL ON REGULAR PRACTICE		AVERAGE TIME ON FIRST IN RETENTION TEST	
No. animals	Minutes		Minutes	
	Av.	Av. M. V.	Av.	Av. M. V.
(18) Group I.	.018	.004	.103	.091
(18) " II.	.013	.003	.140	.179
(18) " III.	.013	.004	.169	.100

The above table on retention, constructed as the table on p. 231, shows clearly that the smaller the number of trials given per day when several problems are learned abreast, the better the retention. The absolute loss during the 60 days non-practice period is greater when two problems are learned in conjunction with box II than when box II is learned alone. Again, when we compare the methods from the standpoint of days, we see that the situation is reversed. The distribution curve (Fig. 47) shows again that within the limits of this experiment the larger the number of trials, the fewer the number of days required to learn.

Sensory habits.—A corresponding series of experiments has been made on sensory habits. Tests upon the dancing mouse indicate that for the white-black discrimination, the fewer the tests per day, within the limits of 2 and 100, the higher the efficiency of the method of training, as measured in terms of the total number of tests necessary for the establishment of a perfect habit, and the lower its efficiency as measured in terms of the number of series given. The table given below shows the total number of errors in each set of 10 trials for each of the four methods used.[21] No

[21] Since sensory habits arise so very slowly, it can easily be seen that, in so far as the conservation of the experimenter's time is concerned, it has been the custom to effect a compromise by giving 10-20 trials per day. This is a purely practical matter and has no bearing upon the physiological problems involved in learning.

TABLE

NUMBER OF ERRORS IN WHITE-BLACK SERIES FOR DIFFERENT METHODS
OF TRAINING

Sets of 10 tests	2 or 5 tests per day Av. no. errors	10 tests per day Av. no. errors	20 tests per day Av. no. errors	100 or more tests per day Av. no. errors
1	6.4	5.3	4.8	5.7
2	4.2	3.5	4.8	3.3
3	3.4	3.2	3.4	5.3
4	3.1	2.5	3.0	5.3
5	2.7	2.5	1.9	3.7
6	1.5	1.3	1.9	1.7
7	0.9	1.5	0.9	3.0
8	0.7	0.8	1.1	2.0
9	0.5	0.4	0.9	2.3
10	0	0.5	0.8	2.3
11	0	0.4	0.4	1.7
12	0	0.2	0.3	1.3
13		0	0	2.3
14		0	0	1.3
15		0	0	3.0
16		0		2.7
17				0.7
18				1.0
19				0.7
20				0

specific experiments have been made to test the efficiency of these methods upon retention, nor their effect when two or more sensory (or one sensory and one motor) habits are required simultaneously.

The delayed reaction.—Economy in learning the delayed reaction has been tested only incidentally. The effect of giving 5 trials and 10 trials during the training period (i.e., establishing ordinary sensory habit) is shown in the following table taken from Hunter:

TABLE

Rat	5 trials No. of trials on learning	Rat	10 trials No. of trials on learning
No. 10	165	No. 12	440
No. 11	160	No. 13	250
No. 14	200	No. 15	220
No. 17	175	No. 16	480

It is clearly indicated here that the use of 5 trials favored rapid learning more than did the use of 10 trials.

No results are given for the effect on retention of the 5-trial method as over against the 10-trial method. It appears, however, that the number of trials given per day in the preliminary training does not affect the *interval of delay*.

VII. Other conditions which affect learning.—Some of the factors which must be considered with reference to learning are (1) the age of the animal, (2) possibly sex, (3) certain general bodily conditions—starvation, arrested growth, etc., (4) relative brain weight as compared with body weight, and (5) removal of parts of nervous system. Only a few of these have been considered with any degree of care; indeed, some have been left wholly untouched.

(1) **Age.**—From some experiments carried out by the author in 1902 he concluded that the young white rat forms motor habits, maze, box I, etc., much more rapidly than the adults. The young animals form the habit of manipulation much less rapidly than do the adults, the general conclusion being that any habit which requires for its learning excess running, climbing, etc., could be learned by any animal at the age of about 35 days more rapidly than by the adult. On the other hand, those problems which depend for their solution upon control of movement, can be learned by the adult more rapidly. This conclusion was probably not based upon a sufficiently large number of tests.

Since the above work was completed two other experiments bearing upon the same problem have been made. The first relates to sensory habits. In the dancing mouse Yerkes has established beyond question the fact that the dancer at 1 month of age can form a particular black-white habit in a much less number of trials than can an older individual. From the first to the seventh month there is a steadily marked increase in the capacity to form habits of this character. From the seventh to the tenth month there is retrogression in this capacity. Furthermore, it would seem that when the difference in intensity between the stimuli is slight, the young animals respond to it more readily than do the adults. When, however, the difference is large, the old individuals respond as readily as the young (Weber law type of experiments).

The other experiment referred to is that of Slonaker upon the activity of the white rat at different ages. It would seem from this work that the most active period in the life of the rat is at the age of (approximately) 100 days. This was determined by allowing the animal to live in a cage which turned on a stationary axis each time the animal left the nest box to obtain water or food. It would thus seem that our early conclusions need confirmation. But it must be remembered that Yerkes worked upon a sensory habit and used punishment, whereas we worked upon a motor habit and without punishment. In regard to Slonaker's work it may be stated that the period of greatest activity as obtained by his method need not at all coincide with the period of greatest activity of the kind involved in attacks upon problem boxes.[22]

(2) **Sex.**—No very systematic studies have been made upon sex differences in learning. All through the literature we find statements to the effect that possibly there was a sex difference, or that there was a slight difference, etc. No experiments which we consider crucial have been made which will enable us to state in what forms of behavior sex differences appear. Personally, from long years of association with animal work, we are prepared to affirm our belief that there are differences everywhere between the males and the females, which may be seen clearly, as every one admits, during the periods of heat, in the female during pregnancy (or brooding, depending upon the phyla). In regard to the differences in the methods of attack upon problems there may be subtle differences which are very difficult to bring under experimental control. Yerkes has come out rather definitely in his statements concerning the sex differences in the dancing mouse. He states, on the basis of several experiments, that the young males

---

[22] Miss Hubbert is making a thorough study of the effect of age upon the formation of maze habits in rats, using the maze with a camera lucida attachment, by means of which the movements may be recorded during the learning process.

acquire the habit of discrimination (black-white) more quickly than do the females, but that between the ages of 4 to 10 months the females acquire the habit more quickly; and that the female makes more mistakes early in training tests than the male, but that this condition gives place soon to greater accuracy of response on the part of the female. This author remarks incidentally that the male dancer is somewhat more sensitive to punishment than is the female. Also, in his book on the dancing mouse, he states that the labyrinth habit (labyrinth C) was acquired by the female more quickly than by the male.

(3) **Certain bodily conditions.**—No definite experiments have yet been published upon the effects of starvation. From some unpublished experiments at the Wistar Institute of Anatomy it would appear that rats which had been stunted by underfeeding and then returned to a normal diet learned more rapidly than normal animals.[23]

Through the work of Osborne and Mendel it has been found possible to hold body growth *in statu quo* and then later to accelerate it at will. This method of controlling growth offers interesting possibilities in the study of habit formation.

(4) **Learning in animals with less than normal brain weights.**—Basset has carried out an extensive piece of work upon a strain of rats the brain weight of which was far below normal. This strain of rats (*Mus noregicus albinus*) was obtained from the Wistar Institute of Anatomy. The strain was strictly inbred for 6 or 7 generations. Through the effects of inbreeding, or some other cause (starting with a mutant in which the relative brain weight was small, etc.) not yet determined, this strain of rats had, relatively to the body length, a much smaller brain weight than the normal rat. The following curve (Fig. 48) shows the distribution of brain weights of the normal and inbred rats actually used in Basset's work. It will be seen that the inbred curve shows the greatest frequency at .88%; the normal curve at

[23] The experiments were made by Dr. J. W. Hayes. See also the report of Langfeld, "Psychophysiological Tests During Prolonged Fast," *Psychological Bulletin*, 1913, p. 83.

.92%. The inbred distribution is from .70% to .95%; that of the normals, from .84% to 1.05%. The average relative brain weight with respect to body length of the 62 normal animals is .93351%; and that of the inbreds, .87335%, or 6.44% less than that of the normals. Basset then tested 62 of the nor-

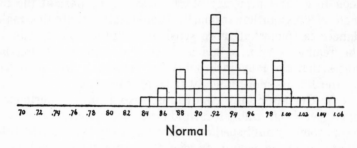

Normal

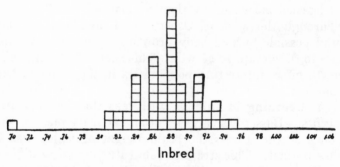

Inbred

FIG. 48. DISTRIBUTION OF BRAIN WEIGHTS IN (UPPER) NORMAL AND IN (LOWER) INBRED RATS

mal animals and 62 of the animals with the small brain weight (inbreds) with respect to the rapidity with which they acquire the maze habit and that of the inclined plane. It appears that the animals with the lesser brain weight require on the average a larger number of days to learn these two problems. Furthermore, the time for relearning was far greater in the case of the inbreds than in that of the normals (see p. 246).

(5) **Motor habits in animals with parts of the nervous system removed.**—It has been shown (Franz) in both

monkeys and cats that newly formed motor habits (problem boxes) (1) are lost if a bilateral lesion in the frontal lobes is made.   (2) Unilateral lesions produce only a slowing in the performance of the acts.   (3) Habits once lost after the removal of the frontal lobes may be regained through training.   (4) Habits of long standing are not lost when such lesions are made.   It would seem from these experiments that the arcs involved in the acquisition of motor habits usually, but not necessarily, embrace the frontal lobes.   From certain recent experiments we are led to believe that the decerebrate frog is incapable of forming habits.   The use of operative technique in the study of sensory habits is discussed on p. 209 and its use in the study of localization of brain function (sensory projection centers) on p. 376.

VIII. **Effect of previous habits upon the formation of new habits: motor habits.**—Neither in the study of human habits nor in that of animal habits have there been thorough systematic attempts to bring the mutual relations of habits under control nor to test the effect of previous training upon the formation of new habits.   There is an enormous field of work here which has just been touched upon.   Research work would yield very rapid results and of such a kind as to be of very great importance in the study of human training methods.   We are able to cite in the animal world the following particulars concerning the influence of previous habits upon the formation of new habits: the dancing mouse not previously trained on a simple labyrinth (C) makes the first correct trip on an average at the end of 19.7 trials.   On the other hand, animals previously trained in another labyrinth (B) will make a successful trip in this labyrinth (C) on the 7th trial.   Mastery of B by untrained animals requires 8.2 trials; by those previously trained on C (a rather difficult maze), 5 trials.   (Yerkes: "Dancing Mouse.")   Similar results have been obtained with the white rat.   Fig. 49 shows the curve of untrained rats on box III and of trained (by previously learning boxes I and II) rats in learning the same problem.   The difference between the two curves is quite marked.   Different

species seem to present characteristic differences in this respect (Richardson). In testing untrained pigeons on a
given maze along with pigeons which had been previously

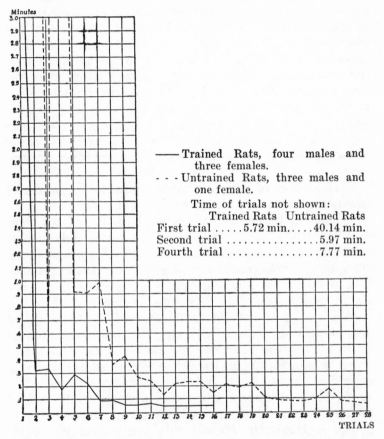

Minutes

———— Trained Rats, four males and
        three females.
- - - Untrained Rats, three males and
        one female.

    Time of trials not shown:
        Trained Rats Untrained Rats
First trial .....5.72 min.....40.14 min.
Second trial ....5.97 min.
Fourth trial ....7.77 min.

TRIALS

FIG. 49.   SHOWING THE EFFECT OF PREVIOUS TRAINING IN ACQUIRING
NEW HABITS (From Richardson, *Psych. Mons.*, Serial No. 48.)

trained on another maze, it was found that the untrained
animals learned in as few trials as the trained. Furthermore, the excess time and errors during the early trials are
greater for the trained than for the untrained. Excess
effort, however, is eliminated more rapidly (in a less num-

ber of trials) in the case of the trained than the untrained. It would seem that the early habits acquired by the trained group persisted in the new work and interfered with the formation of another habit (Hunter).[24] That interference of this kind may exist comes out still more clearly in work on the squirrels. It was found that squirrels trained to open box I and box II are at a disadvantage as compared with untrained animals when they come to learn box III. Boxes I and II require scraping, butting up of the latch with the nose, etc. These acts were carried over to box III; consequently the animals lost time in trying to open box III by persisting in movements organized to meet other conditions (Yoakum). It seems evident, although the above results do not wholly justify the view, that the type of results we shall get in such cases is dependent upon the similarity between the old habit and the habit we desire to instil; certainly also upon the differences in the use of receptors,—an animal in which position habits arise easily is very likely to carry these over into a new situation, whereas an animal with keen vision will likely be attracted by the visual stimuli in the new situation, etc. It will be recalled that the problem under discussion is similar to that involved in the question of specific vs. general training. However, in the case of animals we shall not rest content in settling the matter by argumentation. We shall try to build up by experimentation a series of facts which will show the reciprocal effects of one motor habit upon another; or motor habits upon sensory, or *vice versa;* or sensory habits upon sensory, etc., and to analyze these facts in terms of the organization of reflex arc systems.

IX. Retention.—The term " memory " has been illadvisedly used in the experiments upon the effect of intervals of disuse upon habit functions. The term " reten-

[24] By interference nothing mysterious is meant. We mean nothing more than that old habits persisted in the new work. Consequently the group of random movements released by the new stimulus did not contain in it the successful movement. Not until the old habits had been exercised continuously but unavailingly, with resulting fatigue, did the stimulus call out the new group, which contained the needed movement.

tion '' has been employed in a static sense in this same connection, referring chiefly to the '' persistence of modifications '' in the nervous system.[25] Both terms are ill-defined. It seems possible to keep the term retention and make its meaning more definite. In behavior the term retention covers this phenomenon; viz., that an object to which an animal has learned to respond in a definite way will for a more or less definite period in which the given response has been prevented (i.e., by not presenting the object) call forth in various degrees of perfection the old (or habitual) response. If the response is as definite at the end of the period of disuse as before we say that there has been no loss in retention or that retention was perfect. In most cases the response, after a period of disuse, is not perfect (i.e., there is excess effort). The effect of the period of disuse can be measured (in terms of time, distance, errors, etc.) by comparing the first trial after disuse with the last trial before disuse; or otherwise expressed, the last trial Z of regular training with the first trial α of retraining. If a certain length of time is overstepped the excess effort of trial α may be as great as that of A, the first trial in the training series. In this case the habit appears to be lost. Only complete retraining will tell us whether this is really the case. If the retraining series requires the same number of trials and the same amount of excess effort as the regular training series, the

[25] The neural picture, both during the formation of a habit and during the period of non-practice, has been interestingly presented by William James. Since his *Principles* appeared we have described habit by saying that the neural impulse aroused by the given stimulus in some way digs an ever-deeper trench for itself, and that it in some way modifies the conduction system (molecular rearrangement) over which it passes. Accordingly we would speak of pathways in the nervous system and of their modifications. We would further assume that such modifications persist for definite intervals of time, possibly never wholly disappearing. So far as we know there is no longer any justification for assuming that a neural impulse, which is probably electrical, in any way modifies permanently the conductor over which it passes. While we are ignorant yet of what happens at the surfaces of separation of the conduction systems as regards permeability and the reverse, it seems quite unlikely that neuro-physiology will ever discover any structural modifications in the conductors themselves.

evidence is clear that the habit was really lost. Behavior has not fixed upon definite methods of making retention tests. Shall we compare only the last trial of the training series with the first trial of retraining? Or shall we average the last three trials of training with the first three trials of retraining? Or shall we carry out a wholly new retraining series? In retraining this rather interesting question comes up. It often happens that in the training series we use different methods for the different groups, as we saw in section VII, where the number of trials given per day differed in the different groups. Now, in the retraining series shall we use a common method for all the animals, or shall we retrain with a method identical with that of training? Furthermore, during the period of disuse some systematic method of caring for the animals should be adopted. In most retention tests we read that at the end of the training series the animals were put away until the time for the retention test. No effort is ever made to keep the animals in the "problem solving condition." It is quite obvious that retention tests made under such uncontrolled conditions are worthless from the standpoint of testing pure retentiveness and for purposes of comparison. In the tests which Ulrich and Basset made in the Hopkins Laboratory they adopted the following technique: A long run-way was constructed at the end of which food was placed. At the close of the training period the animal was forced each day at feeding time to travel to the end of the run-way in order to get food. By this method the animal was kept in condition. The amount of food taken was also controlled, i.e., kept constant as in the training period (the animal eating for a certain definite time). Furthermore, the animal was kept from becoming wild and from putting on fat. We suggest the following as a possible standard of procedure. Some standard of accuracy of mastery must be adopted. This will necessarily differ even upon the same problem with the different species of animal used. This standard, where possible, should be based upon more than one criterion. Time is the best single criterion in motor habits. The time allowed for a trial must be determined previously by averaging the results of at least 30 animals which have learned the problem just to the point where no errors appear and no excess distance is traversed. (Such records are gradually collected on all pieces of apparatus in general use in the laboratory.) Distance traversed, where it can be measured accurately (as in the maze, p. 100), is probably the next best criterion. Any distance greater than the measured shortest route is " excess." Mastery of the problem regardless of the time cannot be said to have been attained until there is no excess distance. Freedom from error for 30 consecutive trials has been Yerkes' criterion of mastery for sensory habits. This appears to work well enough. After the animal has mastered the problem it should be worked with and fed each day by forcing it to go for food to the end of a long run-way. It should be allowed to eat the full amount of food that the experimenter knows to be necessary in order to maintain metabolism. The animal should have been made familiar with this method of obtaining food before even the training period is begun. Furthermore, since neither in work upon motor habits nor in that on sensory habits are the animals usually allowed to eat their full quota of food in the experimental room, they should be fed the remainder in this run-way. At the end of the period of disuse retraining should begin. The fairest way seems to be to retrain all animals by the same method regardless of the training method. Furthermore, we suggest that one trial per day only be given in motor habits and that 10 trials per day be given in sensory habits. Retraining should be carried to the point of original mastery. The last trial of training should be separately compared with the first trial of retraining. The whole of the retraining series should then be averaged by successive trials and plotted (i.e., without telescoping and then averaging). It must be remembered that only the first trial appears " pure." Practice effects appear immediately.

In regard to the concrete data upon retention it must be confessed that there is not a single research in the whole field which throws particular emphasis upon retention.

What results we have have been made incidentally in connection with studies on habit formation. Since no approach to uniformity in the method of making tests on retention has been observed by the different experimenters, we can do little more than summarize their findings.

Mammals.—Yerkes shows that in the dancer a perfectly acquired black-white habit will endure for a period of 2

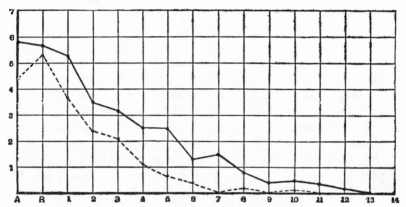

FIG. 50. ERROR CURVES PLOTTED FROM THE DATA GIVEN BY 10 DANCERS IN WHITE-BLACK DISCRIMINATION TESTS

The solid line (———) is the error curve of the original learning process; the broken line (- - - -) is that of the relearning process, after an interval of 8 weeks. (After Yerkes, *The Dancing Mouse*, Macmillan, New York, 1907, p. 257.)

The abscissa shows the number of series of trials, each series consisting of 10 trials; the ordinate the average number of errors made in each series.

weeks at least. The results for 4-week intervals show extreme individual differences in retention. In the case of 2 animals retention tests were made after 3 different rest intervals. At the end of 2 weeks the habit was present in both individuals. After 6 and 4 weeks respectively it still persisted and was apparently improved as the result of additional training received at the end of the 2-weeks period. At the expiration of 10 weeks it had apparently disappeared. Fig. 50 shows the curve both of training and retraining. It would appear from this curve that the mice reacquired the white-black discrimination habit much more readily than they had originally acquired it. Pages 231 and 233 present the two tables from Ulrich's work upon rats. Basset (p. 237), whose general method of testing retention was the same as that of Ulrich, states that normal animals after a 60-day rest required 5.76 days to relearn the circular maze (p. 100), whereas the animal with lesser brain weight required 12.6 days. The final time for traversing the maze on the training series was, for both normals and inbreds, 6 seconds. After the 60-day rest the average of the first trial for the inbreds was 31.8 seconds, for the normals 22.5 seconds. The normals required 4.68 to relearn the latch box, whereas the animals with lesser brain weight required 6.74 days. The final time for solving the problem on the training series was 4 seconds for both normals and inbreds: after 60 days the average time of first trial for inbreds was 81.5 seconds, for the normals 59.6 seconds. Allen shows that the guinea pig retains a very simple labyrinth without great loss for at least 63 days. The retention of the habit was almost perfect. The time for the first success of this animal was 1 minute. Sackett says that the Canadian porcupine retains the Hampton Court maze with some loss for a 10-day period. Its whole time on the trial for retention was 6 minutes and 30 seconds; its second retentive test was 1 minute and 5 seconds. The final time of the training series was 1 minute and 10 seconds. The test of the retention of fastenings showed that at 13 days there was no loss; while at 30 days there had been a slight loss which could be regained at the end of 1 trial; at 50 days there was almost a complete loss. Davis states that the raccoon's retention of simple fastenings remains practically undiminished for periods of no practice of more than a year. In the case of the combination lock (p. 99) the retention was imperfect after a period of 286 days, but the relearning was rapid, only 24 trials being necessary to gain the facility that originally required 107' trials. Cole states that the memory for a combination of 7 fastenings was not perfect at the end of 147 days in the raccoon. Three animals were tested on this box after that period of no practice. Only the first succeeded in working all of the fastenings and releasing himself; he undid the 7 fastenings and came out of the box in 34, 28, 131, and 182 seconds respectively. The other animals worked almost all of them but failed to complete the work. A cat tested by Thorndike on a simple puzzle box showed a perfect response at the end of 20 days. Another cat which opened this box at the end of the training series in 8 seconds, opened the box 14 days later in 3, 9, and 8 seconds respectively in three trials. Colvin and Burford state that the dog retained the habit of reacting to standard color for 3 weeks without loss. In the squirrel 1 month's suspension of time brought considerable loss in the accuracy of the same kind of habit.[26] The following table is taken from Kinnaman's study of the monkey:

	Apparatus	Last 10 tests of training	First series of tests on retraining 50 days later
	1st combination lock	6.4 seconds	13.17 seconds
MALE	2nd combination lock	13.6 "	28.1 "
	maze	59.5 "	88.3 "
	1st combination lock	5.1 seconds	14.2 seconds
FEMALE	2nd combination lock	19.6 "	31.0 "
	maze	55.0 "	120.0 "

Thorndike shows that habits of manipulation in the monkey suffer little loss after periods ranging from 67 to 240 days.

Birds.—Hunter states that the retention of the pigeon for a simple labyrinth is practically perfect for 4 weeks where there has been no intervening training whatsoever. The pigeon would thus seem to be somewhat superior to the cowbirds and sparrows tested by Porter. Rouse mentions incidentally that associations in the pigeon are fairly permanent and remain practically unaltered for at least 6 weeks. There are no records of tests which would sufficiently establish this point. Porter states that the English

[26] Johnson gives a rough statement on the retention of habits of manipulation in dogs (blind and normal). The loss in accuracy (in simple problem boxes) at the end of 60 days was only about 10%.

sparrow did not show any loss of skill in opening a simple food box after an interval of 8 days. He further states that the retention of a simple maze is surprisingly good for birds at the end of 30 days. The cowbird stands first. Her average for the first 10 trials in retraining equals that of the last 10 of the initial training. The vesper sparrow and the female English sparrow do not do quite so well. Retention of simple fastenings after 30 days by the cowbird and pigeon shows some loss; the male pigeon showed less loss than the cowbird. The female pigeon and the cowbird lapsed into a poor method which was used early in the training series. At the end of 120 days the cowbird and the pigeon were again tested upon the simple fastenings. While the loss was considerable the habit was not completely lost and was readily reacquired. Thorndike retested chicks on a simple labyrinth at the end of 20 days and found that retention was practically perfect. Breed shows that of 9 chicks trained to the black-blue habit and tested 30 days later, 5 obtained perfect records. Breed presents evidence to show, too, that chicks which acquire the black-blue habit most readily also show the most perfect persistence tests. Thus of 3 animals that required 100 trials to perfect the black-blue modification 1 made perfect persistence tests; of the 2 that required 70 trials 1 made a perfect record; of 3 that required 60 trials, 2 made perfect records; and the chick that completed its work in the shortest time also made a perfect record.

Amphibia and reptiles.—Yerkes shows that the green frog retains a simple labyrinth habit for at least 30 days. Casteel states that the turtle (*Chrysemys marginata*) retains a simple sensory habit—vertical vs. horizontal line— for 2 weeks without loss.

BIBLIOGRAPHY

Allen, Jessie, "The Associative Processes of the Guinea Pig," *Jour. Comp. Neu. and Psych.*, 1904, XIV, 293.

Basset, G. C., "Habit Formation in a Strain of White Rats with Less than Normal Brain Weight," *Behavior Monograph*, Ser. No. 9.

BOOK, W. F.,[27] *The Psychology of Skill*. Missoula, Univ. Montana, 1908.

BREED, F. S., " Reactions of Chicks to Optical Stimuli," *Jour. Animal Beh.*, 1912, II, 280.

CARR, H. A., and WATSON, J. B., " Orientation in the White Rat," *Jour. Comp. Neu. and Psych.*, 1908, XVIII, 27.

CASTEEL, D. B., " The Discriminative Ability of the Painted Turtle," *Jour. Animal Beh.*, 1911, I, 1,

COLE, L. W., " Concerning the Intelligence of Raccoons," *Jour. Comp. Neu. and Psych.*, 1907, XVII, 211.

————— " The Relation of Strength of Stimulus to Rate of Learning in the Chick," *Jour. Animal Beh.*, 1911, I, 111.

COLVIN, S. S., and BURFORD, C. C., " The Color Perception of Three Dogs, a Cat, and a Squirrel," *Psychological Monograph*, Ser. No. 44.

DAVIS, H. B., " The Raccoon: A Study in Animal Intelligence," *Am. Jour. Psych.*, 1907, XVIII, 447.

FRANZ, S. I., " On the Functions of the Cerebrum. I. The Frontal Lobes in Relation to the Production and Retention of Simple Sensory-Motor Habits," *Am. Jour. Phys.*, 1902, VIII, 1.

FRANZ, S. I., and LAFORA, G. R., " On the Functions of the Cerebrum: The Occipital Lobes," *Psychological Monograph*, Ser. No. 56.

HICKS, V. C., " The Relative Values of the Different Curves in Learning," *Jour. Animal Beh.*, 1911, I, 138.

HICKS, V. C., and CARR, H. A., " Human Reactions in a Maze," *Jour. Animal Beh.*, 1912, II, 98.

HOGE, MILDRED A., and STOCKING, RUTH J., " A Note on the Relative Value of Punishment and Reward as Motives," *Jour. Animal Beh.*, 1912, II, 43.

HUBBERT, H. B., " Time *versus* Distance in Learning," *Jour. Animal Beh.*, 1914, IV, 60.

HUNTER, W. S., " The Delayed Reaction in Animals and Children," *Behavior Monograph*, Ser. No. 6.

————— " Some Labyrinth Habits of the Domestic Pigeon," *Jour. Animal Beh.*, 1911, I, 278.

JOHNSON, H. M., " Audition in Dogs," *Behavior Monograph*, Ser. No. 8.

KINNAMAN, A. J., " Mental Life of Two *Macacus rhesus* Monkeys in Captivity," *Am. Jour. Psych.*, 1902, XIII.

PORTER, J. P., " Further Study of the English Sparrow and Other Birds," *Am. Jour. Psych.*, 1906, XVII, 248.

RICHARDSON, FLORENCE, " A Study of Sensory Control in the Rat," *Psychological Monograph*, Ser. No. 48.

ROUSE, J. E., " The Mental Life of the Domestic Pigeon," *Harv. Psych. Stud.*, 1906, II, 580.

SACKETT, L. W., " The Canada Porcupine: A Study of the Learning Process," *Behavior Monograph*, Ser. No. 7.

SLONAKER, J. R., " The Normal Activity of the White Rat at Different Ages," *Jour. Comp. Neu. and Psych.*, 1907, XVII, 342.

[27] In general the literature on human learning is summarized. See also THORNDIKE, E. L., *Educational Psychology*, New York, Col. Univ., 1913, 2, " The Psychology of Learning."

SMALL, W. S., "Notes on the Psychic Development of the Young White Rat," *Am. Jour. Psych.*, 1899, XI, 80.

THORNDIKE, E. L., *Animal Intelligence.* New York, Macmillan, 1911.

TRIPLETT, N. B., "The Educability of the Perch," *Am. Jour. Psych.*, 1901, XII, 354.

WATSON, J. B., *Animal Education.* Chicago, Univ. Chicago Press, 1903.

——————— "Kinæsthetic and Organic Sensations: Their Rôle in the Reactions of the White Rat to the Maze," *Psychological Monograph*, Ser. No. 33.

WATSON, J. B. and M. I., "A Study of the Responses of Rodents to Monochromatic Light," *Jour. Animal Beh.*, 1913, III, 1.

YERKES, R. M., *The Dancing Mouse.* New York, Macmillan, 1907.

——————— "Formation of Habits in the Turtle," *Pop. Sci. Mo.*, 1901, LVIII, 519.

——————— "Instincts, Habits, and Reactions of the Frog," *Harv. Psych. Stud.*, 1903, I, 579; *ibid.*, 598; *ibid.*, 627.

——————— "Modifiability of Behavior in its Relations to the Age and Sex of the Dancing Mouse," *Jour. Comp. Neu. and Psych.*, 1909, XIX, 237.

YERKES, R. M., and DODSON, JOHN D., "The Relation of Strength of Stimulus to Rapidity of Habit Formation," *Jour. Comp. Neu. and Psych.*, 1908, XVIII, 459.

YOAKUM, C. S., "Some Experiments upon the Behavior of Squirrels," *Jour. Comp. Neu. and Psych.*, 1909, XIX, 541.

CHAPTER VII

FIXATION OF ARCS IN HABIT [1]

Introduction.—Historical outline.—Misconceptions and illogical pre-suppositions.—Enumeration of some of the problems.—Factors involved in fixation.—Application of the principle of *frequency* in motor habits.—Justification for the use of the principle.—Application of the principle of *recency* in motor habits.—Sensory habits.—Substitution.—Repetition of movement in absence of original stimulus.—Conclusions.

Introduction.—We found in the preceding chapter that the most insistent question in the study of habit was one that dealt with the mechanisms by means of which useless movements are eliminated. It follows from our previous discussions that we must be able to account for the elimination of useless movements upon purely objective grounds.

Historical outline.—The psychological literature shows that the problem under discussion has always been the *bête noire* of the parallelist. He avoids it altogether or else goes over either into surreptitiously worded or more outspoken form of interaction. All through the literature we find such statements as the " conscious " guidance or " conscious " control of movements, the effect of having a plan or purpose in mind in learning, etc. In the experimental literature we find the frank statement that all improvement and short cuts in learning come unconsciously: when, however, they have thus accidentally appeared, *consciousness steps in and selects them purposely.* Consciousness is looked upon as exerting a positive influence upon the bodily mech-

[1] In the preparation of this chapter the author has had access to a manuscript of Professor Harvey A. Carr, entitled " Principles of Selection in Animal Learning." This paper appears in the May number of the *Psychological Review* (1914). While the views expressed in the present chapter are in many particulars different from those found in the above paper, we wish to call attention to Professor Carr's prior claims in the matter of authorship.

anism. If a physiologist comes out and frankly admits that he is willing to accept interactionism, as Colvin does,[2] we should not wish to quarrel with him for applying that principle in solving the problem under consideration. Whether he has a right to apply it anywhere depends upon many questions which we have no right to enter upon here. But most of them are not willing to accept interaction in this frank way. The most outspokenly worded form appears from psychologists who speak of the pleasure resulting from a successful movement as stamping an act in, and the displeasure resulting from an unsuccessful act as stamping it out. In order to bring these tendencies clearly before us, we give below the views of a few psychologists.

Statements from various authors:[3]

JUDD states that "the mechanism involved in a habit which has resulted from selecting from among instincts is relatively *easy to explain*. We need only to assume that the stimulation which is given at the first experience has two theoretically possible lines of discharge, either one of which would be through a well-defined instinctive tract. The conditions of the first encounter carry the stimulation in question into one of the two instinctive channels and thereafter this selected channel becomes the natural and easy path of discharge for the stimulus whenever it occurs." (p. 218) . . . "Turning now from the habits which are developed through the selection and modification of instincts, we come to the habits which cannot properly be traced to any single instinct or group of instincts. Let us suppose that a stimulus or a combination of stimulations is introduced into the nervous system of the child *but finds no specific channel of discharge open to it through inherited organization*." Judd insists that the stimulus "will be widely distributed through the whole nervous system because it has no specific channel of discharge and because, as free energy, it must be transmitted through the nervous system until it finds a discharge into the active organs." He cites the diffuse distribution in mature life when one is startled by an unexpected noise. As a case of habit formation with "little or no instinctive background" he describes the method the child employs in learning to write. Once again he states (p. 222): ". . . The nervous impulses which excite the muscles do not follow definite channels. In the case now under consideration the *channels are not yet developed* . . ." The mechanism by means of which the diffuse activity is molded into more definite form is described as follows: ". . . There is a tendency for all parts of the nervous

---

[2] *The Learning Process*, p. xxii.
[3] Italics ours except where noted.

system which are active at the same time to become related to one
another in their activity; and . . . there is always a process of
selection going forward by which those combinations which attain the
end toward which the individual is working are preserved and the
others eliminated.[4] The first of these two principles is not difficult
to understand when the close structural and functional interrelations
of the various parts of the nervous system are recalled. The second
principle is much more difficult to explain. This principle may be
restated in the following terms: If an animal goes through a certain
mode of activity and derives *advantage*[5] from the success which
attends this performance, it is likely to repeat the activity; whereas,
if the activity does not attain success, the animal will not repeat
·it."

ANGELL'S statements of the general problem, while seemingly clear,
on analysis are found to be very hard to state in mechanical terms.
He takes the formation of the eye-hand coördination—the child
learning to reach and manipulate a ball. He too starts with the
idea of "diffusion" of nervous impulses. ". . . *There are few or
no preformed reflex pathways over which such neural excitement may
be effectively discharged.*" In the exercise of these diffuse acts the
child's hand comes in contact with the ball. What happens? "To
begin with the mere *shock of surprise* and *(generally) pleasure* makes
the connection of tactual motor sensations from his hand with the
visual sensations from his eye extremely vivid." . . . "We may
be sure that the child's organism is extremely likely to retain the
memory of the highly vivid connection between the visual sensations
of the ball and these tactual-motor feelings which accompanied the
successful grasping of it." . . . "If the nervous system were an
inanimate mass, we might liken that which occurs to the process by
which a path is made across a meadow. The first wayfarer may have
selected his special route for any cause whatsoever, and his course
may have been devious, like those of the cows which are said to have
laid out the streets of Boston. But he has left a mark in the down-
trodden grass which the next person to cross the field is likely to
follow. Presently the grass is wholly worn away, and thereafter
every one follows the beaten path." He does not accept the metaphor
whole-heartedly, however. "But the moment we recall the fact that
the nervous system is part of a living organism, in which processes
of nutrition and repair are constantly going forward, and when we
remember, furthermore, that the organism itself can in large measure
decide whether a stimulus shall be experienced again and whether a
movement shall be repeated or not, we see that the metaphor of the
pathway in the meadow must be abandoned in favor of some idea in
which the vital processes of the organism are recognized and the
living tissues treated as something other than so much static, plastic
clay, which the accidents of the external world can mold to their
own exclusive purposes." . . . "But the point which we must emphasize is that the organism itself largely decides which pathways

[4] I.e., he frankly assumes the very thing for which we are trying to
provide a mechanism.
[5] To be found on p. 223. I.e., those acts are selected from which the
animal derives advantage. Yet on p. 225 he has a paragraph heading
"Pleasure a result of organization, not a cause."

shall in the first instance become thus established." He goes on to say that such multitudinous connections are possible, "that if the child were left to the accidents of the first external stimulations and to the vagaries of merely passive nervous centers, the chances would favor the acquirement of insane and harmful habits of reaction." [6] Angell gives no more definite account of the mechanism of habit formation than the above. In the paragraph on the inhibition of useless movements he states: "The more firmly the connection becomes established, and the more deeply the pathway is cut between the visual sensory centers and the hand-arm motor centers, the more do the irrelevant movements of face, legs, and body tend to drop away!" This inhibition is largely due to the fact that the newly formed channel is increasingly able to carry off all the neural excitation and in consequence less remains to overflow into other channels.

PILLSBURY makes voluminous reference to the nervous system but makes no effort to apply the theory of synaptical connection in detail. He states that Sherrington believes " . . . that the synapse opposes the passage of an excitation in much the same way that a membrane opposes the transfer of fluids. At first this resistance is very great, but it is lessened with each act." . . . "The change that comes with action is a lessened resistance at the synapses, whether it be due to the coming closer of the processes or to a chemical change that makes more permeable the relatively impermeable membrane that at first separates the neurones." He then likens the synapse to a valve: "At first the valves are stiff and open only to strong currents; with use they work more easily." . . . "At the beginning certain of the neurones constitute a path for an impulse from sense-organs to muscles. These original paths are few and make possible only the most essential activities for the continuance of the life of the individual. *Additional paths* of connection are formed by each activity, *physical* and *mental*. Whenever any two neurones *chance* to act together a *connection* is formed between them, the *original gap* is *bridged* and they come to form part of a *new pathway* from sense-organ to muscle. Sometimes the most important of the neurones that are connected lie within the cortex, and the learning that results is primarily learning of ideas rather than of movements, but the principle is the same as before. Learning, whether of new movements or of new ideas, is a process of making easier the passage of an impulse from neurone to neurone and is fundamentally the same everywhere." Again on p. 55: "If we turn from a discussion of the omnipresence of habit to the question of what goes on in the nervous system when a habit is acquired, we get back to our problem of the synapse and its relations. Each time an act is performed, it matters not how, there is some change in the synapses between neurones. The effect of the act persists and becomes stronger with each repetition. After several repetitions the connection between the cells becomes so close that whenever the particular sensory cell is excited the impulse spreads to the motor cells that were active

_____

[6] Surely this vitalistic terminology is not insisted upon by Professor Angell. He would admit doubtless that were it not for the *parents* or other attendants the child would speedily destroy itself and that it is these same attendants that force the habits which enable it to exist when removed from the society of adults.

before, and the neurones grow more and more to constitute what is practically a single structure. The formation of habits is thus a process of decreasing the resistance of the synapses in the different possible paths of transmission."

BOOK'S statements are contradictory and unclear. On p. 95 he says: " . . . All adaptations and short cuts in method were unconsciously made, i.e., fallen into by the learners quite unintentionally on the good days while practising under strain. The learners suddenly learned that they were doing parts of the work in a new and better way, *then purposely adopted it in the future.*" On p. 171 he makes the following statement after first reiterating the unintentionality and unconscious character of short cuts: " When the advantage of the new method had been noticed it was generally, thereafter, made use of purposely, though even there consciousness seemed to be more of a hindrance than a direct help." In general he speaks of " extreme effort carefully applied to the work on a good day " as being the precondition to a forward step. " Fluctuations in attention and effort " are the factors invoked to explain large variations, lack of improvement, etc. No effort is made by Book to analyze the condition which makes it possible for the short cuts to be fixed. He speaks in several places somewhat as follows: " Continued attention or application is assured by the pleasurable feelings and favorable attitude which always accompany success. The organism as a whole naturally tends to continue the activity as long as improvement is made. When progress stops the activity (mental and physical) becomes disagreeable and attention goes elsewhere."

Similar confusion occurs in SWIFT'S statements (p. 184): " It is interesting that all the subjects improved by hitting upon better ways of working without any further conscious selection. There seems to be a competition of methods. Just how this selection occurs without conscious interference is not easy to say. *Consciousness discovers modes of action already in use, and selects some of them for survival because of their success.*" While it is obvious that if any one has such a vitalistic principle as this within him he needs no physiological mechanism to account for selection, yet nevertheless on p. 185 we find the following: " The question then arises, how are the necessary coördinations brought about? It does not seem difficult to bring the matter into line with phenomena already pretty well known. Let us suppose a successful toss and catch are made. This is followed by a double effect: it leaves, as every action does, a trace in the nervous system which facilitates later repetition of the same action, and the successful adaptation also gives rise to a feeling of pleasure. The effect of pleasurable sensation is a heightening of muscular tonicity or a general tendency to muscular discharge, which in the case of an action just performed—one whose neural effects are still lingering—is equivalent to a partial reinnervation of the same coördinated group of muscles, which again deepens the existing trace. The next actual effort finds the nervous mechanism a little readier to react in this favorable way. In case of an effort that does not lead to success, the slight *displeasure* at failure exerts its natural depressant effect upon the whole neuro-muscular system, and thus does not deepen the neural trace left by the original movement, and even, perhaps, breaks up the incipient coördinations that gave it its particular form. In any case, whatever its mode of action, it has not the reinvigorating effect upon the original neural trace exercised by the pleasurable sensation. In the long run, therefore, the successful movements, and the coördinations upon which they depend, tend to persist, while those that are unsuccessful tend to fall away."

THORNDIKE in his earlier monograph speaks in a highly figurative way of pleasure stamping in an act and displeasure stamping it out. In his book (*Animal Intelligence*, p. 244) the two laws of learning are stated as follows:

" The law of effect is that: *Of several responses made to the same situation, those which are accompanied or closely followed by satisfaction to the animal will, other things being equal, be more firmly connected with the situation, so that, when it recurs, they will be more likely to recur; those which are accompanied or closely followed by discomfort to the animal will, other things being equal, have their connections with that situation weakened, so that, when it recurs, they will be less likely to occur. The greater the satisfaction or discomfort, the greater the strengthening or weakening of the bond.*[7]

" The law of exercise is that: *Any response to a situation will, other things being equal, be more strongly connected with the situation in proportion to the number of times it has been connected with that situation and to the average vigor and duration of the connections.*"[8]

Misconceptions and illogical presuppositions.—It would seem that there must be something radically wrong with the statement of the empirical facts, since it seems so hard to arrive at even a satisfactory theoretical solution of our problems. Examination shows that three misconceptions have crept into the situation: (1) It has been assumed without further ado that the successful act is pleasant, and that the unsuccessful act is unpleasant. Without attempting to venture into the realm of introspection, we shall advance some slight evidence to show that unsuccessful acts can be eliminated in cases where every movement in the situation as a whole is one which is ordinarily avoided by the animal. In Glaser's experiment, where rats were dropped into hot or cold water and allowed to find an entrance, it was shown that the animal formed the habit of

[7] It is obvious that the first law is no law at all, if by law we mean a generalization from a large set of empirical data. It is merely a statement of conviction. Furthermore, he calls it a law of *effect*, whereas it is obvious that it is a law of *cause* if it is supposed to be a statement of the working of the mechanism of fixation, as the second law undoubtedly is. In regard to the second law it is clear that when this is stripped of its unnecessary implications of bonds or connections it is the same principle we have adopted on p. 262.

[8] All italics are Thorndike's.

turning correctly in the hot or cold water and finally reaching the exit. Suppose, e.g., we complicate the situation even further in the following way: instead of having an open vessel filled with water in which the animal can turn at will, we arrange partitions in the water, which the animals may not clamber up, in the form of *culs de sac*. Furthermore, the exit from the maze as a whole should lead into a chamber which is hot but not hot enough to injure the tissue. The rat would ordinarily avoid the water, would ordinarily avoid the hot box, etc. It is extremely probable that the habit would still be formed. The animal is so constructed that it must move when dropped into the water. If it moved at all, it would necessarily move so that certain acts would occur in accordance with the principles we have assumed to be adequate to account for habit formation (p. 262). It is our aim to combat the idea that pleasure or pain has anything to do with habit formation or that harmfulness or harmlessness has anything more to do with the situation. It is perfectly natural in unreflective minds that the idea of good or bad or harmful or harmless should be called in to explain the habits we force upon animals and children. It is a bit strange that scientifically minded men should have employed it in an explanatory way. It unquestionably is a fact that the animals do respond *positively* to certain forms of stimuli and *negatively* to others, and that in the long run, all things considered, a race of animals has positive tendencies for those stimuli which are harmless to the tissue and negative ones for those which are harmful to the tissue. There is a perfectly good reason for this in heredity, viz., those mutants which survived must have had those tendencies to have escaped elimination. One only has to look at the tendencies of young children and those of young animals to see that there are hundreds of misplaced positive and negative tendencies. The child responds positively to a pretty reptile, harmful fluids, fire, swiftly moving but dangerous machinery, etc. Young animals likewise. Children survive by being confined in an environment where they cannot exercise such " misplaced " tendencies; animals by reason of the fact that they (where they have survived in numbers) live in an environment where harmful stimuli (to which they do not respond negatively) are, in the main, lacking. An equally strong case can be made out for misplaced negative tendencies. To call those stimuli pleasant to which the animal positively reacts and unpleasant those to which he negatively reacts, is making a wholesale gratuitous assumption on a par exactly with the assumption made by the unreflective individuals who maintain that the moth flies into the candle because he likes the light or because the light is pleasant to him. Unquestionably we utilize these strong biological tendencies in the formation of habit. I.e., the animal is so constructed that in the presence of " hunger " it moves about; it responds positively (or negatively) to light, etc. The utilization of these and other biological tendencies insures us that our organism must move in certain ways, and if he does he usually forms habits. (2) In the second place we have assumed that only the successful act is always fixed. This assumption is not true to the empirical facts, as can be shown. As an illustration we cite two actual cases, one from the work of Ulrich and the other from the work of Basset. In the latch box Ulrich had one animal that always ran completely around the box before coming to the latch. Basset had one which ran completely around the box on his first trip without striking the plane, but always struck it on his second trip, i.e., he ran swiftly in a spiral. The experiment was tried of gradually extending the number of trials in the case of these animals. But since the useless movement occurred every time the successful movement occurred, no improvement was noticed. There was no evidence that even a very large number of trials would cause the error to be eliminated. In the same way we have found one student making two extra spacing strokes on the Burroughs adding machine before pushing in the "total " key. These extra movements were thoroughly fixed and would never have been eliminated except by accident. If the unsuccessful acts were not fixed along with the successful ones, it is clear that we should be dwelling constantly in a world of virtuosi. (3) In the third place an assumption has been made concerning the neurological mechanism which, to our mind, has been productive of great confusion. It is assumed by a good many writers, as we saw above, that there is an " overflow " or " diffusion phenomenon " and that this diffusion or overflow can spread without having to pass through *preformed neural channels*. In this way accidental connections are said to be made and bonds or associations to be established. But we have tried to point out in several places *that the nervous system is not built to permit such functions. When a stimulus arises in a receptor there is just as orderly a progression of events then as later when the habit is formed, viz., the stimulus is carried off along preformed and definite arcs to the effectors in the order in which the arcs offer the least resistance to the passage of the current. This order may vary with variations in the sum of intra- and extra-organic stimulation. There is no formation of new pathways.*[9]

In order to define the problem with which we have to deal more clearly, we will take an actual illustration. Suppose we present the rat with box I. He exhibits on the first test movements as follows:

1	2	**3**		4	5	6	**7**		8	9	10	11
		Goes					Digs					
		to definite					away					
		place					sawdust					
12	13	14	**15**		16	17	18	19	**20**			
			Crawls						Strikes			
			under						opening			
			floor						with vibrissæ and enters.			

In this case movements **3, 7, 15, 20** are necessary in the act as a whole. While we have numbered these movements serially, it would have been much better to have employed symbols for the movements and to have placed them at the ends of radii running to the center of a circle. The problem box (stimulus) would represent the center of the circle

[9] It is quite probable that the difficulty here is one mainly of terminology.

and the radii the arcs leading to the separate movements. They occur in any fashion depending upon the condition of tension in the conductors. What we call progress in learning comes about through the disappearance (dropping out) of all movements not needed in opening the box, such as 1, 2, 4, etc. When all false movements have disappeared we have the separate acts released in the order 3, 7, 15, 20. Learning is then complete or perfect. Examination of most habits shows that only in rare instances do we ever reach the stage where only the successful movements appear and no others. Learning is usually a compromise. It is obvious that our problem concerns only the causes leading to the disappearance of all movements except 3, 7, 15, 20. *It follows further that when the useless movements are eliminated the correct movements arise serially without any chaining or linking in any material sense* (bonds, connections, etc.). Movement 20 cannot be executed until movement 3 has been executed, etc. Stated in other terms, we find no necessity for speaking of '' associations.'' The '' association '' is given in heredity—the act by which the result is obtained is '' associated '' with the stimulus in the first place.[10] Furthermore, there is no evidence for assuming that there is resolution of one physiological state into another. It will be remembered that Jennings and others have adopted the view that learning means the readier resolution of physiological states. However well the conception may work in the realm of organisms with no nervous systems, it will not work in that of the higher organisms. By physiological states we could mean nothing but the sum of arcs and effectors at work (including under effectors, of course, glands, etc.). The physiological state changes when a new set of arcs begins to function. To say that one resolves into the other is unclear.

Enumeration of some of the problems.—If we glance for a moment at the temporal distribution of the successful movement or movements we find several situations which deserve mention. With regard to I, motor habits, we

[10] In certain cases this apparently is not the case. The " association " seems to be indirect. (See p. 273.)

find: (*a*) One in which the successful act is necessarily the final one of the series, as, e.g., the solution of boxes I, II, and III. (*b*) One in which several acts are necessary for the solution: but during the learning stage, the first necessary movements having been accomplished, there may follow any number of useless movements. Likewise the second and succeeding movements as they are successfully accomplished may each in turn be followed by useless movements. This type of distribution is the one discussed above. (*c*) One which must be looked upon as involving the formation of a *succession* of simple habits like (*a*), above. The maze problem best illustrates this type, the *culs de sac* representing the series of problems, each one of which must be mastered before the problem as a whole is considered learned. It is necessary to say, though, that they do not have to be mastered in order, and furthermore, when they are mastered no separate account of the chaining process is required. The animal *goes forward:* having eliminated the *culs de sac* he necessarily goes straight from the entrance to the food box or exit. (It will be noted that *b* and *c* are not essentially different.) In addition to this type of learning in motor habits we have a similar group connected with sensory habits. (*d*) The animal must learn to go towards one directive stimulus or away from it, when there is no fixed instinctive tendency to react either positively or negatively to it (in cases where we directly utilize the positive or negative reactions to a given stimulus no learning is involved). As an example we cite the experiments on the testing of the limits of the spectrum of the chick, p. 335. (*e*) The animal must learn to go towards *one* directive stimulus or to go away from one or more directive stimuli (depending upon the fact whether we are using two or multiple stimuli methods) where no tendency is present to react positively to the positive stimulus and negatively to the negative stimulus (or stimuli). (*f*) It may be seen that in both (*d*) and (*e*) it is possible, where preliminary tests are made and show a positive tendency to go to one or the other stimuli, to force the animal to go towards the stimulus to which it ordinarily responds in a negative way. There are various refinements and subdivisions possible in these various types, but these represent, in the main, the important ones.

Factors involved in fixation.—We may confess at once that we have no new principles to offer in solving the problems involved in learning; but we hope that by stating our problems carefully and by clearing away the misconceptions referred to, we shall be able to show in a convincing way that the mechanical principles with which we are already familiar and which can experimentally be shown to act in the way we maintain are sufficient to yield the solutions of those problems. We shall call these principles (1) *frequency* and (2) *recency*.[11] Without claiming that they are the only ones operative, let us attempt to apply them in specific cases.

Application of the principle of *frequency* in motor habits.—Let us take the simplest case first, the solving of a problem like that of the latch box (*a*, above). We will suppose that the animal displays movements 1, 2, 3, 4, 5, 6, 7, 8, 9, 10. Ten is the final and successful movement. But movements 1 to 10 inclusive do not embrace all of the repertoire of the animal (actual observation.) Hence on the next trial the movements would need to be numbered (at random) 1, 3, 11, 12, 13, 14, 10; the third trial, 1, 7, 13, 10; the fourth trial, 6, 11, 4, 8, 10, etc. It will be seen by actual count that movement 10 is repeated more often than any of the other movements. The successful movement always appears once in every trial. No other movement necessarily appears in every trial. It is obvious from this description

---

[11] As we have pointed out, it is evident that what most authors mean on the mechanical side by the use of such terms as satisfactory, advantageous, producing pleasure, etc., is that the physiological tone of the organism is raised, and by the opposites of these, that the tone is lowered. Now it is perfectly obvious that heightening or lowering the tone of the organism may respectively increase or decrease the length of time required to form a given habit. So probably would the introduction of caffeine, strychnine or atropine or any other drug which will increase or decrease the reaction time, heighten or lower the irritability, but it is evident that this principle fixes useless as well as useful movements. It cannot be invoked as an eliminating agent.

that if any movement, e.g., 1 above, were repeated as often as 10 it would become as fixed as 10. It is the principle of repetition operating so far.

Justification for the use of the principle.—Our right to use the principle of frequency as a cause rather than as an effect of habit formation may be questioned. It may be argued with justice that movement 10 has nothing to favor it: that there is no reason to suppose that breaking such a chance series of movements each time after the successful act is performed (i.e., by the experimenter taking the animal out at the end of the trial and starting it over again) will cause 10 to appear more frequently than any other movement. This may be admitted. However, we know from the general theory of probability that in any chance temporal arrangement of events the probabilities are equal that any one of them will precede or will follow any other, and that in a large number of such chance arrangements of the same events any given event will precede each of the others in just half of the arrangements and will follow in the other half. But if now each temporal series is *interrupted* at the occurrence of the given event and the occurrence of all that follow is prevented the *given event* will occur *twice as often as any other*. A concrete example will illustrate this point. If ten slips of paper, numbered consecutively from 1 to 10, are drawn at random from a box until a certain number, 5, is obtained, the chances are equal that the required number 5, will precede or will follow any other number, 9, e.g. If the drawing is interrupted when 5 is obtained and all the slips are returned to the box, and this procedure is repeated a number of times, 5 will be present in every series of drawings, the number 9 in only those in which it, by chance, was drawn out before 5. Since this condition is met by only half of the series of drawings, the number 9 will appear only half as often as 5. The required number will appear twice as often as any other. In applying this principle let us suppose that the animal is capable of only two activities, A and B, when subjected to the stimulus offered by the problem box. B is the successful activity and leads to a *change in stimulation which prevents the occurrence of either* A *or* B (i.e., the animal is taken out by the experimenter, or he eats food and goes to sleep, deposits the straw in the nest, etc.). Then if the order in which A and B occur is due to chance only, B will occur twice as often as A. The following schema illustrates the fact that B occurs in every trial, A in only half:

St = situation offered by problem box: stimuli are present, leading either to reaction A or reaction B. But when B occurs (the successful movement) the animal is taken out by the experimenter,[12] which prevents the occurrence of either A or B until it is reintroduced. Call the situation which follows upon B, St′:—

Trials	Sequences	A occurs	B occurs
(1)	St-A-B-St′	+	+
(2)	St-B-St′	0	+
(3)	St-A-B-St′	+	+
(4)	St-B-St′	0	+
(5)	St-A-B-St′	+	+
(6)	St-B-St′	0	+
etc.		—	—
		3	6

For the operation of this principle of frequency it is necessary that the activities set off by the situation of the problem box be diverse—that the animal tend to go to some new activity rather than to continue to react in a circular way—e.g., to spend all his time biting at the wire. For if the chances for the repetition of the act just executed are equal to the chances of proceeding to another act, breaking the series after any given activity will not affect its chance of repetition. This will be evident from the following diagram, where either of the acts A and B may be repeated in any given trial:

[12] Under life conditions there is no "intervener." of course. But the same effect is obtained. The animal gets food, lies down and sleeps, etc.,—i.e., becomes, from the standpoint of the stimuli which may affect it, a different animal. A further illustration follows: A bird in constructing its nest on the ground under a bush must needs pass through a narrow hole in the underbrush just before reaching the nest. In bringing straws he carries them crosswise; he pushes, flies away, tries again, drops the straw, passes through the hole, turns around, and again picks up the straw by the middle and tries to *pull* it through. Finally he catches the straw on the end and pulls it through (B). The straw is then deposited in the nest and the situation develops (St′), which is exactly on a par with the one created by the experimenter when he removes the animal.

Trials	Sequences	A occurs	B occurs	
(1)	St-A-A-B-St′	2	1	
(2)	St-B-[B-A]-St′	0	1	The letters en-
(3)	St-A-A-B-St′	2	1	closed in brack-
(4)	St-B-[B-A]-St′	0	1	ets do not ap-
(5)	St-A-A-B-St′	2	1	pear, since B
(6)	St-B-[B-A]-St′	0	1	ends this series.
etc.		—	—	
		6	6	

The behavior mechanism of the animal meets this requirement nicely. The animal's activity depends upon the immediate conditions of stimulation. The *performance of one act places the animal under new conditions of stimulation* which lead to some other activity rather than the one just executed.[13] A simple example is shown in the following diagram. The figure represents a maze consisting of two arms, *a* and *b, a* being a blind alley, while *b* leads to the nest box. The animal is placed between the arms of the maze, at the original position of stimulation, St. He may go to either *a* or *b* (activities A and B). If B is chosen A cannot follow. If A is chosen B is more apt to follow A than is A itself, since the proprio-ceptive stimuli would tend to force the animal forward, after turning at the end of the alley *a* unless rival stimuli (smell, etc.) were present. I.e., the animal is now oriented towards St′ and would have to turn round in order again

---

[13] In order to keep the explanation in as simple a form as possible we have not brought out certain facts which every investigator knows he must take into account. When the animal is first released the problem box is not the only stimulating factor (complex in its stimulation though it is). Hunger is driving the animal, certain olfactory substances are calling out movements, contact stimulation is present and tending to call out movements, etc. Furthermore, the stimulating value of the problem box changes as the animal advances towards it and recedes from it,—i.e., the olfactory stimulation increases and decreases in intensity, the visual influences change likewise. Oftentimes it is *while executing responses to these various and changing stimuli that the animal happens to be in the neighborhood where the execution of movement* **10** *becomes effective.* The animal has probably executed movement **10** (raising head) several times during the course of the trial but never before in the right place. To attempt to trace out these processes in detail would be futile.

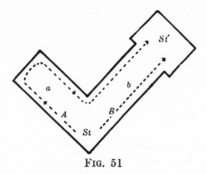

FIG. 51

to perform A.[14]   The situation in the ordinary maze of
the type of the Hampton Court may readily be presented
by the following diagram (Fig. 52) :

Let A and B represent the segments of the true pathway
and X the entrance to any *cul de sac* (let the segments be
chosen somewhere in the middle of the maze).   We will
suppose that the animal is on its way to the position A
for the first time.   The chances of entering B and X are
equal in the long run when the animal is in the position A.
If the animal goes into B the true pathway scores one in
frequency as over against the *cul de sac*.   If the animal

---

[14] At first sight this argument would seem to militate against
the second principle involved in habit formation, viz., recency.   That
the principle of recency is not jeopardized in this case appears when
we consider that in order to test recency we should have to arrange
conditions in such a way that the animal before turning at the end
of the alley was placed again immediately at St, and furthermore,
that he was in approximately the same physiological condition.
After the animal has turned and has become oriented towards St′
additional factors have been introduced which militate against the
recurrence of activity, A.   We have to qualify our statements by
saying "other things being equal" recency is a factor.   In our
original example of the latch box this condition is realized.   A serious criticism may be urged against the use of *recency* when we
consider the fact that an animal learns a problem far more rapidly,
from the standpoint of number of trials necessary, when given only
one trial per day than when given five trials in immediate succession.
It is of course possible to soften the force of this objection by maintaining that recency is operative in the five-trial method but that its
effects are offset and masked by certain disturbing physiological
conditions (as yet unknown) which occur when several trials are
given in immediate succession.

goes into the *cul de sac* X and follows it out to the bitter end it must return.[15]   When it reaches the position of the letter X on the return again the chances of entering B and A are equal.   We thus see that there is a greater probability of the animal's remaining on the true pathway than of his leaving it.   Possibly the case can be more definitely presented if we ask for the probability that the

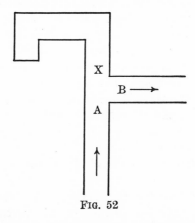

FIG. 52

animal takes the wrong path.   In order that this may occur it must (1) choose the wrong path from A to X and (2) choose the wrong path from X to A.   The probability of each wrong choice is ½; the probability that *both* wrong choices be made is ½ x ½ = ¼.   The complementary probability or the probability that it takes the right path is ¾.   I.e., the chances are three to one that the animal goes out through B rather than comes back to the starting point.[16]   This factor (frequency) alone is

[15] It does not always return.   Sometimes it goes to the end of the *cul de sac* and lies down.   If this happens often enough the animal very quickly forms the habit of going to the end of the *cul de sac* and lying down and going to sleep.   This is just as good and just as true a habit as if the maze had been completely traversed and learned.

[16] A type problem is this: What is the probability that heads be thrown at least once in two throws of a coin?   The *equally probable* cases are these: HH, HT, TH, TT.   Only the last is unfavorable whence the probability is ¾.   The argument that there are three cases HH, TH, TT, the last of which only is unfavorable (whence

probably sufficient to account for the formation of the maze habit.[17] Apparently it is difficult to obtain any explanation based upon other factors. Even those who would maintain that the obtaining of food, or " satisfiers," to use Thorndike's term, is the thing which stamps in movements, cannot apply that principle in these cases because of the fact that the " satisfier " is not obtained until the end of an extremely long series of movements is reached. Furthermore, actual observation shows that the *culs de sac* occurring early in the series are eliminated oftentimes *before* those occurring later and hence in closer proximity to satisfaction.[18] Hence there is no immediate connection between the obtaining of food and the elimination of errors, as must necessarily be called for on Thorndike's first law. This phenomenon in itself is enough to make us hesitate before applying it. In the case of the less restricted activity permitted by the problem box, it is more difficult to define the relation of successive activities, but this difficulty is due, not to any difference in principle, but only to the greater complexity of the conditions.

Application of the principle of *recency* in motor habits.—It should be clear that if there exist any factors which tend to influence the arrangement of the series of

p $=\frac{2}{3}$), is fallacious unless we take account of the fact that the three cases are *not equally probable*. The probability of case TH is $\frac{1}{2}$; of cases HH and TT each $\frac{1}{4}$. This evaluation of the cases leads to the argument. We are indebted to our colleague, Professor Coble of the mathematics department, for this development of the problem.

[17] If it happens by chance that any *cul de sac* is entered as frequently as any segment of the true pathway, it becomes as firmly fixed as the true segment. We often find that certain *culs de sac* are favorably placed (position in the series) and it is these which are hardest to eliminate. Sometimes, indeed, they are never eliminated. It seems worth mentioning that the animal in the maze does not always choose the shorter of two pathways when a longer and a shorter are offered.

[18] Miss Hubbert, who has been making an extensive study of this question, states that in the circular maze (p. 100) white rats eliminate the errors in alley 4 first, if we neglect 6, the alley nearest to the food box. The justification for neglecting 6 arises from the fact that it contains no stop. The animal upon entering it may turn either to the right or to the left—i.e., it must run completely around the food box in order to make an error. As it passes the entrance the smell stimuli of course become directive.

activities—to make one or another come earlier in the series—the progress of habit formation will be altered. *Recency* in problems, like that of opening boxes, seems to be such a factor. Its effect would tend to make the last act of the series (i.e., the successful one, 10 in our illustration) appear earlier. This will tend to decrease the probability of the occurrence of all other activities and hence quicken the rate of the learning process. In applying the principle in the particular case (problem above) we need to assume that on the first trial the initial resistance in arc 10 has been overcome and its reaction threshold lowered. Since the stimulus originally tended to call out this reaction along with the others (was primitively or instinctively associated with it) and since there is no instinctive spacing (no instinctive order of release, as often is the case with instincts) of the separate acts, it is most natural to suppose, other things being equal, that movement 10 will appear earlier on the second trial than on the first. We might go still further and maintain that if we could start with a case where the thresholds of stimulation in all the arcs involved in the whole ten acts were equal, 10, being the most recent, would be the only one to appear on the second trial and on all succeeding trials. But the organism is never constructed in this way. The principles of repetition and recency must operate many times before the threshold of 10 becomes lower than that of any other set of arcs. In general it must be admitted that recency is a much less potent factor in habit formation than is frequency. In certain habits such, for example, as those involved in the maze, its influence cannot very well be made out.

Sensory habits.—The problem in sensory habit is much more complicated. We will take (*e*) of our illustration (p. 261). The animal must learn to respond positively always to one of the two stimuli, say *yellow*, or what amounts to the same thing, negatively to the *blue*. Whether in any given situation the animal actually does both we cannot say until careful tests have been made. The observed result is the same—the animal, in the illustration chosen, always reacts to the *yellow* regardless of its right or left position (we are assuming that the wavelength difference is always effective from the standpoint of reaction, regardless of the energy difference of the two stimuli, i.e., that the two objects really offer different stimulating values). In order to understand what happens we ask leave to simplify the problem slightly. Instead of two lights, *yellow* and *blue*, we will substitute two problem boxes, respectively A and B, in their places, leaving the other conditions the same, i.e., the two boxes are separated by a partition, the animal is released from the home box as before, etc. In order to further simplify the problem we will use at first only one box, A, in place of the *yellow* (positively reacted to). We will keep the box on the right side for the first set of trials. Releasing the animal now as before we find exactly the same situation that we found above, i.e., random movements giving place to the definite act of opening the box. After a time the animal, immediately upon release, goes to the right-hand side and opens the box. The next step is to place the box on the left-hand side. The animal, on release, will probably run to the right-hand side, then here and there, finally locating the box and opening it. We then change its position back to the right and repeat the routine. After a time this movement likewise becomes definite. What have we done? Two acts have been established, viz., one of opening the box and the other of following the box. In this case the act of opening was established first and that of following later, but it is easy to see that the act of following must be executed before the act of opening can be executed. Henceforth we shall call the act of following the box (1) and the act of opening (2). Now introduce the second box, B, on the left side, leaving A on the right side. It is essential to our hypothesis that B be somewhat different from A (i.e., offer different stimulating value). Were box B not present the animal would rush immediately to A and open it. But putting box B on the left-hand side introduces a different stimulation, the intensity of which is such that it on its own account tends to release both the act of *following* (1) and the act of *opening* (2). Will the animal go to A or B? That depends purely upon the strength or intensity of the new stimulus (naturally we should consider here the momentary set of the animal and other intra-organic processes, etc). Suppose we introduce now the electric shock, and further, that the animal actually goes to B instead of to A. Before the subject reaches B the electric shock produces the avoiding reaction with the consequence that the animal turns over to A. The response to A becomes the most recent act. On the next trial we will assume that the same thing happens. We begin immediately to get the effect of repetition. The operation of the two factors, recency and repetition, combined with the process of *substitution,* which is discussed in the next paragraph, will finally result in the establishment of the habit (provided the stimuli actually possess different stimulating values for the animal). If now we will go back and substitute the two lights, *yellow* and *blue,* for the boxes, A and B, and for the act of opening box A, that of going around to the food box, etc., we will see clearly that this simplified scheme has given us the essential factors in the formation of sensory habits. We see that the sensory habits are much more complicated than the motor, but that they are not fundamentally different. It may be argued that we have no right to develop the problem in this simplified way: that the habit may be formed when both stimuli are present from the beginning. We admit that the habit may be developed under such conditions but we argue that while the reactions called for on the part of the animal are more complex under those conditions, yet in the end the fixation process takes place as a result of the factors we have invoked. In this connection we call attention to the almost unanimous verdict of experimenters to the effect that when both stimuli are present from the beginning the habit arises with difficulty or not at all. A reference to our work on the rat (p. 222) where yellow and blue of high intensity were introduced simultaneously at the beginning of the experiment, will show that the animal never formed the habit. It was only by using the positive stimulus alone until a perfect habit resulted that we were finally enabled to introduce the negative stimulus and thus to complete the test.

Substitution.—By substitution we mean that a stimulus which originally did not call out a given response comes later to call it out. Two examples illustrate this very clearly. A green light at first does not call out the salivary secretion *in large amounts* in the Pawlow type of experiment (p. 66). After food has been presented immediately after the green light (or simultaneously with it; simultaneity is not necessary) for a number of times, the green light calls out the secretion in large amounts. Or again: the experimenter claps his hands (A) and lays fish (B) upon the top of a cage containing a cat. The cat climbs to the top of the cage (R) and eats the food. We may put the course of events down in serial form: A, B, R. After a time the cat climbs up (R) immediately after the experimenter claps his hands (A): thus A, R; B seems to have become unnecessary. It is to meet this type of problem that has led Jennings to posit the concept of the "readier resolution of physiological states." While the two types of behavior differ in several particulars, the processes involved are probably in general the same. We have to suppose, e.g., in the case of the cat's reaction to the signal that on the first trial A aroused general reflex activity (S), while B aroused the definite instinctive (or habitual) act of climbing up (R). In such a case we have to assume further (there is apparently no other hypothesis open) that while A could not arouse R until B had aroused it and thus lowered the resistance across the effector division of the arc (Y) nevertheless it attempted to discharge into Y as well as into the more segmentally placed X. I.e., *A discharged or tended to discharge into R but at that moment the resistance was great and the impulse passed out over X, producing the movements (S), e.g., of clawing at the wires, purring, etc.* We offer the following simplified neural diagram, Fig. 53. Granting the connection between the sensory division of the arc AS and the effector division of the arc BR, we need to account for only one thing, viz., how it comes about that the stimulus aroused by A now passes through Y instead of through X, its original channel. If we watch the training of the animal we find that A and B have to be gone through with serially many times before R will follow upon A. Before the substitution is established the response (R) has become extremely easy to set off (note the premature response which often occurs in human reaction experi-

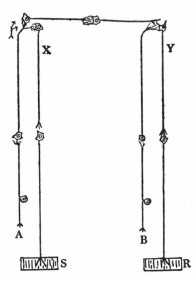

FIG. 53

ments). Resistance has been decreased by use until even the (assumed) weak impulse aroused by A is sufficient to call it out (it is not necessary to suppose that the resistance across X has changed).

Repetition of movement in absence of original stimulus.—In both human and animal work we get cases where a series of movements is executed in a fixed order in the absence of the stimulus which originally called them forth. The process is again one of substitution, but somewhat more complex than the one considered above. One of the most interesting of such cases is the learning and later repetition of nonsense syllables. Presentation of a series of nonsense syllables to the eye may be illustrated as follows (Fig. 54):

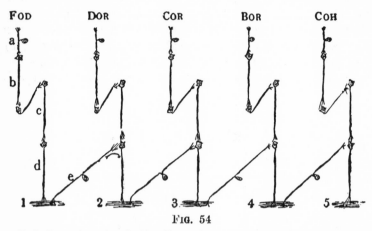

FIG. 54

Fod, Dor, etc., visual stimuli; a, b, c, d, arc running from eye to laryngeal muscle 1; e, segmental sensory neurone ending in muscle 1.

As is well known, we are dealing here with the rearrangement of established habit systems. The visual stimulus *Fod* sets up an impulse which releases activity in the laryngeal muscle 1 (either silent or overt saying of the word) and the rest of the syllables act in the same way. We know further that after this series has been gone through with a few times presentation (by any method whatsoever) of *Fod* forces the recall of the remaining syllables. We may illustrate the scheme where all extra-organic stimuli except the original stimulus are removed, as follows (Fig. 55):

In order to understand this we must go back to our first diagram. We see that when muscle 1 is thrown into activity by the visual stimulus aroused by *Fod,* a neural impulse is set up in the muscle spindles in 1. This impulse passing inward over the segmental (proprio-ceptive) neurone, *e,* may discharge theoretically into any muscle of the body but by reason of the high development of

laryngeal habits, it comes about that the discharge back
into the other muscles of the larynx is the easiest. But
into which one? Before activity has ceased in 1, muscle 2

FOD

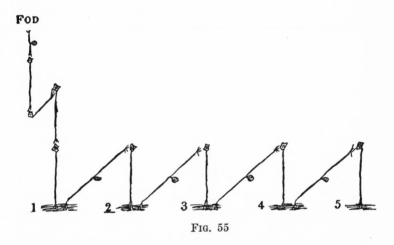

FIG. 55

has been forced into activity by the external visual impulse. We make the assumption then that ease of discharge into muscle 2 is greatest, and that next in order
come 3, 4, 5, 6, etc. From this time on muscle 2 may be
called into activity equally through the kinæsthetic impulse
passing over *e* or through the visual impulse aroused by
Dor. Consequently when *Fod* is presented and the remaining syllables are not presented, it is clear that the appropriate kinæsthetic impulses discharge in order into muscles
3, 4, 5, 6, etc. We are dealing here with systems already
so highly organized that a single reading of a series of seven
syllables will often make the repetition of this series possible. It is probable that these segmental arcs are " fixed "
as a result of such factors as we have already considered.[19]

Physiological principles operative.—Unquestionably
the principles of reënforcement, inhibition, and summation
of stimuli are constantly operative. When the separate

[19] As is well known other arcs than e become established, viz.,
an arc running from 1 to 3, from 1 to 4, etc.; also from muscle 1 to
the muscle which functioned previously to the functioning of muscle 1.

stages of habit have been more carefully analyzed we can more readily see how such factors operate in detail.

Conclusions.—It is to be hoped that even this tentative and unsatisfactory presentation of the most important principles in fixation will lead to a more definite study of the mechanisms involved. The problem is in such a state that only careful experimentation will enable us to go further in its solution. It is a great deal easier to assume that pleasure stamps in the successful movement and that displeasure stamps out the unsuccessful and to let the matter rest than to institute the necessary experimentation. But behavior has reached a critical stage and such explanations, however satisfactory in the past, no longer content us.

BIBLIOGRAPHY

ANGELL, J. R., *Psychology.* New York, Holt, 1908.

BOOK, W. F., *The Psychology of Skill.* Missoula, Univ. Montana, 1908.

CARR, H. A., "Principles of Selection in Animal Learning," *Psych. Rev.*, 1914, XXI.

GLASER, O. C., "The Formation of Habits at High Speed," *Jour. Comp. Neu. and Psych.*, 1910, XX, 165.

JUDD, C. H., *Psychology.* New York, Scribner's, 1907.

PILLSBURY, W. B., *The Essentials of Psychology.* New York, Macmillan, 1911.

SWIFT, E. J., *Mind in the Making.* New York, Scribner's, 1908.

THORNDIKE, E. L., *Animal Intelligence.* New York, Macmillan, 1911.

CHAPTER VIII

THE ABRIDGMENT OF THE LEARNING PROCESS

Introduction.—So far in the treatment of habits we have discussed mainly those that have been formed without tuition, i.e., by the animal through its perseverance method. That there are so-called higher forms of learning has been warmly advocated by many experimenters and investigators. Such forms have been treated under the general head of imitation. Examination of the concept of imitation shows that there is little agreement as to the meaning which the term should connote. It would seem wiser to treat the subject of imitation solely from the standpoint of behavior. From this standpoint real or genuine imitation should refer to a *relatively instantaneous regrouping of old habits* (1). It is presupposed that all elements (unit habits) are present and that the stimulus (pattern, act to be imitated or copied) leads to a response which, from the observer's standpoint, is like the pattern. On the other hand, all that experimenters seem to have meant by imitation is that we can, by adopting certain methods of procedure, abridge the process of learning, or make learning possible in cases where the animal has failed to form the habit by its own unaided efforts (2). When the problem is approached from the standpoint of (2) it must be readily admitted that there are many factors which can both abridge the process of learning and lengthen it. Some of these factors have already been discussed on p. 235. Whether there is real imitation in the sense of (1) in the animal world cannot be affirmed so readily (p. 281).

Lloyd Morgan's classification of imitation.—The point of view suggested above has not, in general, been adopted. Examination of the literature shows that experimenters have usually chosen some anthropomorphic type of classification of imitation, such as that outlined by Morgan, and have conducted their experimental tests in such a way as to throw into relief the expected kind of imitation. (1) *Mimicry* is the lowest type so far as classification goes. It lies, according to this writer, generally below the level of imitation. It is found widespread among insects. On account of the many enemies which prey upon animals it has been supposed by the Darwinians that under the process of natural selection animals have become inconspicuous, i.e., they have come to resemble (visually as a rule) the objects in their environment. This is supposed to afford protection from enemies. Once the race is established it is easy to see how the variants will be killed off on account of their conspicuousness. On the other hand, conspicuousness may be allowed under natural selection where that character is combined with inedibility. Now many conspicuous edible forms are not eliminated because they have come to resemble the conspicuous inedible forms. We have already discussed the improbability of races arising in this way through the action of the Darwinian mechanisms (p. 166). However that may be, the mere fact of resemblance as outlined above is unquestionably true. (2) *Instinctive imitation.* This kind of imitation depends upon inherited mechanisms. As examples we may cite the following instinctive group of activities; drinking, peering into cracks and holes, etc., warning cries taken up by birds and other animals, etc. Care is not always taken in these illustrations to insure against the possibility of response to a common stimulus, i.e., the stimulus which may have set off the response in the first animal may also have acted upon the other members of the group. There seem to be genuine cases, though, where the stimulus acts upon one animal, inducing an instinctive mode of behavior which in turn becomes the common stimulus causing group activity.

In regard to the first of these types, mimicry, it may be

said that there seems to be no valid reason to consider such phenomena under imitation at all. Mimicry, except in certain cases, is not a form of behavior at all, but a morphological or anatomical character.[1] The second division, instinctive imitation, falls under the general head of instinct since such acts as we have included in this group are seen at once to be congenital and not in any way involving the process of learning. It is better to group such responses under some such title as that of social instincts. Morgan's third division, (3) *intelligent imitation,* is the type usually referred to in discussions on imitation in general. It is in this third class (and in its finer subdivisions, such as inferential imitation, etc.) that we find confusion of meaning. It is openly anthropomorphic. Experimenters have reported the finding of imitation of this type through the use of the following devices: (1) by the experimenter showing the animal how to do an act; (2) by allowing a trained animal to perform before an untrained animal; (3) by " putting the animal through " the act; (4) finally by " encouraging " the animal. Before trying to evaluate the effects of the above devices, it is presupposed that the animal has failed to learn by his own unaided efforts, or at least that he has worked at the problem indefinitely until the situation no longer offers stimulation for activity, or finally that we are reasonably sure of the number of trials that the animal would take to learn the problem by the perseverance method. If we examine these devices and strip from them their anthropomorphic implications we find that all of them except (3) are methods really for localizing and enhancing the intensity of the stimulus [(3) is separately considered on p. 282].

Localizing and enhancing the stimulus.—In actual practice the stimulus may be localized and enhanced in a variety of ways: by the experimenter doing the act before the animal; by pointing to the apparatus and moving cer-

---

[1] Numerous exceptions to this statement may be found in fish, e.g., the flounder, and possibly in certain reptiles (the chameleon). There is no justification for considering such responses as these under the head of imitation at all since they depend upon reflex and inherited mechanisms.

tain parts of the mechanism, etc.; by allowing one animal
to learn by the perseverance method and using him as an
imitatee. His attack upon the apparatus will serve the
same purpose as that of the experimenter.[2] When using
this method two things should be kept sharply in mind as
was indicated above, p. 277: either (1) the experimenter is
trying to call forth a new combination of old habits (i.e.,
imitation according to our definition; or (2) he is trying
to get the animal to form the habit *de novo*. We have never
sharply separated these two issues. Usually we might say
(1) has always been in the mind of the experimenters. All
of us, in such experiments, have plunged *in medias res* by
giving the animal exceedingly complex acts to imitate without being sure that all of the elements are present, or
whether there was flexibility enough in the elements (p. 49)
which were present. What can we hope to get from such
an unscientific procedure? Behavior seemingly is establishing the point that each simple coördination (not congenital) is acquired by the perseverance method, hence the
pattern, or the act to be copied should be made up of simpler acts already acquired. The novelty present in the act
as a whole is the method of combination (temporal spacing
of the elements). It may be argued that in all the tests on
imitation we are sure that the unit acts are all present before we start. Each one of our monkeys knows how to put
his hand up a shute, turn a button, lift up a latch, etc.—
we have trained him to do this before setting the pattern
for imitation. The reply is " Yes, those coördinations are
present, but they are not flexible enough." Nearly every
human being knows how to move his feet alternately backward and forward and to turn while moving them, yet the
average man learns a new dance with appreciable difficulty.
Merely watching the movements of some one else in dancing
is not usually a sufficient stimulus to set free the appropriate
movements. Most of us have to be pushed, pulled, twisted
through it before the act follows of itself (i.e., through the

[2] Hobhouse holds that in the case of some animals a mere hint, i.e.,
a mere motion towards the correct act, is sufficient to make the
animal go through the act correctly.

action of the proprio-ceptive arcs.)   On the other hand,
the dancing master and many women, through long practice,
have trained their feet and legs as well as their hands and
arms, and can execute the variations of the dance the moment the pattern is set.   If it is agreed that the above
analysis of what is involved in the act of imitation is, in
large measure, correct, it is obvious that very few experiments so far reported upon animals (and very few of
those on children), really touch the problem of imitation
(i.e., of making new combinations immediately from among
old habits) at all.   It may be argued with justice that we
can never be sure in advance that there are a sufficient
number of coördinations at hand, and that practically all
we can do is to take the animal as we find him, subject
him to the influences of the devices enumerated, and see
what happens.   Until it becomes possible to take some anthropoid apes and bring them up practically as children
are brought up, with varied training and with wide education of hands, it is probable that what we shall mainly be
doing in such work is the testing of the *formation of habits*
with stimuli enhanced.   But the results of this type cannot
be differentiated from the hastening, or the reverse, one
gets through introducing pain stimulation, drugs, heightening tonicity through more potent stimuli,—as when toasted
cheese is used in the case of the rat instead of bread, sex
in the case of the rabbit, etc.   Under proper manipulation
such factors can be made to hasten or retard a given habit,
depending upon the fact whether these stimulations are
arranged to reënforce the desired response or to inhibit it.
To illustrate what is meant: one can take the female rabbit
and enclose her in a cage along with food, and close a
door which may be opened by the turning of a button.
Activity of the sort calculated to produce the first success
will be hastened in the male, which is placed on the outside.
Now, if the box is arranged as before with food alone on
the inside, and the female is left with the male, the latter
will respond to the more potent sex stimulus to the neglect
of the problem before him.   Rats which have lain down
in the maze,—given up the problem,—can be made active

again by the introduction of another animal. Chickens hasten more rapidly through the maze if they can hear their fellows pecking on the outside, etc.

Putting the animal through the act.—A reference to the literature will show that positive results are being accumulated by the use of this method. The theoretical envisagement of the problem involved in the interpretation of these results is difficult. All we can do, apparently, is to admit the general fact and to wait for more extended work to bring analysis. If putting the most motile organ (paw, beak, etc.) of an animal slowly through the various parts of an act brought a hastening of the act as a whole, interpretation would at least be theoretically possible. But with the exception of Cole, in his work upon the raccoon, all have failed to get positive results from this method. On the other hand, it is possible to get both the rat and the raccoon to climb to the top of a box and drop through a trap to the floor of the box (which is quite foreign to their instinctive organization) after they have been passively dropped through the trap on various occasions. It would seem that in this method we have an additional (i.e., to the perseverance method) way of establishing a simple coordination in an animal. Yet we are not willing to admit this until there has been made a very thorough analysis of the factors which enter into it (p. 293).

Presentation of experimental results: introduction.—From these preliminary statements concerning the general problem of higher forms of learning it will be seen that it is impossible to present the results which have been obtained in any thoroughly systematic and unitary way. The technique of making the tests has been as varied as the presuppositions held by the different investigators. Accordingly the results will be presented in some detail.

A. Primates.—Thorndike concludes in general that learning in the monkey (*Cebus*) cannot be hastened by the methods under consideration. He found that opening the door of a given box for the monkeys had no effect upon the rapidity with which they learned to open it. Thorndike's usual method was to " attract the attention " of the monkey or to wait until the animal was looking at the experimenter, and then to open the box slowly, emphasizing the movements. The monkey would then be given a trial without tuition; or the experimenter would repeat his act several times before allowing the animal to try the box. All experiments of this type failed to yield positive results. They profited just as little by the tuition of other trained animals. One animal was allowed to open the box by the perseverance method. This animal was then used as the *imitatee*. The imitatee worked with the *imitators* near at hand. Negative results were again obtained. Monkeys fail to learn, according to the same writer, by being put through the movements. Thorndike made several such tests upon the monkeys. One animal was carried to the top of a table and fed there, and then tested to see if it would go to the table of its own accord. This was repeated ten times, and then the animal was released. In no case did this monkey or any other give an imitative response. Watson's experiments were made upon monkeys (*M. rhesus*) which were quite tame. Two of the monkeys were quite friendly with each other. J was an adult monkey and B a young one. In a short time an attachment sprang up between these monkeys which persisted for several years. B was wild and restless and became excited when J was away from him. J on his part would run to B on certain cries and put his fore-paws around B's neck. B would nestle up to J and clasp him around the chest. If B did not become placid under this treatment, J would rock him from side to side and give out a little companionable chatter. Under these conditions, it is quite evident that J's reactions influenced B's greatly. When J went to one part of the cage B followed. If, while sitting on the shelf, a pan of water or bowl of milk was placed upon the ground, B would not come down to drink if J did not precede him. J formed the habit of jumping on to the experimenter's shoulder when he entered the cage and called. B formed the same habit, but if J for any reason refused to come, B refused also. If B were loose in the room when the experimenter passed with J on his shoulder, B would run to the experimenter immediately. But, on the other hand, if J was not on his shoulder, B paid not the slightest attention to the experimenter's commands. At times J and B were left loose in the animal room. Sometimes J was refractory and did not care to go into the cage. B would never go in unless J did. It was necessary to threaten him at times with a long stick. J would walk around the cage two or three times before entering it, but always just out of reach. B trailed J and when the latter finally darted through the door of the cage B darted in also. It was almost impossible to force B in unless J had preceded him. Several types of problems were given the animals in the work upon imitation. (1) Drawing in food with a rake, animal to imitate the experimenter; (2) drawing in food with a cloth, animal to imitate the experimenter; (3) obtaining food from bottom of bottle by the use of a fork, animal to imitate the experimenter; (4) pushing out food from middle of long glass cylinder by means of stick, animal to imitate experimenter; (5) manipulation of old-fashioned latch, animal to imitate experimenter; (6) box with a door in top not held in place by any fastening, animal to pull open door by means of a handle, B to imitate J; (7) box with door in top held in place by push button, B to imitate J. The monkeys very quickly form by their own unaided efforts such habits of manipulation, but so far as our observations went they were entirely uninfluenced by tuition. In the simple problems, such as pushing out food from a glass cylinder, pulling in food with a rake or cloth, etc., we failed wholly in obtaining positive results. When the animal is placed in such situations it at once begins to strain at its tether and to reach out after food with its paw. It would often pick up the stick or cloth, bite it, and then discard it, but it would never attempt to go through with the act of pushing out the cloth or stick, throwing it over the object, then pulling it in. In other words, our conclusions exactly harmonize with those of Thorndike and are entirely against Hobhouse's type of results. We did find evidence for certain types of reaction which are generally included under the head of instinctive imitation. With Kinnaman we found that if one monkey discovered a hole and peeked into it, another would generally push him aside and peek into it in his turn. This was observed several times. More recently we have confirmed these observations many times in the case of a mother and baby. One day the baby left the mother's arms and peered under a sill at a brass lock which could be seen from his viewpoint but not from hers. He pushed his arm through and attempted to pull the lock forward. The mother left off eating, came and adopted the same position and reached her arm through and attempted to grasp the lock. The two acts were identical in technique. We found also that certain acts which resulted in a sound would be rhythmically repeated. In one case one of the monkeys (*Cebus*) filched a large tablespoon. He was found standing the spoon on one end and then immediately releasing it. Dropping the spoon seemed not to be accidental but actually a part of the act. He repeated this act 15 times in unvarying order and, so far as could be judged, at definite intervals of time. This corresponds, in our opinion, very closely to the child's act of repeatedly hammering its spoon against the table. Hammering with a nut or any small, hard, preferably round, object was another favorite trick of the *Cebus* monkey. In one case the animal tapped with a small hickory nut 150 times in one half hour. In the forest this is possibly connected with some kind of food-getting process, although we have no assurance of this. *Rhesus* J also gave evidence of a similar type of action. Occasionally he would sit and play with a small hard object, let it slip through his fingers to the board on which he sat, pick it up again, and drop it. One instinctive act could at times be called out in J, that of flea catching. As is well known, this is probably the most frequent act indulged in during their quieter moments. The smacking sound used by the monkeys in this act is easily imitated. On one occasion J allowed the experimenter to hunt fleas over him. After performing this act J perched upon his shoulder but made no attempt to pick him. The experimenter then held up the hairy portion of his arm to J but he made no effort to hunt for fleas! The smacking sound was then made with the lips. J immediately made the sound in turn and began searching the arm, and then proceeded to the experimenter's neck (the experimenter was wearing a rubber cap which extended down over his ears). Haggerty worked for several months on the *rhesus* and *Cebus* monkeys. The animals were placed in the presence of simple mechanical devices the manipulation of which opened doors, disclosed openings, or dropped food into the cage. Each animal was given a fair opportunity to imitate in a series of preliminary trials,—usually 15 in number, each 15 minutes in length and given on successive days. In almost every case the animal had either solved the problem by the end of that time or had lost interest in it. Imitation experiments were then begun upon the animals which had failed. The trained animal was allowed to perform in the presence of the imitator. After this the imitator was given an opportunity to try the mechanism. He was allowed to work 10 minutes, and longer if he seemed on the point of making the successful movements. If he failed the test was repeated. He was not considered as having failed to imitate until 100 opportunities for profiting by tuition had been given. Under these conditions Haggerty obtained 16 cases of imitation, 3 of which were immediate, and 5 cases of partially successful imitation. Of the 11 animals used by him but 2 failed to exhibit imitative behavior in one test or another. Haggerty mentions the fact that animals imitate best when not too thoroughly accustomed to one another. He states that these cases are cases of imitation of the inferential type. We are not able to agree with him. In the first place, his method of allowing the animals to have 100 chances for imitation before considering tuition without effect must always give ambiguous results. With an animal as agile and as varied in his interests as the monkey, it is never possible to tell when a burst of activity will lead to the solution of the problem by the perseverance method. On the other hand, it is possible to assume that the only effect of the act of the imitatee was to set off two congenital forms of response on the part of the imitator. The one was the

following instinct,—i.e., to go to the place where a group
of monkeys had just been and to peer into the same holes
that other monkeys had just peered into, etc.; and the other
the tendency to attack moving objects first. The general
perseverance method of the animal took care of the remaining factors. Kinnaman reports instances where he observed
that the acts of the male monkey (*M. rhesus*) influenced the
responses of the female. In one case where food was to be
had by pulling out a plug, and in another where food
could be obtained by bearing down upon a lever, the female
had had opportunity to learn without tuition but had failed.
The male had learned by his own efforts. He was allowed
to perform in front of the female. She went at once in
each case, after seeing the male get the food, and operated
the mechanisms, and then repeated the acts later several
times. Witmer was not very successful in getting Peter,
the chimpanzee, to imitate the trainer in fitting the form
blocks into their appropriate holes. He states that better
success was obtained with him in the imitation of the letter
W, which was placed upon a blackboard. Witmer also cites
the case of a monkey (*M. cynomolgus*) in opening a door.
He maintains that this door was opened for the first time
by the monkey. There is nothing in his paper that would
show that he knew anything about the previous history of
the monkey. Opening a door is one of the easiest things
that a monkey does. Time and time again we have had
them unhook doors, twist off wires which were wrapped
around doors, break wires, take a round knob and turn it
with the hind-feet while holding on to a nail in the wall
with the fore-feet. All of these acts were readily learned
without tuition and in the absence of the experimenter. It
is very easy to be deceived about the accomplishments of an
animal not under daily observation. Shepherd repeated
several of the tests made by Watson and by Hobhouse. In
one of his imitation tests he used a glass tube 15 inches in
length and $\frac{7}{8}$ of an inch in diameter fitted with a plunger
which could be easily taken out and inserted. All failed to
imitate. The animals would take up the plunger, throw it
down, pick it up, insert it in the mouth, bite it, and then

again discard it. They were also tried with a T-rake. Nearly all failed. None pushed out the rake and hooked the prong over the food. Monkeys 3 and 7 learned to push out the rake and with much slashing about of the T end to succeed in drawing in the food. The act was very awkward for them. One of the monkeys would many times knock the bit of food away. The best that can be said is that the animal learned to imitate the experimenter in pushing the rake out, but only awkwardly in hooking the rake around the food and pulling it in. These coör- dinations were never smoothly executed by the two monkeys. There is some slight evidence that one of them learned something from the tuition of the other. In another type of test positive results of a fairly satisfactory kind were obtained. A banana was suspended by a string from a horizontal rod attached to the wall of the room. The banana was entirely out of reach of the monkey unless he would push a horizontally placed pole (pivoted at one end and supported by a railing at the other) under the banana. Having done this he was able to mount the pole from the ground and to reach the banana from the pole. While in general the monkeys learned this problem by the perseverance method, there were certain indications that imitation was involved. In the case of monkeys Hobhouse cited the behavior of the chimpanzee P which had learned previous to the tests under consideration to throw his rake out and over the food that was out of his reach and then clumsily to roll it in. Hobhouse taught P to substitute a stick with a crook at one end for the rake. Food was placed in a light box. The chimpanzee learned in time to hook the end of the stick into the box and pull it in. The animal learned rapidly to use a short stick to bring in a longer one—the latter enabling him to obtain food which was beyond the reach of the short rod. Hobhouse tried to teach the chimpanzee to throw a rope with a noose in it over the box and bring in the food in this way, but even when he got the noose around the box he did not complete the response by pulling it in. The *M. rhesus* mon- **keys** were much slower in learning to use the stick. They did not succeed apparently any better than those used in the author's experiments. Hobhouse's *M. rhesus* did not at first learn to use the short stick to pull in the longer one. He later learned to use a stick quite frequently and when it was out of reach even to use substitutes for it, such as a child's skipping rope, wire, cord, etc. Hobhouse reports an interesting act in the *M. rhesus:* food was placed on a table just out of reach of the monkey. However, the tether was long enough for him to reach the food provided a chair or box was pushed between him and the table. He rapidly learned to push the chair into position and to mount it.

B. Cats.—Berry states that the Manx cat is very much influenced by the behavior of its associates. In learning a problem box a trained animal was used as the imitatee. In one case it was shown that cat M refused to turn a button which would have released her until cat X had turned it several times in front of her. In rolling a ball into a hole cat Y refused to do it until the trained animal had performed in front of him. The presence of imitation was found in such acts as pulling a knotted string which would release a door. Instinctive imitations such as going to the same place and looking down the same hole, scratching at the same place, and so on, are also reported by Berry. Thorndike failed to get cats to imitate. Trained animals were allowed to perform in front of the untrained animals. Several simple experiments like the following failed to yield positive results: The cats were placed in a large box with a door in the top; the experimenter went to the box and opened the door to get the animals out. The first cat up was always taken out first and fed before the others. Usually they climbed up to the door on the approach of the experimenter. Of 3 recently purchased animals 1 had not acquired the habit by the end of the tenth day. Even though a piece of fish were held up to him he would not climb up. It is reasonable to suppose that imitation, if at all prominent in their lives, would have overcome this sluggishness. Thorndike then put 2 trained cats in the cage with this animal and had them climb up

80 times before his eyes and get the food. No positive results were obtained. In one other interesting test they again failed. All animals of a certain group were taught to climb to the top of a large cage on the *approach* of the experimenter with food. Two animals, then, were trained to go up on a signal. One of these trained animals was put into the cage with the untrained animals. On the signal the trained cat would go up, but the untrained animals would not go up until the approach of the experimenter. This association was not very quickly formed, although it was learned in time by the perseverance method. Warren reports a case of delayed imitation in the cat. One of the two pets formed, through efforts of its own, the habit of climbing into the experimenter's lap, then on to his shoulder and out over his outstretched arm to a piece of meat held on a fork. The companion of this cat made no attempt to perform the trick, although watching the trained animal feed in this way daily. This second cat had often been coaxed to make the effort. One day, however, (after the owner had been absent for some time) after watching the trained animal feed, it suddenly sprang into the experimenter's lap, walked out over his arm, and seized the meat. After this it became the sturdy rival of the cat which had first learned the trick.

C. Dogs.—Thorndike has made similar tests upon the dog. After the dogs had failed to open a given box, the experimenter went through the act. The dogs failed in all cases to profit by such tuition. One dog had been taught to jump up on a box and " beg " when a piece of meat was held above his head. He did this 110 times in the presence of an untrained animal. The untrained animal never learned to imitate. Putting the animal through the act proved just as unavailing as in the case of monkeys. In such experiments the animal was left at its task for a few minutes, and if it failed to work the mechanism the experimenter would place his hand in the cage, take the dog's paw and force it through the act of pulling the string or working the lever, as the case might be. This he would repeat again and again. At the end of 10 to 15 minutes he would test the animal alone. None of the animals failing to learn by its own unaided efforts ever learned by being " put through."

D. Raccoons.—On the question as to whether raccoons imitate there is much difference of opinion. Cole says that they imitated his movements in pressing down the lever of a card displayer (which finally resulted in their obtaining food). Sometimes they apparently worked the lever as the experimenter had done and at others at least attempted to work it in that way. After a few days they began to watch the experimenter's hand very closely. He admits that they do not imitate their mates. He finds further that the raccoons learn by being " put through." He tried Thorndike's experiment of dropping the animals into the experiment box. The animal was picked up by the back of its neck and dropped into the box. It had to open the door to get out and obtain a bit of food. At the end of 33 to 57 trials the animals learned to turn and go back into the box if the door was left open. If they found the door closed the raccoons would climb up the sides of the box and drop in through the hole at the top. In the case of these animals there is some evidence that they learn more quickly if passively " put through " the movements of working a simple mechanism. The main effect appears immediately after they are " put through " the act. The effect is very transient. An animal never failed to work the mechanism if given a " put through " trial at first. He otherwise often failed in the early stages. Cole states that they can be made to learn an act by tuition after having failed to learn it without tuition. The animals did not always duplicate the act exactly, although they could be taught to do even this. Shepherd failed to get such satisfactory evidence of imitation in the raccoon. His animals had been trained to solve problems involving the manipulation of levers, etc., for about 3 months. His imitation apparatus consisted of an inclined plane of poultry netting 25 cm. wide supported at one end by a box. From the box the plane extended diagonally across the room to a platform. The raccoons could mount the box from the floor of the room. At a given signal the trained raccoon would mount the box and walk up the plane to the platform where he was fed. This animal was the imitatee. Two others were used as imitators. Several experiments failed to show a more rapid learning on the part of the imitators than would be called for by the assumption that their learning was of the perseverance type. Davis reports one case of doubtful imitation in the raccoon. For the most part he failed to find any trace of it. Two experiments are cited: A blind coon was taught to climb to a platform in the middle of the room. Upon this he would stand and beg for food. Another raccoon was taught to climb up with the blind animal, but although this animal had seen the blind coon stand up and beg for food many times it would never, on its own account, imitate the act. One animal was taught to jump for food up to 3 feet in height. He was always in the midst of the pack when he performed this act, yet none of the other animals ever attempted to imitate it.

E. Rodents.—Berry states that the white rat will imitate simple actions. If one rat begins digging another one will come up and begin to dig also. In other experiments less instinctive acts were said to have been imitated. It is extremely questionable whether the rat has sufficiently developed visual receptors for such a complex stimulus as the performance of another animal to lead to such complicated motor results. Such results would be very difficult to account for when we consider that it has been shown that the rat learns with great difficulty to respond to even large differences in size, pattern, and intensity of visual stimuli. Dr. Florence Richardson in her work at the University of Chicago was not able to obtain positive results on rats when they were tested in an apparatus as nearly like Berry's as could be made from his description. Imitation of the *following* type has been admitted by every one since the work of Small appeared. Hunter finds that the white rat can learn by being " put through " an act. As a part of the daily routine of an experiment upon a group of rats it was found necessary to deposit each animal, after completing his quota of work, in a small box.

This was accomplished by lifting the animal up and dropping it through a hole in the top of a box resting on the table which held the living cage. The animal remained in the box until all the members of the group had been worked with, after which the group as a whole was removed to the living cage and there fed. On the two hundred and fourth day after experiments had begun the door of the living cage was left open by accident. Two of the 5 rats climbed to the top of the small box and dropped to the floor of their own accord and remained there, as was their custom during the regular routine of experimentation. A regular set of tests was then initiated. Several results of this character were obtained.[3] Yerkes failed to get imitation in the dancing mouse. He allowed a trained animal to escape from a box by climbing up a ladder. This trained animal performed before untrained animals many times. The untrained animals failed to profit by the copy. A similar condition of affairs resulted when discrimination tests were tried. The animals responded individually. Seldom would one even follow the other. Again, some of his animals were taught to pull and others to push in a door of an experiment box. Those which had learned to push out doors did not learn to imitate those which had learned to pull in doors in situations which demanded the latter type of response. Although abundant opportunity was given in a variety of acts, no imitation was found. This has been confirmed by other observers on different varieties of mice. Allen states that the guinea pig can be " tolled " through certain movements (thus supplying

---

[3] It is possible, but probably unwise, to interpret this act in a rather simple way. After the animals are dropped into the box a habit of remaining there is formed. The floor of the interior of the box often reacted to may, whenever sensed, lead to the old response of jumping down upon it. The rats, when let out inadvertently, do as all rats do, run over every available inch of surface. On arriving at the top of the box the stimulus of the floors and sides leads to the old response. Rats often climb over the interior of a box and over its cover, jumping at times to the floor. There are many obvious ways of controlling this response, by the use of blind and anosmic animals, by putting the animal through a door in the side, etc. Until some one does this, we shall not know what factors are involved.

its own motor impulse) which has the effect of hastening the formation of the habit.

F. Birds.—Thorndike gave his chicks the chance of imitating the act of pecking at a door, jumping up and with the neck pulling down a string, stepping on a platform, pecking at a tack, etc. In no case was imitation found. Porter offers a new criterion of imitation, as follows: Bird No. 1 is allowed to open a problem box by the perseverance method. Bird No. 2 which has not learned to open it, or else has a different and possibly a poorer method of opening it, is allowed to work upon the problem with bird No. 1.[4] If either bird changes its method, discarding a poor one for a better one, or if the untrained animal should suddenly pick up the method, imitation is present. In all cases, except where the tests were made upon blue jays, Porter found positive evidence of imitation. The birds giving positive results were English sparrows, cow birds, juncoes, white-throated and field sparrows, song sparrows, Baltimore orioles and crows. Birds of the same species imitate one another more readily than they do birds of a different species. Baldwin in personal conversation mentioned a case of delayed imitation in the parrot. He tried to teach this parrot to sing '' Over the Fence Is Out.'' The bird would never attempt to repeat the words while the experimenter was present. One morning, though, as he came down the steps, the bird started in with the melody.[5] The observations of Scott and of Conradi, showing that the type of song which develops in a given bird is largely dependent upon the nature of the songs of the other birds confined in its neighborhood, have already been mentioned in another connection (p. 142). Lashley has recently confirmed this work and ex-

---

[4] The two birds are likely to fight. Porter supposes that by this process he makes the stimulus to get at the food or to work at the problem far greater than by the ordinary method; e.g., he states that '' rivalry '' is a strong motive.

[5] He has since published a similar observation: Baldwin, J. Mark. '' Deferred Imitation in West-African Gray Parrots.'' Extrait du IXᵉ Congrès international de Zoologie, tenu à Monaco du 25 au 30 Mars, 1913, 536.

tended it. He finds that when an Amazon parrot
(Chrysotis), which does not talk, is confined with a bird
which does, the untrained animal begins to repeat at first
very indistinctly the words of the trained parrot. These
gradually become more definite. The untrained animal
in this case profited much more rapidly from the tuition
of its fellow than from that of the experimenter. This
same investigator has tested to what extent a well-trained
parrot can reproduce articulate and inarticulate sounds.
This bird possesses 50 to 100 distinctly articulated words
which can be called out by appropriate stimuli. In addition,
he sings, whistles, barks, mews, cackles, and laughs. When
tested on ability to respond in kind to such sounds, he gave
30 whistling tones to 30 whistling stimuli produced by the
experimenter's lips and by blowing a small metal whistle.
He responded to 31 singing tones from violin, cello, piano,
and voice 29 times by singing tones and 2 times by whistling tones. The bird was able to reproduce varied types of
sounds as is shown in the following table:

Stimulus	Times given	Response	Times given
Guttural speech	10	Guttural muttering..	10
Whistling	10	Whistling	10
Whispering	10	Whispering	10
Cough	10	Cough	10
Smacking of lips....	5	A similar sound	4 ⎫
		Whispering	1 ⎭

Further tests tend to show conclusively that there is
actual reproduction of vibration frequency. The bird was
not able to reproduce a given succession of notes (not in
his repertoire) given by the experimenter.

Summary.—It will be seen from the above summary
of the work on imitation that the results are not harmonious. Indeed, in some cases two authors working upon the
same species have arrived at exactly opposite conclusions.
On the whole, however, enough positive results have been
obtained to show that in some way the process of learning
is modified when certain forms of tuition are used. If
further work were conducted along lines which are not anthropomorphic—if the experimenters would confine their

work to determining just what the animals do without being concerned about the fact that they may be acting as human beings would under similar circumstances—the control of behavior by such methods in both human and animal work would more speedily be realized.

BIBLIOGRAPHY

ALLEN, JESSIE, "The Associative Processes of the Guinea Pig," *Jour. Comp. Neu. and Psych.*, 1904, XIV, 293.

BERRY, C. S., "An Experimental Study of Imitation in Cats," *Jour. Comp. Neu. and Psych.*, 1908, XVIII, 1.

————— "Imitative Tendency of White Rats," *ibid.*, 1906, XVI, 333.

COLE, L. W., "Concerning the Intelligence of Raccoons," *Jour. Comp. Neu. and Psych.*, 1907, XVII, 211.

DAVIS, H. B., "The Raccoon: A Study in Animal Intelligence," *Am. Jour. Psych.*, 1907, XVIII, 447.

HAGGERTY, M. E., "Imitation in Monkeys," *Jour. Comp. Neu. and Psych.*, 1909, XIX, 337.

HOBHOUSE, L. T., *Mind in Evolution.* New York, Macmillan, 1901.

HUNTER, W. S., "A Note on the Behavior of the White Rat," *Jour. Animal Beh.*, 1912, II, 137.

KINNAMAN, A. J., "Mental Life of Two *Macacus rhesus* Monkeys in Captivity," *Am. Jour. Psych.*, 1902, XIII, 98, 173.

LASHLEY, K. S., "Reproduction of Inarticulate Sounds in the Parrot," *Jour. Animal Beh.*, 1913, III, 361.

MORGAN, C. L., *Animal Behavior.* London, E. Arnold, 1900.

PORTER, J. P., "Intelligence and Imitation in Birds; a Criterion of Imitation," *Am. Jour. Psych.*, 1910, XXI, 1.

RICHARDSON, FLORENCE, "A Study of Sensory Control in the White Rat," *Psychological Monograph*, Ser. No. 48.

SHEPHERD, W. T., "Imitation in Raccoons," *Am. Jour. Psych.*, 1910, XXII, 583.

————— "Some Mental Processes of the Rhesus Monkey," *Psychological Monograph*, Ser. No. 52.

THORNDIKE, E. L., *Animal Intelligence.* New York, Macmillan, 1911.

WARREN, E. R., "Delayed Imitation in a Cat," *Jour. Animal Beh.*, 1912, II, 222.

WATSON, J. B., "Imitation in Monkeys," *Psych. Bull.*, 1908, V, 165.

WITMER, LIGHTNER, "A Monkey with a Mind," *Psych. Clinic*, 1909, III, 179.

YERKES, R. M., *The Dancing Mouse.* New York, Macmillan, 1907.

CHAPTER IX

THE LIMITS OF TRAINING IN ANIMALS

Introduction.—From time to time there loom above the level of the behaviorist's horizon reports of individual animals or groups of animals that affirm that at last a prodigy has been found which possesses something special in the way of a behavior equipment. Such animals have never been discovered in the laboratories devoted to the study of animal behavior. That the highly gifted animal should not thus appear in the laboratories is understandable when one considers that investigations have heretofore been rather narrowly concerned with the instincts and the sensory and motor habits which appear in a laboratory environment. The gifted animal has usually been developed by the amateur. Through the animal's contact with its owner and with other animals there arise highly complex modes of response. The training methods are not controlled and no scientific attempts are made to analyze the exact nature of the stimulus to which the animal responds. From an anthropomorphic standpoint the animal apparently is reacting as a human being would act under the same circumstances. In a short time the doings of the animal get noised abroad and it becomes necessary for some trained investigator to step in and reduce the chaos to some semblance of order (interpretation of acts where there is ignorance of training methods is not an easy task). Within recent years several animals have appeared which have caused a certain amount of consternation among investigators who have gone to examine into the phenomena. The situation is exceedingly like that which appears in the investigation of so-called occult phenomena.[1]   Some new medium arises.   Some prominent man visits the medium and becomes mystified.   A scientific man, usually a physicist, is selected to investigate her.   The physicist reports an elaborate series of tests which shows that the medium is not using concealed wires, magnets, mirrors, or other physical equipment.   The physicist himself may become " convinced."   The mystery grows.   Finally the psychologist makes the test and finds some simple trick which will account for the phenomenon.   The number of such alleged occult phenomena from telepathy to spiritualistic converse, which have been investigated and found wanting in scientific or philosophical interest, has been so numerous that now it is very difficult to get a psychologist who values his reputation to undertake such an investigation. In the same way, when a wonderful animal appears, zoölogists, botanists, and physiologists are hastened to the scene.   A commission is appointed and the mystery deepens.   Usually when some man who is familiar with the methods of training animals and with animals' methods of responding is found, the explanation, while not necessarily simple, smacks not at all of the mysterious.   This situation in the past, with regard to the animal world, has not been wholly without beneficial effect.   In the first place, it has brought the behaviorist face to face with the fact that there may be depths in the animal to which he has not descended and cannot descend except by adopting a part, at least, of the technique of the amateur, viz., that of living a large part of his time with the animal and complicating the methods of training (as is done for the child). That this meritorious effect has been produced is shown by the fact that there are investigators in behavior who are willing to devote a large number of years to the study of a single animal or at most a small group of such animals.   The German station on the Canary Isles is a case

---

[1] Attention is called to President Sanford's " Discussion of Animal Prodigies," *Amer. Jour. Psych.*, 1914, p. 1.

in point. Along with certain biological investigations will go detailed studies on the behavior of the anthropoid apes. It is certain that this tendency to specialize on one or at most a few animals will become more common. Since the higher anthropoids are nearest to man in their equipment and since their tenure of life is long under natural conditions it is to be expected that students will undertake work upon them with greater willingness than upon lower forms. To do such work effectively there is great need of an anthropoid ape station open to American students. The second generally good effect the study of the gifted animals has had upon the behavior work comes from the fact that in making an analysis it is often necessary to undertake a study of the sensitivity of their receptors, field of vision, limen of sensitivity for moving objects, etc.

Some gifted animals.—On account of its bearing upon the limits to which training in animals may be carried, we wish to examine into the behavior of some of the better known gifted animals. We shall discuss in order (1) the horse, Clever Hans, (2) the horses of Elberfeld, (3) the chimpanzee Peter, (4) the talking dog Don, and (5) the dog Jasper. In considering their behavior it seems well to bear in mind that *all behavior, human and animal, is analyzable in terms of stimulus and response,* and that the only difference between man and animal upon this assumption would be in the complexity of behavior. The fundamental difference between man and animal from our point of view lies in the fact that the human being can form habits in the throat (and other bodily language habits),—neglecting his finer sensory-motor equipment. All other habits pale into insignificance when contrasted with these. While this at present is affirmed on the basis purely of theory, we feel that the assumption has a good many points in its favor (p. 322).

Clever Hans.—In 1890 Mr. von Osten, a gentleman of Berlin with some mathematical training, noticed what he considered remarkable behavior in a horse which he then possessed. When that horse died he purchased another (1900) and began training him about a year later. This horse, Hans II, was destined to arouse an enormous amount of interest both in popular and in scientific circles.

Mr. von Osten's method of instructing the animal was very simple. He began by teaching the horse to respond properly to the different words for spatial localization, such as left. right, above, below, etc. Simple arithmetical problems were next attempted. He would place one, two, three, etc., objects upon a table, kneel down and take the fore-foot of the animal and make him tap once for each object. In a remarkably short time Hans learned to "count" and to perform simple additions and multiplications. But these attainments did not satisfy von Osten. He desired to give Hans a wider medium for the expression of his talents. Accordingly von Osten arranged for him a conventional alphabet. Having mastered this the horse was able to read and to answer simple questions. At the height of his career Hans showed the following scientific accomplishments (summarized from Pfungst): he had mastered the cardinal numbers from 1 to 100 and the ordinals to 10. Upon request he would count objects of all sorts, the persons present, even to distinctions of sex; then hats, umbrellas, and eyeglasses. All forms of simple arithmetical problems involving addition, subtraction, multiplication, and division. He could do fractions, changing them first into decimals. E.g., "How much is $\frac{2}{5} + \frac{1}{2}$?" Answer, $\frac{9}{10}$ (tapping first the numerator and then the denominator). Or again: "I have a number in mind. I subtract 9 and have 3 as a remainder. What is the number?" (12). "What are the factors of 28?" Whereupon Hans taps consecutively 2, 4, 7, 14, 28. He was able to read German readily, whether written or printed. If a series of placards with written words was placed before the horse he would step up and point with his nose to any of the words required of him. With his alphabet he would answer simple questions, e.g.: "What is the woman holding in her hand?" Hans spelled without hesitation "Schirm" (parasol). Furthermore, his memory was excellent. He carried the entire yearly calendar in his head. He could give not only the date of each day without having been previously taught, but also the date of any day one might mention. He could tell the time to the minute. His musical ability was especially well developed. He had absolute pitch memory and a feeling for intervals. He could analyze compound clangs without difficulty, and could inform his experimenters as to what changes should be made in a discordant clang in order to produce consonance.

Naturally Hans' fame spread and different people visited him. These at first were connoisseurs of horses, officers, who—astonished—told about Hans' accomplishments. Soon the public at large became interested and von Osten's court-yard became too small to accommodate the curious. The newspapers discussed it as the "Case of Hans." Violent polemics followed between those who believed in the animal's intelligence and those who suspected some trick. These latter did not agree among themselves,—some talked of optical signals, others of acoustical signals, which von Osten gave his horse. Others supposed that electrical wires placed under the pavement of the court allowed the master to communicate secretly with his pupil. Still others laid it to telepathy; the N rays (a fad of the moment) and to " suggestion."

A scientific commission was appointed, which delivered its report on the 12th of September, 1904. It was composed of Messrs. Stumpf and Nagel, professors of psychology and physiology respectively at the University of Berlin, of the director of the Zoölogical Garden, a director of the circus, veterinarians, and cavalry officers. The report denied the existence of any tricks used by von Osten, for the very good reason that the experiments had the same results even in his absence. For the rest, the conclusions of the commission were entirely negative. It was said merely what did *not* exist, but the answer to the puzzle was not revealed. The mystery deepened. Haeckel, who had assisted at one of the séances, declared for the authenticity of the mental activity of the horse. A second commission was formed, composed of Stumpf and his students. This time one point was seemingly established. Hans could not read, calculate, or count unless some one present knew the answers. Pfungst established this, indeed, beyond even a doubt by putting a series of questions to the horse, the answers to which were not known to the questioner. A card containing a certain number was picked at random by the experimenter and exhibited to the horse in such a way that no one could see it (the answer being unknown to the experimenter himself). When tested in this way, procedure without knowledge, the horse returned only 8% of correct responses, whereas he responded with an accuracy of 98% in those cases where the questioner knew the answers. Exactly the same state of affairs was found to exist with respect to arithmetical calculations and to reading. It will be recalled that reading was accomplished by first tapping out the number indicating the horizontal row in which the first letter appeared and next the place in the row. This complicated procedure had to be repeated for each letter in the word. It was found that when the questioner was ignorant as to the letter and row, Hans never responded correctly. Calculation was tested similarly. It was found that if von Osten whispered a number in the horse's ear so that no one present could hear, and then the questioner similarly gave the horse a number and told it to add the two, the answer was wrong 28 times out of 31, whereas in a procedure with knowledge the relation was 29 right and 2 wrong. Hans could not even count on the abacus when the questioner remained in ignorance of the number of balls which were pushed aside. The memory tests and tests on musical ability (all questions of this kind being answered by tapping) all failed to yield correct responses in a procedure without knowledge. Taking all such tests into consideration showed that where the questioner knew the answer 90-100% of the responses were correct. When the experimenter was ignorant of the answer, only 10% at most of the answers were correct. These tests tell us little as to how the experimenter's knowledge aided the horse in giving correct responses. Carrying the analysis one step farther, Pfungst found that vision was necessary for correct response. When the horse was perfectly blinded almost no correct responses could be obtained (only 6% were correct). The final link in unraveling the '' mystery '' came when Pfungst discovered the signs by means of which the horse responded. These signals were the minimal movements of the questioner's head. '' As soon as the experimenter had given a problem to the horse, he involuntarily bent his head and trunk slightly forward and the horse would then put his right foot forward and begin to tap, without, however, returning it to its original position. As soon as the desired number of taps were given, the questioner would make a slight upward jerk of his head. Thereupon the horse would immediately swing his foot in a wide circle, bringing it back to the original position. (This movement which, in the following exposition we shall designate as '' the back step,'' was never included in the count.) Now after Hans had ceased tapping the questioner would raise his head and trunk to their normal position. This second, far coarser movement, was not the signal for the back step, but always followed it. But whenever this second movement was omitted, Hans, who had already brought back his foot to the original position and had thereby put it out of commission, as it were, would give one more tap with his left foot." These minimal movements turned out to be exceedingly small (1/5 mm. and upward). If this analysis of Pfungst's is correct the responses of Hans are exactly similar to those with which we have long been familiar in the laboratory.

The horses of Elberfeld.—Not every one accepted Pfungst's conclusions, yet interest in von Osten and in Hans rapidly abated. Von Osten died in 1909. Hans was entirely forgotten until Karl Krall's book appeared which raised the question of the completeness of Pfungst's explanation. Mr. Krall, a wealthy and highly respected merchant of Elberfeld, having known von Osten and having worked with him during his last years, inherited Hans. He states that Hans works well under circumstances where it is impossible for him to see his master or to distinguish the minimal movements of the questioner. E.g., Krall affirms that Hans replies correctly in complete darkness, or with blinders on that permit him to see only the blackboard or the objects about which he is questioned. Krall determined to render justice to his old friend by proving the truth of von Osten's contentions. He bought two stallions,—Muhamed and Zarif,—and began to train them.

According to Krall their progress was, as in the case of Hans, astonishingly fast. Moreover, the two horses displayed different aptitudes. Muhamed was much quicker at arithmetic. Instruction began with this subject with an hour and a half to two hours of "study" a day for each animal. At the end of three days they could recognize the first numbers, 1, 2, 3 written upon the board, and would touch with the muzzle the one called for. At the end of ten days Muhamed could count up to 4. Several days later the tens were explained to them and they were taught to designate them with the left foot, the right being used for the units. On the 14th of November, 1908 (the horses were purchased on November 1st, the first lesson beginning on the 2nd), Muhamed performed correctly such small additions as $1 + 3$, $2 + 5$, etc., and also subtractions such as $9 - 3$.   He passed to multiplication and division on November 18th, to fractions and the addition of fractions on the 21st.   In December he was taught French and replied equally well to questions asked in French or in German.   In the following May Muhamed could extract square roots and cube roots, and could do sums like the following:

$$\frac{(3 \times 4) + \sqrt{36}}{3} \qquad\qquad \frac{\sqrt{36} \times \sqrt{64}}{\sqrt{4}}$$

In February, 1909, spelling lessons commenced.   Spelling was made possible by means of a conventional alphabet (where each letter or diphthong is represented by a number between 11 and 66, e.g., 11 would represent e, 22, h, etc.) as follows:

	1	2	3	etc.
10	e	n	r	
20	i	h	l	
30	a	d	g	

etc.

The horse spells by tapping with his foot (the tens are tapped with the left foot, while the units are tapped with the right foot) the number corresponding to the desired letter.   By this method Zarif, at the end of four months, could spell, in his own fashion, words spoken to him which he had never seen written.   Below are presented some of the different spelling of " Pferd " as spelled by Muhamed and Zarif:

Muhamed: bfert, bfrt, färd, färt, fert, frt, fäart, faerd, faert, färb, fpferd, frrt, pärd, pfärt, ppverd, pfer, pferd, tfert, fed;

Zarif: bferd, färed, fferwt, fvert, pfrde, sdfert, pfert, bffet, fdaerp, etc.;

Zucker was spelled zkr, zukr, züqr, zuqr, czukr, sucr, szukr, zuäkr, cukr, zucher zuker, zucher, suqker, etc.; Muhamed spelled his name, mäemuaämt, muahmet, muamät, etc.; Zarif spelled his, tsarem, zarif, sfrai, zuarif, zuruf. Finally Mr. Krall, noticing that the horses tapped "out of lessons," took down their tappings to see if he could make anything out of them. Sure enough! While the discourse was at times as incomprehensible as the first babblings of an infant, nevertheless there were fragments which could be understood. One day Krall told Muhamed that he was going to give him carrots: "fünuf" (i.e., fünf, 5) replied Muhamed spontaneously. At another time he replied: "iohn, hfr, gbn" (iohann hafer geben, John gives oats). Soon he detected genuine conversation between the two pupils. One morning when Zarif had shown himself lazy his companion was asked: "Warum war Zarif nicht lieb?" And Muhamed answered: "weil vaul isd" (because he is lazy). "And why is he lazy?" "Weil r sagt begin wiil nijd wisn" (because he said at the beginning that he didn't want to know anything).

Notwithstanding the lesson taught by Hans, Krall's exaggerated report was received favorably by many distinguished men. Haeckel wrote to Krall: "Your careful and critical experiments show in a convincing fashion the existence of reason in the animal, which I have never doubted." On the other hand, Ettlinger attacked Krall's experiments with a great deal of vigor. Professor Dexler, in a strongly worded article, declares that "Krall's book is a vile blot on our contemporary literature. Born in the poisoned atmosphere of humbug and of trickery, it is a monument raised to the cult of the beast." Argumentation, however, is not the method to settle behavior questions. Many tests have been made upon the horses but none by thoroughly trained investigators of behavior. The two reports by Claparède are probably the most reliable we have at present. The first was made in August, 1912; the second in April, 1913. The first set of tests is not really scientific in character since Krall himself acted mainly as questioner, and since even when Claparède acted as questioner adequate controls were not introduced. Claparède's second set of tests were undertaken in a much more critical spirit.

CLAPARÈDE'S EXAMINATION: Results of the first set of observations: Zarif was first brought in. Krall showed us (summarized from Claparède's report) that his pupil understood French. He wrote on the board (phonetically without the subleties of orthography) fät sero, (the horse made the sign of negation with his head, which signified zero in his language), then, Komptä dis (the horse tapped once with his left foot, correct answer). Having written 34 he asked the horse to read the number both ways (reply 34, then 43, right), then to multiply the two figures (3 x 4) (reply correct), and then to square the larger of the two figures. That time Zarif made an error and replied 15 instead of 16. When asked to correct it he replied 15, then tapped 24. Zwei und zwanzig was written on the board. The horse failed twice to read this number. Then Krall wrote "adire zu elf" (add it to 11). He replied 33. The horse was rewarded for this answer. "Adire zu ein und dreizig" (reply correct). "Zu vängt troa" (phonetic for 23). This time the answer was 44 instead of 45. When told to correct it Zarif gave 54 (which is the reverse of 45) and on a third trial gave 45. Krall wrote on the board "dus" (12). The horse read 22. "Add 12 and 2." Reply 24, then 14. Krall wrote on the board $\sqrt{25} \times \sqrt{49} =$. The horse replied 24. Krall said it was wrong. He repeated 24. Zarif showed signs of embarrassment (at least as interpreted by Krall); he dropped his head like a shamed school boy. Krall told him that several people were present, one of them a professor who was taking notes and putting down all the wrong answers. Then the horse began tapping of his own accord. Krall put down on the board the numbers he tapped: 14, 26, 23, 54, 13, 13, 32. Translated the corresponding word is *schlprrd*. What did it mean? Krall said he could not make it out. We quote Claparède: "But it was not hard for me to discover between these letters and the letters of my name a striking analogy. Krall said it was impossible that Zarif had attempted to spell my name for he did not even know it, but in the afternoon he told me that he remembered having mentioned my name before Zarif while talking to a third person. Was it my name which he voluntarily spelled, wishing to convey the information that he knows that it is I who is taking notes? Cruel enigma!" In order to end this séance which had lasted twenty minutes, Zarif was recalled to his problem (the multiplication of square roots): he gave the correct answer, 35. Then Hänschen was brought in. He resembled an ass, but only externally! Indeed with astonishing quickness, considering the fact that he had been a pupil only a few months, he did a dozen correct additions of numbers of two figures written in a column on a little blackboard before him in an inclined position, for he was too little to use the board fastened on the wall. For the sum of $23 + 12 + 20$ he answered first 65, then 45, then 55, which is correct. Strange to say he corrected himself. He hardly finished one sum before he started another. The problem $2 \times 32 + 12$ brought out a number of wrong answers. The order "zweimal drei und dreizig" (2 times 33) brought first 86, then 66. During Hänschen's exercises, which lasted twenty minutes, Krall stood completely behind the animal. He did not leave his position except to write the problems on the board, which was done in such a manner that no one near by could see it. The groom remained perfectly motionless the entire time. C. was beside him and watched him closely. He did not detect the least sign which could be suspected of being given in correlation with Hänschen's replies, who had his head lowered, with muzzle almost on the board.

At last Muhamed was brought in. He is the genius of the group. He is much more lively, much wider awake than Zarif. Krall wrote upon the board $\sqrt{36} \times \sqrt{49} =$. Muhamed first answered 52, then, when told that that was wrong, 42, which is correct. Krall then substituted the $+$ sign for the $\times$ sign in the problem. The answer was correct, 13. Krall then gave him the following problem:

$$(\sqrt{1296} - \sqrt{81}) \times (\sqrt{144} - \sqrt{49})$$

and went out of the room. Muhamed looked at the problem and immediately answered 115, which is wrong. (The hundreds are tapped with the right foot, but are given after the tens, which are tapped with the left foot. This distinguishes them from the units, which are also tapped with the right foot, but which precede the tens.) Krall then called to him from without to try it again. He tapped 25, then 125 (which is still wrong, the correct answer being 135). When an answer is wrong Krall prefers not to insist on it, and changes the problem, only to return to the original problem in a moment. Claparède was then asked to choose from a large list of squared numbers a number for Muhamed to extract the square root. He chose at random 64516, the root of which is 254, but Muhamed persisted in tapping numbers of only two figures, which made us think that he wanted to say something by means of the conventional alphabet, which contains only numbers of two figures. So these tappings were noted with the following results: *rihgvgdhaig.* It was incomprehensible. He was asked to repeat it. The second attempt was: *rmigdjg.* This was no clearer. But the similarity between the two series of letters was too striking to be entirely haphazard. But Krall could not unravel it. Muhamed was then asked how many syllables were in the word he wished to spell. He answered three. "Is the word finished?" "No," he replied. "Unfortunately we could get nothing more out of him." Krall then went back to the two problems which he had not solved and which were still written upon the board, and this time, with no difficulty, Muhamed replied 135 to the one and 254 to the other, which are correct. As a reward he was given three carrots: "How many carrots have you eaten?" he was asked. "Three," he replied. To the card $\sqrt{117649} =$ Muhamed answered 4, then 13, then 346, then 347, then 343, which is right. To the card $\sqrt{383161} =$ he answered 58, 317, then, after two "bavures," 619 (right). By "bavures" are meant incomplete wrong answers given by the horse,—incomplete because Krall, seeing that the number of units is wrong, interrupts the horse without letting him go on to the tens and hundreds. Upon this last correct answer, the exhibition ended.

The remaining séances were equally productive of startling results. It is unnecessary to present them in detail. From such a set of tests absolutely nothing can be concluded, and yet Claparède, being much under the influence of his emotions, devotes many pages to speculations concerning the analysis of his observations. The results of the tests made in April of the next year show that Claparède's attitude has become scientific and critical. We give them in some detail.

LATER TESTS BY CLAPARÈDE: On the 26th, 27th, and 28th of March, 1913, Claparède paid another visit to the horses, accompanied by Dr. J. de Modzelewski and Dr. Weber-Bauler, both of Geneva. Mr. Krall was not at Elberfeld during the first series of tests. We give below a rather careful summary of the tests on the various horses:

TESTS ON MORNING OF THE 26TH OF MARCH.—HÄNSCHEN: During the tests on this horse Claparède, with the two gentlemen named above were present. The horse was led in by the groom, Albert, who remained in the room. The pony was shown two cards designating the number 53. He responded correctly. The digits were next transposed, making the number 35. The response was correct. Every one then left the room exept Claparède. Having shuffled a series of cards on which numbers were printed he drew out one at random and placed it under the eyes of the horse without glancing at it himself (procedure " without knowledge "). The horse tapped 42, which was wrong, the correct answer being 45. Twice more this type of test was repeated. The horse tapped 73 for 25; 53 for 84. We have here three wrong answers when the observer tested by the procedure " without knowledge." For the sake of comparison he repeated the test, first glancing at the cards (procedure " with knowledge "). The results were no better: 52 was given for 33. When asked to repeat it he gave 31. The experimenter wrote down 63; the response was 16. He then wrote 43 on the board: the answers were in order, 42, 52, 53, 64. Calculation was next tried: 34 + 25 was written on the board: the replies in order were, 22, 42, 73, 66. The horse was next tested with 24 + 12: responses in order were 37, 46, 36, the latter being correct. At this moment the assistant came back. He wrote on the board 34 + 25. The horse returned 73. After this there followed a long series of tests the answers to which were mainly wrong, although now and then a correct one would be given. Under such conditions it seemed useless to give tests where the experimenter was in ignorance of the answers. The horse having tired, he was removed.

BERTO: The blind stallion Berto was next tested. The animal had double congenital cataract. The horse had learned speedily by the contact method of training employed with blind human beings. It must be remembered that the type of response called for here is much simpler than that demanded by the other horses, at least so far as the " reading " of numbers presented through contact is concerned. At the end of five lessons, the animal, according to his trainers, could add simple numbers, such as 5 + 1 and 5 + 2. When the horse was brought in Claparède verified the state of the animal's vision. The horse was completely blind. (" Il ne peut y avoir aucun doute à cet égard: l'animal n'apercoit pas une carrotte que l'on place sous y eux." It is hoped that Claparède does not mean seriously to affirm that such a test is really crucial. The testing of complete blindness in an animal is very difficult. It is doubtful if any physician can determine this surely except in cases where complete degeneration of the retina is revealed by skioscopic methods.)   Berto was quite restless and in order to soothe him the groom held the halter. The groom retired during the reply of the horse. In certain tests the groom was not allowed to hold the halter even while the question was asked. The groom first asked the horse to tap out the following numbers: 2, 14, 42, 33, 40, 2, and to add 2 and 3 and to multiply 5×3. Only a part of the answers to these questions was right (see appended table). The horse was able to give a number traced upon his rump. In view of the blindness of the horse, procedure " without knowledge " could not easily be undertaken.

MUHAMED: The horse Muhamed was given (by cards) the number 35. The reply was incoherent. Several of them finished with the digit 5, e.g., 15, 25, etc. For 67 he returned 37, then correctly 67: for 48 a series of wrong responses with none correct. An exercise in spelling was next attempted with complete failure. There was incoherence all along the line. Under such conditions it was useless to attempt to make tests under rigorous conditions.

AFTERNOON OF MARCH 26TH:—Simple exercises with numbers were continued but the results were deplorable. Zarif read very nicely the first number Claparède gave him, but after that one correct response nothing further could be obtained in the way of correct responses. Two incidental observations were made on the general behavior of the horses during the period of response. When one insisted that his reply was wrong, once, contrary to his habit, he began to watch the groom while tapping, but the response was wrong all the same. On another occasion the horse, which ordinarily tapped with machine-like precision, hesitated with right foot poised in air before beginning the reply. Muhamed was hardly more brilliant than in the morning. There were several good responses which were interesting in view of the fact that only Claparède and his colleagues were present. The horse read correctly and on the first trial the numbers: 5, 42, 49. To the addition $3 + 4$ given on the card he replied 34. All then left the room except Claparède. Several numbers were then presented (procedure " without knowledge "): all responses were wrong. E.g., 46 was read 44; 43 was read 75; 7 was read 6. To $22 + 15$ the horse replied 37, which was correct. After that response no further correct ones could be obtained regardless of the method of procedure. Berto was then brought in. He gave a pretty series, Claparède doing the questioning. He responded correctly to 2×11 and to 3×11. When asked to substract 3 from 7 he tapped 10. Hänschen was next brought in. He did not give a single correct response.

AFTERNOON OF MARCH 27TH: At this session Krall, de Modzelewski, and Claparède were present. They examined successively Muhamed, Zarif, and Hänschen without getting any correct responses. Berto, the blind stallion, alone gave good replies. A recital of these would be without interest. The horses replied wrongly even to Krall.

MARCH 28TH, MORNING AND AFTERNOON: Claparède, de Weimar, and Krall were present. Several fruitless attempts were made to get correct responses. Krall advanced as a possible explanation of the poorness of the results the fact that the horses were shedding.[2]

Tables of results.—From de Modzelewski's note to Claparède's report, we copy the following table showing the number of correct and incorrect responses returned during the several tests:

TOTAL NUMBER OF RIGHT AND WRONG RESPONSES

March 20		Poor	Right but with help	Good
Hänschen,	A.M.	42	5	5
"	P.M.	47	6	2
Berto,	A.M.	23	5	2
"	P.M.	24	10	13
Muhamed,	A.M.	9	2	0
"	P.M.	46	6	4
Zarif,	P.M.	9	2	3
	Total	200	36	29

Of 265 questions, 29 were good, 11%.

RESPONSES TO THE MORE DIFFICULT PROBLEMS (OF THE ABOVE LIST)

	Poor	Right but with help	Good
Hänschen,	31	3	1
Berto,	5	2	6
Zarif,	1	1	1
Muhamed,	12	2	1
Total	49	8	9

Of 66 responses, 9 were good, 13%.

TOTAL NUMBER OF RIGHT AND WRONG RESPONSES

March 27	Poor	Right but with help	Good
Muhamed,	77	4	2
Zarif,	13	1	5
Berto,	26	8	9
Hänschen,	111	8	4
Total	227	21	20

Of 268 responses, 20 were good, 7½%.

RESPONSES TO THE MORE DIFFICULT PROBLEMS (OF THE ABOVE LIST)

	Poor	Right but with help	Good
Muhamed,	26	1	1
Zarif,	9	0	3
Berto,	33	4	1
Hänschen,	11	4	4
Total	79	9	9

Of 97 responses, 9 were good, $9\frac{1}{3}$%

[2] Yet another gentleman only a few days later obtained very successful results. Krall then stated that Claparède's failures were due to the fact that he had not gained the confidence of the horses.

As will be seen upon comparison with Pfungst's work on Hans, the percentage of correct responses in Krall's horses is about the same that he obtained by the procedure " without knowledge." How shall we account for the 8-11% of correct responses? Surely chance will account for a certain percentage. It would be impossible to train horses in this way for months to respond to cards and figures upon the board without two things appearing: (1) Training upon special numbers, cards (of square roots, etc.) establishes a set of special simple reactions. It is quite probable that many of the combinations (even those suggested by the outsider) are ones upon which the horse has been specially drilled. (2) If the horses really tap in groups (numbers?) spontaneously, by the theory of probabilities some of the " answers " must be right. What lend color to such a view are the statements of de Modzelewski to the effect (a) that the very simplest problems are answered with no greater percentage of accuracy than the more difficult ones; and (b) that no matter how simple or how difficult the problem is, the horses start mechanically upon the answer; and (c), finally, the horses do not even look at the letters and figures upon the board. Furthermore, it lies well within the bounds of probability that there are certain means of rapport between the horse and his questioner which may serve the horses of Elberfeld as " minimal movements " served Hans. We say this without prejudice and without any intention of intimating that fraudulent means are employed. This would account for the high percentage of accuracy which is sometimes obtained by Krall. (And since in many cases where positive results have been obtained in Krall's absence the grooms have not been excluded, a similar explanation is at hand to account for this fact.) On the whole, it seems not improbable that we are dealing here with responses which do not rise above the level of those given by Hans.

Peter.—The chimpanzee has always been a favorite subject of eulogy. Very few of the highly trained animals have come under observation where experimental conditions could be sufficiently controlled. Several experiments

upon imitation have already been noted on p. 282. Witmer
has given a report of some observations made upon Peter
in the *Psychological Clinic*. Peter's vaudeville performance, which we have several times witnessed, is most im-
pressive. He skates readily and with accuracy; drinks
from bottle or glass; lights and smokes a cigarette (sometimes after a good deal of "help" from the trainer);
eats with a fork; and can "ring for the waiter." Furthermore, he has varied motor accomplishments ranging from
the riding of a bicycle to the threading of a needle, and
from locking and unlocking locks to tying and untying
knots in a string.

When Peter entered the clinic Witmer's secretary bent down and
he shook hands with her and then kissed the back of her hand. He
then began to skate around the room in a lively manner and next
examined a camera, attempting to turn the screws and actually
manipulating the shutter. The trainer gave him a cork-tipped
cigarette and offered him a box of matches. The cigarette was put
into the mouth with the cork end first. He next took a match from
the box held out to him and struck it on the side of the box. A
different kind was offered him wrong end first. He at once reversed
it and put the right end (tube) in his mouth. Peter was able to
string beads. An incomplete string of beads was held out to him
and then a bead was taken from a box and strung before his eyes.
This was twice repeated. Then the box and beads were handed to
the monkey. He promptly put a bead into his mouth, feeling it
with his lips and tongue. He then took it from his mouth and
strung it. One bead after another was taken from the box and
strung; each was tested with the lips in order to get the hole in
the middle in the proper position for stringing. When tested on the
pegging board, after being shown how to put the pegs in, he put
them in irregularly. The impulse to pull the pegs out was strong but
was inhibited upon a word from the trainer. The pegs were given to
him one by one. When tested on the lock which he used in his
vaudeville performances he locked and unlocked it mechanically. A
small padlock with a staple attachment was then given him. The
staple had to be pulled entirely off the lock at the end opposite the
hole. The key was a small one, difficult to insert and difficult to turn
after it had been inserted. It was unlocked for him and the staple
attachment taken out. The staple was put back and locked with
key withdrawn. Peter reached for the lock, inserted the key, and
unlocked it more rapidly than the experimenter. When told to put
the staple back and unlock it, he inserted only one prong of the
staple. He was told that it was wrong and had his ears boxed by his
trainer. The lock was taken from him, the staple slowly pulled out
and moved several inches away, then reinserted. This was repeated
several times. When tried, he seized the lock, slowly and carefully
pulled out the staple, then carefully reinserted it and shoved it

home with a smack of his hand. A small box with a tiny keyhole was next given him. The key was on a ring with a large number of other different sized keys. It was the smallest one on the ring. When handed the ring, he tried first the largest key, then the next largest, and then the third largest, etc. The box was then opened for him and lumps of sugar shown on the inside. The small key was pointed out to him. The box was locked and the bunch of keys shaken up and again handed to him. He was unable to pick out the smallest key. It was picked out and handed to him. He then opened the box with the key and obtained a lump of sugar. He failed again on the second trial. A double-headed hammer and a piece of board on which were some nails and screws were then given to Peter. When the hammer was handed to him he proceeded to drive several nails into the board with the proper head of the hammer. He never mistook a screw for a nail. When given a screw instead of a nail, he stuck it into a hole in the board and at once selected a screwdriver, paying no attention whatever to the hammer lying on the table. The screw was long and wobbled as he turned it. He turned the screw always in the right direction. He used both hands on the handle instead of employing one hand to steady the screw. With the hammer and the nails, he steadied the nail between two fingers of his left hand and used the hammer with his right. Once he pounded his fingers and instantly put them in his mouth. When tested with the form board he showed total inability to place the blocks in their proper compartments. He seemed to be able to articulate the word "mama." Witmer states that he did this with great effort. His response to words was not tested scientifically enough to enable us to pass judgment upon his ability in this direction. When asked certain questions as: "Where is mama?" "Where is daddy?" "Where is Peter?" "I beg pardon!" "Give mama a kiss," "Give daddy a kiss," "Give mama a drink," and so on, he did the correct thing, seemingly in response to the words. No attempt was made by Witmer to substitute different words with the same intonation, etc., and no attempt was made to give the words from behind a screen, etc. (See tests on Don and on Jasper, below.)

The behavior of Peter, while described by Witmer in a grossly anthropomorphic manner, shows us at once that we are dealing with an organism which is far more complicated than any horse at Elberfeld. Witmer states that he ought to be compared rather with the child. Unfortunately neither the behavior of the chimpanzee nor that of the child has been subjected to sufficient analysis to make comparison feasible. At least two general statements may be made of the chimpanzee by way of showing similarity to and difference from man. In the first place his motor development seems capable of being extended to a point where in some instances he can actually compete with man, and in the second place his lack of language habits puts him forever below the plane of comparison with man.

DON: The analysis of the vocal efforts of Don, " the talking dog," has been undertaken by Pfungst. The analysis is of interest only by way of the light thrown upon the instinctive sounds which can be made by the dog. Don is a German setter about 8 years of age belonging to the royal game warden at Ebers in Gardelegen. His vocabulary is supposed to contain 8 words which may be called out when food is present and the following questions given: " Was heisst du? " " *Don.* " " Was hast du? " " *Hunger.* " " Was willst du? " " *Haben haben.* " " Was ist das? " " *Kuchen.* " " Was bittest du dir aus? " " *Ruhe.* " Don was supposed further to answer questions by *Ja* and *Nein* and to speak the word *Haberland.* On examination it was found that the vocabulary is given always in order beginning with *Don* and ending with *Ruhe.* If the order is varied we find him calling himself *Kuchen* and stating that he desires *Hunger!* The first vocal effort sounding like a word was supposed to have been *haben.* This attracted the attention of the owner and thereupon began a series of lessons in which Don was fed for correct response. Ten repetitions some weeks apart sufficed for completing this response. The word *Ruhe* was supposed to have been uttered first on command of the owner's daughter. It was " fixed " in the same way. It will be seen immediately that there is nothing in the behavior of Don which is different, from the standpoint of interpretation, from what we find in the parrot. Furthermore, close analysis of even the words he speaks shows that they are not true words in the mechanical sense—not all the vowel and consonant sounds being included. Indeed, even the number of syllables is not always constant. The dog makes only one vowel sound lying between *o* and *u.* His one guttural aspirant is like the German *ch* and does duty both for *k* and *h.* There is also a nasal sound lying between *n* and *ng.* When not prolonged it will pass for *d* as in Don. He does not really make the sounds *b, d, k, l,* or *r.* What he really sounds is [(*ch*) *unguo*] in the word which passes for *Hunger.*[3]

JASPER: The bull terrier owned by Mr. Dixie Taylor is in many ways a remarkable animal, but not nearly so remarkable as his owner believes him to be. Jasper has been several times under the observation of the author. There are many things in his performance which are deserving of a more careful study than we have been able to give him. Jasper's claims to consideration come from his extraordinary ability to do certain acts in response to words. Mr. Taylor thinks the dog can respond properly to several hundred words, including those indicating direction; e.g., up, down, right, left. We have not been able to agree with Mr. Taylor respecting the dog's ability to go in a given direction. In one case in a three-story house we took Jasper to the stair-landing on the second floor. Mr. Taylor remained on the first floor, completely hidden. The author was alone with the dog. The owner then said to the dog, " Go up the stairs, Jasper." Once

---

[3] Those of us who have seen Don's performance in this country will surely agree with the above analysis of Pfungst.

he went to the window and looked out (another act he is supposed to do on command), once he tried to go below, but the third time he found the stairs and started up them. Not many tests were made on this point since there were several others which we desired to bring out. The most significant act brought out on command was the following: Jasper was told to " go into the room and turn over the waste-paper basket "; or to " go into the room and bring the waste-paper basket." When the tests were made in the Hopkins Laboratory Mr. Taylor had first gone into the room and touched the articles. We repeated the experiments upon another occasion in which Mr. Taylor had never even seen the articles. The commands were given by the owner from such a position that the dog could not see him. On command the dog would go into the other room and mount the table and look out of the window, or he would close the door. On command, " Go to the next room and bring me a paper lying on the floor," the dog would go and execute the command. Many common objects which are left lying on the floor will be brought in on command. When the situation is complicated by laying several objects in a row near together, e.g., a handkerchief and a one-dollar bill, the dog does not always bring the object designated by the word. Not enough tests have been made to give the percentage of correct responses when two objects are used, nor to tell the decrease in accuracy when three or more objects are placed side by side. Two other tests were made in the open. After reaching the street Mr. Taylor said to Jasper, " Go behind me and put your feet on the bicycle." The bicycle was about 50 feet behind Mr. Taylor. The dog trotted immediately to it and did as he was told. The command to go down the street and put his feet on an automobile (about 100 yards distant) was executed with equal readiness. Many other tests of this character were made, but they were so poorly controlled that no very accurate conclusion can be drawn. For the past 18 months Miss Elizabeth Gilman has been training a cocker spaniel of pure breed (registered) along these same lines. The dog (now about 20 months of age) was purchased a few weeks after birth by the laboratory for this special purpose. He is living in the home of Miss Gilman and is a great pet. So far, although trained every day upon the execution of simple commands, little success has attended Miss Gilman's efforts. This fact has increased our respect for Jasper's accomplishments regardless of the possibility that subsequent analysis may show that his repertoire of responses to spoken command is much more limited than we now believe it to be.[4]

Summary.—Unsatisfactory as this chapter is from the standpoint of the strictly factual material it presents,

[4] Recently the Airedale terrier Rolf, owned by the Moekel family of Mannheim, has come into prominence. This dog is supposed to possess the same mathematical ability and conversational powers as the horses of Krall. No thorough scientific tests have been made upon him. William Mackenzie (" Le Problème du Chien Pensant de Mannheim," *Archives de Psychologie*, 1913, XIII, 312) has given a popular presentation of this dog's accomplishments. Claparède (" À Propos du Chien de Mannheim," J. Larguier des Bancels et Éd. Claparède, *Archives de Psychologie*, 1913, XIII, 377) has made a few observations upon Rolf. It seems worth while to mention that Krall " discovered " the dog of Mannheim.

nevertheless it serves to show that the behavior laboratories must be prepared to admit that the sympathetic upbringing of animals in the home where they are thrown into constant contact with human beings does produce in them a certain complex type of behavior for which the laboratory concepts, as they now exist, are inadequate to supply explanation. It is quite obvious that the behaviorist has no right to be content until the newly born chimpanzee and the newly born child are brought up side by side and subjected to the same training. At definite intervals stock should be taken and the lines of divergence and of parallel growth be determined. Such studies can be adequately conducted only in a station where the chimpanzee can be bred.

BIBLIOGRAPHY

CLAPARÈDE, ED., " Les Chevaux savants d'Elberfeld," *Archives d. Psychologie*, 1912, XII, 261.
——————— " Encore les Chevaux d'Elberfeld," *ibid.*, 1913, XIII, 244.
DEXLER, H., " Über den dermaligen Stand des Krallismus." Prag, *Lotus*, 1914, 62.
ETTINGER, MAX, " Der Streit um rechnenden Pferde." München, *Natur und Kultur*, 1913.
JOHNSON, H. M., " The Talking Dog," *Science*, N.S., 1912, XXXV, 749. (Abstract of Pfungst's Study.)
KRALL, KARL, *Denkende Tiere, Beiträge zur Tierseelenkunde auf Grund eigener Versuche*. Leipzig, Engelmann, 1912.
MENEGAUX, A., " L'Éducation des Chevaux pensants d'Elberfeld," *Bull. de l'Inst. Gén. Psych.*, 1913, XIII, 111.
PFUNGST, O., *Clever Hans, the Horse of Mr. Von Osten*. New York, Holt, 1911. (Translation by Karl Rahn.)
SANFORD, E. C., " Psychic Research in the Animal Field: der Kluge Hans and the Elberfeld Horses," *Am. Jour. Psych.*, 1914, XXV, 1.
WATSON, JOHN B., " The Need of an Experimental Station for the Study of Certain Problems in Animal Behavior," *Psych. Bull.*, 1906, III, 149.
WITMER, LIGHTNER, " A Monkey with a Mind," *Psych. Clinic*, 1909, III, 179.

CHAPTER X

MAN AND BEAST

Introduction.—We have now considered several forms of habit, from the simple ones we find in the rat to the more complex ones we find in the chimpanzee. We saw that in the former we could, with a measure of success, reduce habit to the functioning of a relatively simple set of arcs. In the complex coördinations of the higher animals we found analysis difficult, yet even in the most complicated cases we saw no reason to lose faith in our methods. It is probable that a more careful study of such acts will enable us ultimately to reduce them to their lowest terms and to state the laws of their genesis and of their combination. Stated in other words, our science does not feel the need of changing its methods and principles in passing from simple forms of behavior to more complex ones. It is probably the search for a new principle of explanation that has created so much diversity of viewpoint in the study of behavior. Strange to say, it has been the biologists and not the psychologists who have introduced this confusion, although a great many of the psychologists have followed their lead. We find among biologists generally the tendency to treat simple reflexes and habits in a perfectly objective way, but suddenly when the reactions begin to get complex we find them introducing the concept of the psychic. It is introduced apparently as a *deus ex machina* to account for complexities in response. Even Loeb has not escaped the tendency.

Certainly his earlier work makes a wide distinction between tropism and associative memory. Throughout this work we have tried to be consistent. If tropism or reflex is the ultimate unit of analysis of behavior in the lower vertebrates, it serves the same purpose in the higher organisms, including man. No new principle is needed in passing from the unicellular organisms to man. As we pass from the responses of the simple organisms to the more complex ones of the higher animals we find (1) a greater number of units, and (2) more complex forms of combinations of these units. Jennings has stated that if the amœba were the size of an elephant, we should feel pretty much about the amœba as we do about the elephant. We doubt if he means to be taken literally in this matter. If we knew as much in proportion about the elephant as his studies have revealed about the amœba, the disparity in behavior would seem even greater than it does at present. Jennings' point, though, is well taken, and means that the amœba's responses are usually very complex when carefully scrutinized; probably fully as complex as the elephant's responses appear to be when not closely analyzed. (By this we do not mean to affirm that behavior becomes complex in proportion to the mass of the animal which displays it!)

Man and animal.—This leads to a consideration of the question of the dividing line between the behavior of man and that of brute. Hitherto we have not found any peculiarly subtle differences among the brutes themselves. We have found innumerable differences among the different phyla with respect to the presence or absence of certain types of action systems, in the range of sensitivity of receptors, the delicacy of the functioning of these receptors (amount of energy of stimulus necessary to arouse them to action), in the development, range, combinations, effectiveness, etc., of the muscular systems. Our studies on habit and instinct have brought out such points and continued study will make them increasingly apparent. It is evident that we find in the primates, at least in rudimentary form, all types of reactions that we find in man (with one exception, which we shall discuss later), such as complex forms of response to complex objects, imitation, use of tools, etc. (We say nothing of reasoning since we do not admit this as a genuine type of human behavior except as a special form of language habit.) Appeal to the nervous system yields us no better results. Man has neither the greatest absolute brain weight nor the greatest brain weight in relation to body length. While it is true that the complexity of the convolutions are greater, yet many animals have an encephalic surface which is respectably convoluted (especially the anthropoid apes). It is quite improbable that convolution of surface means anything *per se*. It is well within the bounds of possibility that had man appeared with a smooth brain three times as large as at present but having the same number of conductors and the same number of functional connections as at present, he would have shown the same superiority over his nearest competitor, the anthropoid ape, as he does now. Certainly the idea that convolutions mean anything specific in the way of differentiation would not arise under such circumstances. Neurologists have told us faithfully enough that convolutions are simply indicative of greater cortical surface, hence of an increased number of long and short reflex arcs. Furthermore, the development of the frontal lobe has often been used as another neurological instrument for sounding the superiority of man over animal. It is in this region that Wundt has assumed that the apperception centers reside. It must be admitted again that the increased development of the frontal lobes is a genuine fact, but that any special mechanism resides in it, i.e., in the so-called silent areas, is most improbable. While it is generally admitted that complex fiber tracts connect this area with the sensory projection centers, with motor centers (and more recently admitted) with the basal ganglia, this does not furnish any proof that it exerts anything special in the way of "control" over the projection centers, as is often assumed in theories of "attention." Since it was the last brain tissue put on in evolution, and is to be found chiefly in man, we have hastened to assign to its care all those functions in which man is thought chiefly to excel the brute. Its presence does unquestionably increase the number of neural elements and the number of synaptical connections. It is quite thinkable, though, that the same effect would have been produced if these increased connections had been placed in the parietal or occipital lobes or even in the basal ganglia. Of course to those who are wedded to the Darwinian theory and who believe that simply because we have the tissue it must have a life and death significance, this argument will not appeal. But as a matter of fact we have always been skeptical of this attempt to put " something not found elsewhere " in the frontal lobes. It is extremely questionable whether (aside from its purely motor function) it has anything like the significance of the silent areas in the parietal and occipital lobes. How, then, shall we account for the notion that man is something and has something which the brute is not and has not? The feeling that a cataclysmal difference exists has been strong through all the centuries, and is as firmly fixed in the popular mind today as ever. Among scientific men the conviction that the gap is not so wide as was formerly supposed is growing; yet we find scientifically-minded men still searching for the " missing link." [1] The feeling that a gap exists is shown all through the behavior work from studies on amœba to those on the anthropoid ape. This feeling has manifested itself in various ways: in the search for (1) imitation, (2) reasoning, and (3) imagery in animals. Since man was supposed to possess such functions and animals to be lacking in these respects, what more natural than to scrutinize closely the behavior of animals in order to discover them at least *in ovo* and thus to bridge the gap? We will discuss (2) and (3) on p. 333. (1) Imitation we have already

[1] E.g., Witmer states: " Speculation has at times arisen concerning the existence of a ' missing link ' between the higher apes and man. Such a ' missing link ' ought to present an anatomical form intermediate between the highest anthropoid ape and the lowest type of man. This *gap* (italics ours) has been partly filled by the discovery of the Neanderthal man and the ape-like remains found in Java."

treated at length on p. 277. If the analysis given there is correct, it is clear that the absence of any high degree of imitative capacity in the anthropoid ape should not be looked upon as any special form of break since apparently all that is amiss in the Simiæ is, on the one hand, too little complexity in their coördinations, and on the other hand, too great rigidity in habits once they are formed. The differences between man and ape in these respects are closely similar to the differences we find along the same lines between the ape and the squirrel.

In thus arguing against a fundamental difference between the behavior of man and brute it must not be supposed that we are trying to support the continuity theory of the Darwinians. We have just seen that we have had to admit characteristic differences in the receptors and action systems in different forms. Historically, however, the existence of the " break " has been urged most strongly in connection with those animals which have bodily structures essentially like our own. It has often been said that where there is similarity in structure, as an observed fact we find similarity in function. When we are observing the behavior of animals lower than man we are willing enough to abide by our dogma. Yet when we reach man we find a certain hesitation in applying it. Logically we must apply the principle consistently. If we find man doing something which the animal does not do, it is due to one of two things: (a) the animal does not possess the structure, or (b) he does not possess it in a highly enough developed form. If we examine man and animal from the standpoint of (a) and (b), we find that there is a difference in structure which at once accounts for the popular and the scientific feeling that a break exists between man and animal. We refer to the lack of well-developed speech mechanisms in animals and to the consequent lack of *language habits.* So far no language habits have ever been found in animals, nor has any one succeeded in developing such habits in them.

The lack of language habits forever differentiates brute from man.—In taking the position that the chief difference between the behavior of man and animals flows out of man's ability to form language habits, we shall neglect the plainly observable difference in man's more finished use of the skeletal muscles and in the greater delicacy of his receptors, etc. It is possible, however, easily to overrate these differences. In many cases it is clearly observable that the difference between Peter's motor and sensory equipment and that of the guinea pig is probably more marked than that between Peter and the ordinary man. In taking this position we hasten to add that it is not fair to us to suppose that we believe that the putting on of simple language habits in the gibbon, e.g., would make him a fit subject to compete with a cultured European from the standpoint of complexity of behavior. We do mean that if we could *establish* in the anthropoid even a primitive language and were then to compare him with the primitive Australian bushman, we should at once lose the feeling that there is some qualitative difference between his behavior and our own, i.e., we should lose the feeling at once that he is a brute.

Instinctive basis of language.—In the general discussion of habit on p. 186 we spoke of the fact that before habit can be formed the stimulus must call out a large group of reflexes. Unless the stimulus does this no habit can arise. Examination of the child shows that such reflexes are early called out with such abundance as to foreshadow the fact that the speech mechanism is eminently suitable to the formation of habits. The stimuli which may lead to these reflex movements in the vocal apparatus are exceedingly varied. Stimulation of any appropriate receptive surface by bright objects, oft reacted to objects, as the face of nurse and mother, sound of the human voice, loud noises, etc., will call them out. In addition to these random reflex movements, we have in the case of the throat mechanism something similar to that which we found in the general bodily mechanism, viz., there exist rather distinct concatenations of reflexes which we designate as instinctive *cries* and *sounds*. These in mammals at least are racially typical and must be con-

sidered definite instincts. These instinctive acts, executed
with the vocal apparatus, have, just as is the case with
instinctive acts executed with the trunk, arm, and leg
muscles, more or less definite stimuli which call them forth
(e.g., the mouse calling out certain responses in the cat).
The animals, as a rule, possess a fairly definite and fixed
group of these. This has given rise to the misguided
efforts of Garner and others to show that the primates
have a language. What the primates have is a much
larger number of such vocal instincts than the other
mammals, and a much larger number of stimuli can call
them out, e.g., injury to bodily tissue calls out one group;
hunger calls out a certain group; sex stimuli (mate, etc.)
another; and similarly, cold, swiftly moving objects, tones,
strange animals, call out others. When attachments are
formed between the female and her offspring, another
large group is called into action. There is no evidence to show in the case of mammals that these vocal
instincts are modified by the sounds of other animals.
We have brought up dogs, rats, guinea pigs, rhesus monkeys, Cebus, etc., in the same room. We have shown
elsewhere that although songs and call notes develop in a
bird reared in isolation, they are not necessarily the ones
that would have developed had the bird been reared with
the adults of its own or of a different species. These
throat habits may be cultivated to such an extent in birds
that we may get an approximation, more or less complete,
to a few such habits possessed by the human being. Such
throat habits, however, are not language habits, as will be
clear from our later discussion. It is pretty clear that
the mutant man, when thrown off from the primate
stock, sprang forth with a vocal apparatus different from
that of the parent stock, and possessing abundant richness
in reflexes, even far surpassing that found in the bird. It
is interesting to observe too in this connection that within
the narrow space occupied by the vocal apparatus we have
a system of muscular mechanisms which has within it,
looking at it now as a whole, the same possibilities of habit
formation that we find in the remaining portion of the

bodily musculature. Once we can establish more definite systems of examining the muscular apparatus we can undoubtedly watch the rise and growth of both simple and complex language habits, plot their curves, etc., and in every way come to look upon that mechanism as we now look upon the system of bodily musculature. It is probable that in a few years we shall undertake the study of such habits from exactly the same standpoint we now employ in studies upon the acquisition of skill in the human being. This will lead to a clearing up of the misunderstanding which exists concerning imagery. On p. 18 we denied the necessity of assuming imagery (1) because there is no way of accounting for it on neurophysiological grounds without doing violence to our conception of brain physiology, (2) for the reason that there is no objective evidence to show that it exists, (3) for the reason that we can substitute for what it is supposed to do a mechanism which is exactly in line with what we have found to exist everywhere else, viz., an enormously developed system of language habits. From this point of view, all organization, no matter what its character, shows directly for what it is worth in the appropriate muscles. At present we are told to believe that there are two distinct orders of organization, that which can be read off by the observer directly in the muscles or groups of muscles of his subjects, and that which can be read off only by the subject in which the movement is taking place. This latter organization consists of visual, auditory, tactual, etc., copies (substitutes for the stimulus which leads to the response of the muscles), copies and symbols of various kinds of the movements themselves (see James' system of " remote cues "). Furthermore, these images can come and go without showing necessarily at all in the muscles. On p. 17 we touched upon this matter. We wish to enlarge upon the general position adopted there. The whole matter can be simplified by calling this second type of asserted organization thought (imaginal). The position which we have earlier sketched took the ground that imaginal thought needed no new principles of explanation and required no different interpretation in behavior from that of other habits; and that if behavior could adequately treat of the overt bodily organization, it could, by the same principle, just as adequately treat of the thought processes. Unfortunately language habits have not been studied from the standpoint of behavior and we have little data of a positive kind which will bear out our assertion. Anna Wyczoikowska in her work on the speech mechanisms states that when a subject was told to *think* of a word or sentence, there followed a definite movement of the tongue, and that sounding the word or sentence within the range of the subject also produced a tongue movement. Unfortunately her work stops far short of showing what we believe exists. If it could be shown that the sentence, '' Mary had a little lamb,'' when spoken in front of the subject, produced a very definite form of movement (habit), and the same general type of movement followed when the subject was told to think the words (they need not be identical in form), the evidence would be favorable. Her records are not treated in this way and too few were made on any given subject. Furthermore, no time relations are shown. We give (Figs. 56-60) some of the curves presented in her paper. Explanatory legends attached to each will show to what the curves refer.

The tongue is a poor organ to deal with: we need to get some direct way of observing the vocal cords, throat formations, etc. It will be extremely difficult to get definite evidence either for or against the present theory. In the section below we shall see that there are forms of language habits other than those appearing in the vocal apparatus. For this reason it is clear that robbing a man of the laryngeal mechanism would not rob him of thought, since usually in those cases in which a man has been robbed of this apparatus there has been a tumorous or cancerous growth that has been slow in its onset, and for this reason *bodily language* habits have grown up. Furthermore, even in cocainizing the vocal apparatus, we do not destroy the possibility of throat and laryngeal movement. Only the sensory nerve endings in the mucous membranes will be

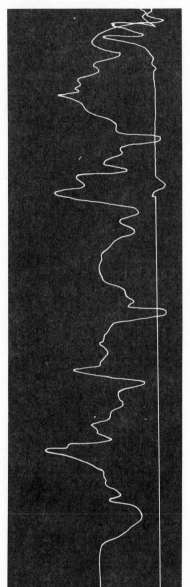

Fig. 56

The subject is asked to " remember " the verse, " When I am dead, my dearest, sing no sad songs for me."

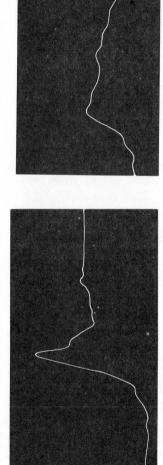

Figs. 57 and 58

The subject is asked to think the words " experimental psychology."

touched by the cocaine. The deep-lying sensory endings of the muscles which are the only essential (sensory) ones from our point of view, will not be affected by the cocaine. If we could find a case where a man suddenly lost his laryngeal apparatus without any serious injury to the other bodily mechanisms, we should have a crucial case. From our point of view there would be, or ought to be, a serious limitation in this man's thought processes. It is extremely unlikely that such a case will ever occur. We have had under consideration many methods which might

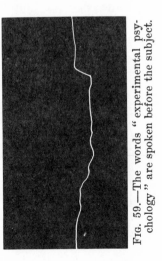

Fig. 59.—The words "experimental psychology" are spoken before the subject.

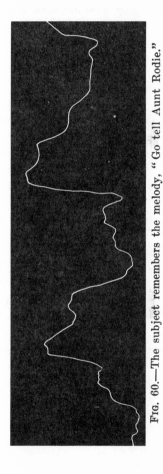

Fig. 60.—The subject remembers the melody, "Go tell Aunt Rodie."

lead to the closer observation of the movements of the vocal mechanisms. It probably would be premature to give any sketch of these. As stated above, Madam Wyczoikowska shows one method which, imperfect as it is,

presents some of the things which we believe to be true in
every case of thought. Even that unsatisfactory method
can be refined and made to give facts which will either
support the argument here presented or else show its un-
soundness. To advance the argument, which we admit
is highly speculative, we will suppose that future analysis
will enable us ultimately to show that every word, syllable,
and letter, whether spoken or thought, produces a characteristic form of response which, when recorded, must be
looked at from the same standpoint which we adopt when
looking at habits elsewhere. At present we can take a human
being or an animal and in a shorter or longer time get a
fairly complete record of his bodily habits, i.e., of their
number, of the accuracy in each, of their complexity, the
ease with which habits are formed, etc. This does not
mean that we ever have done this or that we ever will do
it in any complete way, but there is nothing theoretically
impossible in the problem.[2] In the same way we should be
able to determine man's language habits, what habits are
being used at the moment (i.e., what thought processes are
going on), etc.

The nature of language habits.—Not all habits formed
in the vocal cords are true language habits. The parrot
and many other birds learn to speak and sing words;
the dog even may possibly form certain vocal habits.
If we turn to the child we find the genesis of such habits.
The child begins with certain sounds that are essentially
instinctive,—"ma-ma-ma, gu-gu, goo-goo," the guttural or
velar r (ℝ) is also common, etc., differing slightly in
different races. His first simple vocal habits depend upon
the language which surrounds him. For a long time such
habits in the child do not differ from those formed by the

---

[2] Practically, however, the technical difficulties are very grave
indeed. On the possibility of recording and reading sounds of the
human voice, musical instruments, etc., see the article "Vocal
Sounds," by John Gray M'Kendrick and Albert A. Gray, in Schäfer's
Text-Book of Physiology, p. 1206. For a recording device see an
article by M'Kendrick, "Demonstration of an Improved Phono-
graphic Recorder, and Remarks on the Curves Thereby Obtained,"
Proceedings of Edinburgh Royal Society, 1895, XXI, p. 194.

parrot. The vocabulary of the " parrot stage " in the child may be fairly large, consisting of as many as a hundred or more words. By the time this stage is reached the child is ready to begin the process of forming true language habits. Vocal habits do not become language habits until they become associated with appropriate bodily habits, and even substitutable for these acts. If we examine the bodily habits which have been formed prior to this time we find that the use of the hands, arms, and fingers, organs of locomotion, etc., has been more or less perfected, i.e., hundreds of habits of response to objects have been formed. The child has learned to respond by appropriate acts to its doll, bottle, small boxes, and to hundreds of other objects. These habits of response to objects are essential to the formation of language habits. So far the animal and the child are on the same basis. The parrot responds with words to an auditory stimulus, or to an intra-organic stimulus (spontaneous words of the parrot) : that animal can also form habits of opening boxes, etc. What, then, constitutes the difference between the parrot and the child ? They are not different at this stage ! If we watch the development of the child from this point on, however, we find that the next step he takes carries him to a plane to which no animal has risen. The stimulus (object) to which the child often responds, a box, e.g., by movements such as opening and closing and putting objects into it, may serve to illustrate our argument. The nurse, observing that the child reacts with his hands, feet, etc., to the box, begins to say " box " when the child is handed the box, " open box " when the child opens it, " close box " when he closes it, and " put doll in box " when that act is executed. This is repeated over and over again. In the process of time it comes about that without any other stimulus than that of the box which originally called out only the bodily habits, he begins to say " box " when he sees it, " open box " when he opens it, etc. The visible box now becomes a stimulus capable of releasing either the bodily habits or the word habit, i.e., development has brought about two things : (1) a series of functional connections among arcs which run from visual receptor to muscles of throat, and (2) a series of already earlier connected arcs which runs from the same receptor to the bodily muscles. When the box is presented now, which set of arcs will function? Evidently either (1) or (2) or both simultaneously. It is at this time that the influence of the environment upon shaping the language habits comes again clearly to the front. The object meets the child's vision. He runs to it and tries to reach it and says *"box."* The box happens to have been put beyond his reach. The nurse, seeing the child's efforts to reach it and hearing the word " *box*," hands it to the child. This situation being repeated day in and day out, not only with this object but with hundreds of others, brings it about that the arcs running from receptor to throat muscles offer the least resistance so far as concerns the neural impulses aroused by the box (frequency, p. 262). Finally the word is uttered without the movement of going toward the box being executed. There has been a substitution (mechanical process) of a language habit for a bodily habit. One other step and the process is complete. We found in our studies on the maze that every *cul de sac* represented what we might call a simple unit habit. These simple habits when perfected arise serially. When learning is complete we can put the animal down anywhere in the maze, and after a few trial movements the remaining part of the journey is executed without a break. Something similar of course occurs in all complete systems of bodily habit and in language habits as well. Habits are formed of going to the box when the arms are full of toys. The child has been taught to deposit them there. When his arms are laden with toys and no box is there, the word habit arises and he calls " *box;*" it is handed to him and he opens it and deposits the toys therein. This roughly marks what we would call the genesis of a true language habit. The expositions of the formation of these simple habits are often put in unscientific form, e.g., language is said to be social and words arise only in virtue of the fact that man is a social being. It probably is perfectly true that if the child were taken at birth to a desert island and fed by the ravens (granting the climate were kindly) that no true language habits would be formed. Certainly none which would characterize the adult reared under such circumstances as belonging to any known nationality. We have no objection to saying that language is social in its essence, provided we recognize the essentially mechanical nature of the formation of such habits. In the same way a human being reared in a world in which no monochromatic lights were present would never form habits of reacting differently to differently colored objects, the reason being that no stimulus would be on hand to call out such responses. In the same way no true language habit (laryngeal) would be formed by a normal child dwelling in a community of deaf mutes. No stimulus would be at hand to call out the response in such a way as to force the formation of the habit. It is essential to recognize that the process of forming the language habit of " box " would probably advance just as quickly if the " Tik Tok Man of Oz " were put in as a nurse and his mechanism so arranged that he would speak at the right time and move the box in the right way at the right time.

Early predominance of language habits.—It is not our purpose to treat the steps by which such habits are developed. We are interested simply in the steps by which one such habit might arise. The moment the child forms the first language habit, he is forever differentiated from the beast and henceforth dwells apart in another world. He still uses his bodily habits, certainly, but not even a stroke of paralysis, paralyzing all other skeletal muscles except the laryngeal ones, could rob him of his right to be called a human being.

Forms of language habits.—It is immediately suggested that there are many deaf mutes in the world and many pathological subjects lacking a sufficiently developed throat mechanism for the formation of language habits. It would be impossible to enter into any detailed study of the various forms which language habits may take. We can, however, at least mention some of the principal

forms. We have (1) the typical process sketched above
where the word either uttered aloud or uttered in silent
speech (thought) sets up a stimulus which effects a response in the musculature of the arms, legs, trunk, etc.,
or else initiates another word, which may in a similar way
serve as a stimulus to arouse a bodily habit. This reciprocal process of bodily acts arousing the (thought)
word: the word or series of words arousing another act,
etc., is persisted in during the whole of the waking day
and, if the psychoanalysts are right, during most of the
period of sleep. In sleep, however, since the body muscles
are largely inert, the drama as a whole must be played
with the larynx as the stage.[3] It should be emphazised
here that in adults the situation (sum of present extra- and
intra-organic stimuli) determines whether the thought or
spoken word will serve as the stimulus for a bodily act or
for another word. In reverie the bodily muscles are re-
laxed and (thought) word initiates (thought) word; at an
afternoon tea or at a reception where the words or phrases
are stereotyped, the heard word initiates a series of overtly
spoken words on a par with the bodily habit of walking.
When the situation is changed to scenes of action, the emphasis falls again upon the bodily muscles. Strenuous
objections naturally arise to the viewpoint just expressed.
It is asked, " Do we always think in terms of words? "
We should certainly reply in the negative. Observation
shows that we have even short-circuited (substituted for)
the word system of thought.[4] We find (2) a somewhat

[3] It should be a relatively easy matter now to test whether, e.g.,
the related tongue movements are present in sleep.

[4] In this connection it will be instructive to glance for a moment
at the complexity in habit systems with which we have to deal in
daily life. We may illustrate this in a very easy way by a suitable
example: before me as I write is a calendar with " Friday, January
9 " upon its face. The habit of tearing off these leaves has been
forced upon me in past years. The effectors of hand and arm are
used in this operation. The city bell rings 12 P.M.. I say aloud
" another day over, it's January 10! " I glance at the calendar and
say aloud, " tear off leaf." Immediately the movement is executed.
Two stimuli are present simultaneously, both of which act upon
the same effectors, viz., the intra-organically aroused one (exercise of
the throat muscles) and the one extra-organically aroused, i.e., by

highly involved system of language habits which, strange
to say, while formed (as we believe) after vocal language
habits, have their locus in the general bodily musculature
such, e.g., as the nod of the yes or no, closing the lids
slowly for yes, winking, which expresses a whole series of
words, the shrug of the shoulders, and bodily sets and
attitudes.   These movements are often spoken of as being
mimetic.[5] But the fact is they have nothing at all to do
with thought, until by a process of substitution such as we
have already described they come to function as do words.
The muscular movements originating in these groups
can arouse there a stimulus which incites to response, e.g.,
to an extension of the arm, bringing about the removal
of the leaf of the calendar in our illustration. Since these
mimetic movements often follow, are reflexly aroused along
with movements in overt or silent speech, it is perfectly
natural to suppose that a substitution process could occur

the spoken word. The reaction must follow equally well if another
spoke the word (even if I were lacking in a laryngeal language
apparatus). On the other hand, I may *think* the words " Saturday,
January 10, tear off leaf," and the act will follow. (It is just at this
point that the upholders of the image say that you can not only think
it by silent speech, but that you can also *imagine* the act and the
movement will follow. Our contention is that in thought the words
must be uttered silently before the habitual act arises. See also
p. 324. Neural activity begins always in a receptor, in this case in
the vocal cords. What starts movements in the vocal cords? A
previous movement in the cords or another form of stimulation,
either intra- or extra-organic). Of course, since the act is habitual
and was formed prior to the language habit, a word is not necessary
to initiate the act. If I were blind and had no speech the sound
of the bell might release the act of extending the hand and tearing
off the leaf (if I may, by courtesy, be allowed to suppose now that
the calendar has become one of the raised letter type). Finally the
act might follow in the absence of the bell. If I were a blind
deaf mute and happened to feel my watch at 12, I might be led to
extend my hand and arm and tear off the leaf. It is clear that if a
suitable stimulus is at hand, the act of the hand and arm follows.
Now this stimulus can have its origin in any receptor (or in any
muscle, considering them now as receptors). We have found such a
group of receptors to be the throat muscles themselves, i.e., the
movement of these muscles, as in the silent speaking of the word,
will initiate the impulse which drives the muscles of the arms and
hands. All such processes are at bottom really identical in nature.
  [5] Sante de Sanctis: *Die Mimik des Denkens.*

by which they would come to function independently of
the word. Of (3) writing habits, (4) deaf and dumb
sign language, and (5) formation of words on lips we say
nothing, since the processes involved here are all essentially upon the same plane.

**Futility of searching for reasoning, imagery, and the
like in animals.**—From our point of view it can readily be
understood that the search for reasoning, imagery, etc., in
animals must forever remain futile, since such processes
are dependent upon language or upon a set of similarly
functioning bodily habits put on after language habits.

**Division of labor between human and animal behav-
iorists.**—If the highly speculative position we have tenta-
tively put forth here represents in any measure the true
state of the case, it would seem that the field of behavior
could be divided largely among three groups of investigators: (1) a group interested in the instincts, sensory and
motor habits of animals below man, (2) another group
interested in the same type of problems in the human being,
and finally (3) a group interested mainly in the language
habits of the human being and in the possible development
of such habits in the anthropoids.

BIBLIOGRAPHY

JENNINGS, H. S., *Behavior of the Lower Organisms.* New York,
    Columbia Univ. Press, 1906.
JUDD, C. H., *Psychology.* New York, Scribner's, 1907.
WITMER, LIGHTNER, " A Monkey with a Mind," *Psych. Clinic,* 1909,
    III, 184.
WYCZOIKOWSKA, ANNA. *Op. cit.*

VISION

Introduction.—Very little of the early work on the responses of vertebrates to light was conducted with sufficient care to give reliable results. This is especially true where monochromatic lights have been used as the specific stimuli. In reading the summary of results given here it must be remembered that this department of behavior is a very active one and what is said should be considered as portraying only the present conditions of affairs. We have to admit that many of the conclusions appearing here are in need of confirmation.[1]

I. Limits of Spectral Sensitivity and the Relative Stimulating Effect of Different Regions of the Spectrum

Mammals.—The majority of mammals tested under experimental conditions are insensitive to light of long wave-lengths. At least for them such rays have a relatively low

[1] This summary of the color work makes no pretense of being exhaustive. It does not embrace all of the results upon any given

stimulating effect. The following mammals have been under observation: The dancing mouse, white rat, hooded black and white rat, rabbits, and monkeys. The range at the red end cannot be given in terms of wave-length. There has been no satisfactory experimentation upon the range at the violet end. It is probable that the shorter rays of the spectrum have a relatively high stimulating value. Tests upon rats and rabbits show that the blue and green have a relatively high stimulating value as compared with the yellowish-red.

Birds with day vision.—From C. Hess we learn that when a light-adapted chick is taken into a dark room and placed before grains illuminated by the whole spectrum (spectrum of medium intensity) and allowed to peck freely, it will begin with the grains illuminated by the red and orange rays. It pecks continuously until the blue-green region is reached, beyond which point it refuses to peck further. A well dark-adapted chick in a spectrum of the same intensity will always begin to peck at the grains illuminated by the red; then in order, orange, yellow, green, and blue-green. While under these conditions the spectrum is widened at the short end (i.e., while the birds may peck further into the green) they still refuse to pick up the grains illuminated by the blue and violet rays. The behavior of the pigeon under the same conditions is closely similar to that of the chick. The range at the red end for it is normal, but at the violet end it is even more contracted than is the case with the chick. Chicks 48 hours of age have the same spectral range as the adults. In a spectrum of low intensity they feed first in the region which has the highest stimulating value for the human eye. This in the chick is shifted somewhat towards the red end. In connection with the author's work upon the homing sense he has determined the limits of sensitivity at the two ends of the spectrum for the dark-adapted (not complete) chick (90 days of age.)[2]

form, nor does it trace such studies consistently through the various phyla. This two-fold selection process is necessitated by the volume of the work done and its relatively unsatisfactory nature.

[2] This summary is taken from a work as yet unpublished. It

In this work precaution was taken to eliminate all extraneous white light.[3] The Nernst lamp was used as the source at the red end, whereas the arc was used as the source at the violet end. The limit at the red end is approximately $715\mu\mu$. It is probable that if a greater amount of time had been taken to determine the limit for the chick very accurately, it would have been found to coincide with that of the human being, which is ordinarily placed at $760\mu\mu$. The limit at the violet end is approximately $400\mu\mu$, which again is almost the same as that of the human eye, $396\mu\mu$. In a long series of experiments the relative stimulating effect of the different regions of the spectrum was determined for the dark-adapted chick in the following way: All of the monochromatic bands, the wavelengths of which are shown on the abscissa (Fig. 61), were equated in energy. Experiments were begun upon the chick with the green, $550\mu\mu$. By cutting down the intensity of the light with the Brodhun sector (see description of whole apparatus on p. 76) a point was reached at which the chick could not respond correctly (this can be determined accurately since the chick is positive to light

was conducted under the auspices of the Marine Biological Laboratory of the Carnegie Institution. I am indebted to Dr. Alfred G. Mayer and to the Carnegie Institution for permission to use this summary and the descriptions and cuts of apparatus shown on pp. 64 and 76.

[3] A word should be said concerning the state of adaptation: The chicks were brought into the dark room in a fairly tightly-woven wicker basket. They were left in total darkness for 15 minutes. The experimenter then entered the room and turned up a 16-c.p. tantalum light, placed 1 meter above the home compartment of the animal box. The chicks were taken out and run in the same order every day. One chick at a time was placed in the home compartment; then the light was turned out. A wait of 5 seconds ensued and then the door was opened and the animal confronted with the stimulus. As soon as the correct response was made the light was turned up. The chick ate of the grains for a few seconds. It was then driven into the home compartment, when the light was again turned out for 5 seconds and the routine repeated. That darkness-adaptation was well advanced appears from the fact that the point of highest stimulating value for the author's eye lay at $520\mu\mu$. If the threshold had been taken upon the eye in the (approximately) light-adapted state the point under consideration would have shifted over to about $580\mu\mu$ to $600\mu\mu$.

and since only one light was used) or else would not leave the home box at all. The sector reading which is directly proportioned to the energy was noted. When the reaction threshold had been satisfactorily determined in this region, another wave-length was selected and the same routine repeated. We thus obtain the threshold at any given wavelength in terms of the sector opening. For purposes of comparison, an assistant took the author's threshold each day after the work on the chick had been completed. Care was taken to keep adaptation for his eyes the same as for that of the chicks. It is clear that the greater the energy required by any given monochromatic light to stimulate the retina, the less the sensitivity of the retina to that ray; i.e., the reciprocals of the energy value ($1/e$ where e equals the energy necessary for stimulation) will, when plotted against wave-length, give the usual sensitivity curve. In examining the curve it is well to remember that the higher the point on the curve is above the base line, the less the energy required to produce stimulation. We do not know in absolute terms (ergs) the standard energy carried by each beam with which we worked, but we do know that all had the same initial energy and consequently that the final sector openings at which the various thresholds were obtained, are all directly comparable and proportional to the absolute energy required for stimulation. Hence it is legitimate for us to take the reciprocals of the sector openings. Below we give a table showing the actual sector openings for chick and man, and the reciprocals of those values.

Wave-length	Sector in mm., chick	Reciprocal	Sector opening mm., man	Reciprocal
660 $\mu\mu$. [4]	870.00	.0011	900.00	.00111
600 "	10.72	.0932	7.36	.1358
580 "	9.90	.1010	2.82	.3546
550 "	1.52	.6578	.54	1.8518
520 "	1.40	.7142	.42	2.3809
480 "	1.98	.5050	.95	1.0526
452 "	2.66	.3759	1.82	.5494

[4] The opening at 660$\mu\mu$ is of course merely proportional. At all other wave-lengths a smoked wedge was used after the energy was calibrated. the transmission curve of which, from 396$\mu\mu$ to 760$\mu\mu$, was known (calibrated by Bureau of Standards). At 660$\mu\mu$ the efficiency was so low that the wedge had to be removed.

If now we allow each millimeter on the ordinate to represent .01 these reciprocals, when plotted against wavelength, yield the two curves shown below in Fig. 61.

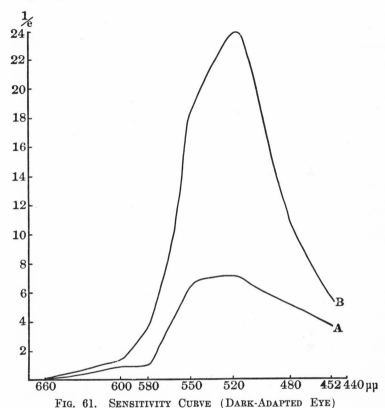

FIG. 61. SENSITIVITY CURVE (DARK-ADAPTED EYE)

A, chick; B, man. The ordinate shows the reciprocal (1 mm. = .01) of the energy value necessary to stimulate the retina at the wave-length given on the abscissa.

It follows from these experiments that the chick is not blind to blue and violet rays. On the contrary, these rays are highly efficient in stimulating effect. In general the sensitivity curve for chick and man are strikingly alike. The absolute threshold for man is lower than that of the chick except in the extreme red.

Birds with twilight vision.—Several birds with rod

retinæ, and especially birds with twilight vision, have been under laboratory observation. Among these are the kestrel (a bird similar to our sparrow hawk), house hawk, small owls, and the horned owls. A bright-adapted kestrel, according to Hess, has a range in the red coextensive with that of man. Its range is short at the violet end. A dark-adapted kestrel has a somewhat wider range at the violet end than the light-adapted animal. But even a dark-adapted animal responds to food stimuli less accurately and quickly in the blue and violet regions than in the red and yellow. When the kestrel and the chick are tested together simultaneously, the one with bits of veal and the other with grains illuminated by the whole spectrum, it is found that each will eat the food from the red to the green, but the kestrel will find the food further along in the green than the chick. When tested with food illuminated by blue and red ray filters it was found that the kestrel rarely ever touched the food illuminated by the blue, even after 20 hours of adaptation, unless the blue was made very intense. The horned owl has a range both in the violet and in the red much more nearly like that of man. Even the owl is slow and clumsy in its movements in blue and violet light. The dark-adapted owl eats first in a spectrum of weak intensity in the regions offering the greatest stimulating effect to the human eye.

Hess' absorption theory.—It is well known that the chick and most other day birds have retinæ richly supplied with cones but lacking in rods. Hence we have in the day birds little or no visual purple. Just the reverse is the case with birds possessing twilight vision. Their retinæ abound in rods but contain few cones. In some forms, like the owl, cones are almost completely lacking. In the cones of the day birds we find red to reddish-orange-colored oil globules and similarly in the retinal rods of the birds with twilight vision we find orange to greenish-yellow-colored oil globules, at times colorless globules. Hess supposes that the shortened range in the violet of the birds and other forms possessing these oil globules is brought about by the physical fact that the short waves are stopped by the globules. This affords the possibility of accounting, on physical grounds, for the asserted lack of sensitivity in the violet. Our own experiments showing that the spectrum is not shortened in the violet for the chick at least tend to prove that one of two things must be true: (1) either the oil globules do not absorb the short rays as Hess maintains, or else (2) the chick's retina is so sensitive to these rays that the loss is compensated for by greater sensitivity.

In fish.—Hess shows that the dark-adapted fish *(Atherina)* collect almost immediately in the neighborhood of the yellow-green to green, between the lines E to b. That this is the point of highest stimulating value comes out clearly from the fact that when the container is shaded one can drive the fish at will towards the red end or towards the violet end. This method (p. 69) enables one to test sensitivity at the two ends of the spectrum. It is found that their range at the red end is shorter than that of the human being normal in color vision. This was shown by shading all of the spectrum up to orange. As the card is moved along the fish advance before it, collecting in the light. Long before the human limits are reached in the red the fish begin to respond as to darkness: i.e., to swim aimlessly under the shadow of the card, out into the red, and then into the infra-red—i.e., they cease to collect. In general it is found that the common fresh and salt water fish collect in the neighborhood of the yellow-green to green. The stimulating value of the spectrum decreases from this point towards the red end very quickly. The stimulating effect is remarkably decreased by the time the pure yellow is reached. The orange and the red rays have exceedingly little stimulating value. The decrease in stimulating efficiency is much less apparent as one goes from the yellow-green towards the violet.

In reptiles and amphibia.—The limit at the red end for reptiles (turtle) is the same as for man, but their range is even more limited at the violet end than that of the chick.[5]

---

[5] Again in the case of the reptiles Hess falls back upon his absorption theory. In the retina of the turtle only cones are present. The cones contain reddish-orange oil globules.

By methods similar to those we have already considered Hess shows that several species of frogs have a range in the spectrum coextensive with man's. This is in agreement with the work of Gotch which appeared several years before that of Hess.[6] Gotch showed that in the excised eye of the frog the photo-electric responses fail or become extremely feeble if the eye is stimulated by infra-red or ultra-violet rays. It follows from this that the range of light vibrations within which the frog's eyeball gives definite photo-electric changes corresponds very closely to the range which produces visual response in the human being. The point of greatest stimulating value (spectrum of low intensity) for dark-adapted amphibia is in the neighborhood of the yellow-green to green. This point can be made to shift for amphibia as for birds by changing the animal's state of adaptation and by increasing or decreasing the intensity of the spectrum, i.e., here also a Purkinje effect is demonstrable (Hess).

II. Darkness-Adaptation; White Light

Introduction.—The current view in sensory physiology holds that darkness-adaptation is connected with the accumulation of visual purple which takes place while the eye is undergoing adaptation to darkness. Two phenomena have been urged in support of this theory: (1) The asserted lack of adaptive increase in sensitivity in foveal vision, after adaptation; (2) the supposed fact that birds with day vision, whose retinæ are sparsely supplied with rods and consequently contain little visual purple, do not possess the power to adapt to darkness. It has been shown by Piper and others that the fovea in the human being does have the power to adapt to darkness. The work of Hess cited below shows conclusively that the course of darkness-adaptation in day birds is not very different from that found in man or in birds with twilight vision. We have not repeated Hess' work in detail, but of the fact that an enormous increase in sensitivity comes with dark-

[6] But not mentioned by Hess.

ness-adaptation where the chick is the subject there can be no question. We have had in sensory physiology to give over the attempt to make of the visual purple a photo-chemical substance responsible for the general phenomena of color; it would seem necessary also to give up the attempt to connect it with the phenomena of adaptation to light.

Darkness-adaptation in birds with daylight vision.— When chicks are bright-adapted for one hour and then taken suddenly into a dark room and placed before grains of food illuminated by white light passing through an Aubert diaphragm (working over a ground glass disk), a very noticeable increase in sensitivity can be shown. If the pecking threshold is taken in terms of the Aubert diaphragm, it may be shown that chicks cease to peck at the points at which the grains become invisible to the human observer. E.g., in one test it was shown that immediately after entrance into the dark room, the light-adapted chick ceased to peck when the Aubert diaphragm was set at 21 mm. The grains ceased to be visible to the human observer at 20 mm. After five minutes' adaptation, the limit for the chick was 9 mm. The grains ceased to be visible to the human being at 9 mm. In another case a human being, a chick, and a white pigeon were tested simultaneously. The subjects were bright-adapted and then taken into a dark room. After one hour's darkness-adaptation the limits were taken (in this case with an iris diaphragm). The relations may be shown in terms of the divisions on the iris diaphragm as follows:

$$\text{White pigeon} \ldots \ldots \ldots 3\tfrac{1}{2}$$
$$\text{Man} \ldots \ldots \ldots \ldots 6$$
$$\text{Chick} \ldots \ldots \ldots \ldots 7\tfrac{1}{2}$$

In all cases one hour in darkness produces complete adaptation. It follows from this that the course of adaptation to white light in day birds is closely similar to that in man.[7] It is interesting to note that chicks, when long

[7] The increase in sensitivity produced by darkness-adaptation may be shown roughly in birds by a very easy experiment. If a chick

dark-adapted, are not blinded by strong light. Small grains placed before a dark-adapted chick and then suddenly illuminated by bright sunlight, are picked up readily by the birds. Birds and turtles stand in interesting contrast to man in this respect. Man is blinded by strong light after darkness-adaptation. Whether this is due to the fact that man possesses rods, and hence visual purple, is not clear at present.

In birds with twilight vision.—Tests by Hess upon the light-adapted kestrel with the Aubert diaphragm (see above, p. 343) show that the animal ceased to eat immediately after entrance into the dark room when the Aubert diaphragm was set at 40 mm. The food ceased to be visible to the human observer at 12 mm. In another test with the iris diaphragm the limits of visibility for the observer were 7 to 8 mm. (diameter of opening of iris). After a half hour's darkness-adaptation the kestrel's limit on successive trials was $7\frac{1}{2}$, $5\frac{1}{2}$, and $5\frac{1}{2}$; for the human being, even after 5 minutes in the dark room, the limit on successive trials was $6\frac{1}{2}$, $4\frac{1}{2}$, and $4\frac{1}{2}$; after 10 minutes in darkness, $4\frac{1}{2}$, 4, and $4\frac{1}{2}$. On other specimens the following course of adaptation was obtained:

Bright-adapted kestrel on entrance	After ½ hour	After 1¼ hours
22 mm.	9 mm.	3 mm.
21 "	7 "	
24 "		

Human being immediately upon entrance	After ½ hour	After 1¼ hours
6 mm.	3 mm.	2½ mm.

The range of adaptation to white light in the horned owl corresponds a little more closely to that of the human being. The bright-adapted owl upon entering the dark room had a limit on the Aubert at 24 mm.; the human observer at 18 mm. After a quarter of an hour in darkness the owl's

with one eye blindfolded is light-adapted and then brought suddenly into a dark room and the bandage removed from its eye, it will, when placed before a row of grains, take the food on the side of the dark-adapted eye.

limit was 14 mm., and the human observer's was also 14 mm. The owl is not light-shy in the common meaning of that term. The animal sees very well in bright light. With the possible exception of the owl adaptive increase in sensitivity in birds with twilight vision is not greater than in the day birds. Under decreasing illumination they seem to see much more poorly than the human being. The increase in sensitivity comes on much more slowly. The total range of adaptation is about the same as in man, although, with the exception of the owl, the absolute threshold is not quite so low.

In fish.—After 10 to 15 minutes darkness-adaptation sensitivity to light is increased over one-thousand-fold in fish. This adaptive increase is in part physical, due to the wandering of the retinal pigment towards the vitreous humor under exposure to light. In darkness the pigment recedes and clears the retinal elements for the reception of the light. In man the pigment is almost stationary. A large part of the effect in fish, however, is due to the general physiological processes with which adaptation is connected (Hess).

In reptiles and in amphibia.—Reptiles (various species of turtles have been mainly worked upon), although possessing a retina totally unsupplied with rods, nevertheless show a marked increase in sensitivity to light when dark-adapted. If a light-adapted animal is placed with its back to the apparatus admitting graded white light, it is found to be an easy matter to find the limiting intensity at which the food will be struck; a dark-adapted animal will strike at a piece of moving meat which is invisible to the bright-adapted human eye. The course of adaptation is almost identical with that of the human eye when the latter is covered with a piece of orange glass (to compensate for the absorptive effect of the red oil globules). The turtle responds to objects surprisingly well in very high illumination. The process of adaptation in the amphibian eye (frogs of various species) seems to follow closely that of the human eye. But the absolute increase in adaptive sensitivity seems to be somewhat less. An interesting way to test the process of light-adaptation in such animals is for the observer to light-adapt only one eye. This eye is kept in the bright light for the same length of time that the subject's eyes are light-adapted. Then when the animal is taken into the dark room the experimenter, with his dark-adapted eye, can arrange the apparatus, while with his light-adapted eye he can test the course of adaptation in himself and compare it directly with that of the animal under observation (Hess).

III. DARKNESS-ADAPTATION: MONOCHROMATIC LIGHT

In birds.—Chicks are somewhat similar to man and reptiles in the range of adaptive increase in sensitivity to monochromatic light. On account of the presence of the oil globules in the retinæ of the chick man needs, as in testing reptiles, to put an orange-colored glass before the eye when examining the course of adaptation. When man and chick are tested under these conditions, close similarity in the course and the range of adaptive increase can be noted between them from the green region to the red (Hess).

In reptiles and in amphibia.—The course of adaptation to monochromatic light in reptiles is similar to that in the chick. In an actual experiment, where food was illuminated by a red ray filter, the intensity of which could be altered by moving the lamp behind it, it was found that to the bright-adapted human eye the food was just invisible when the distance between the lamp and the filter was 8 cm. The reptiles under these conditions snapped at the food with some sureness. After one half hour's darkness-adaptation the food was visible to the human being with the lamp 17 cm. behind the filter. The turtles, dark-adapted for the same period, had their threshold at 17 cm. In general the course of adaptation is exactly the same in the turtle as in the human being when the latter observes the spectrum through an orange-colored glass. This holds until the blue is reached, beyond which point the spectrum of the turtle does not extend—i.e., has such a high threshold that comparison between human beings and reptiles is impossible. Here again, as in day birds, we have animals which are lacking in cones, and hence in visual purple, showing a considerable range of adaptive sensitivity to monochromatic light. What is still more surprising is the fact that these animals are almost exclusively nocturnal. When the frog's eye and the human eye are tested under comparable conditions the course of adaptation for the two forms is closely similar throughout the range of the spectrum. It will be recalled here that the spectrum is not shortened in the violet for the amphibian. The range of adaptive increase for the several amphibians tested was practically the same as for man (Hess).

IV. SENSITIVITY TO WAVE-LENGTH

Of mammals.—All of the tests, taken at their face value, upon monkeys seem to point to the fact that they are sensitive to difference in wave-length. Most of the work upon them has been carried out with colored papers or colored foodstuffs as stimuli. It was shown several years ago that the *M. rhesus* can learn to respond positively to one of a series of colored boxes or glasses, regardless of its position in the series. When the rhesus is presented simultaneously with bits of food dyed with a given coloring matter and soaked in a solution of quinine, and with bits of food dyed with a different coloring matter and left free of quinine, it learns with astonishing quickness to select only the bits free from quinine. The writer's own experiments upon the rhesus and cebus, carried out with monochromatic light, gave similar evidence of discriminative ability. In one animal the habit of responding negatively to yellow and positively to blue arose very quickly. Popular literature is full of assurances that the dog is sensitive to wave-length difference. When tested with colored papers, colored metal plates, etc., the results are everywhere confirmative of the popular view. The dog can learn to bring red, green, yellow, and blue balls upon command, as was shown long ago by Nagel. But in such experiments there has been no serious effort to control the various factors which must be taken into consideration in every such test. The more careful work of Nicolai, using the method of Pawlow with ray filters as the source of monochromatic light, fails to confirm the view that the dog can respond to wave-length difference. The dog, according to Nicolai, reacts wholly upon the basis of intensity. Even careful tests with colored papers (Smith) show that the dog's sensitivity to wave-length difference must be very rudimentary. Several other mammals have been tested in the various laboratories by the colored paper method. Among the animals so tested are raccoons, cats, and porcupines. The porcupine and raccoon strangely enough show little ability to respond to colored papers in such a way as to indicate sensitivity to wave-length difference. The cat has recently been more carefully tested with colored papers. It is found that *yellow* and *white* of the same flicker equivalent have apparently the same stimulating value; that Bradley standard *blue* has the same value as dark gray cambric. On the other hand, *red* is not reacted to differently from *black;* whereas *green* has the stimulating value of " *dark gray.*" It appears that a gray can be found which will break down the adjustment to any color (Cole). White rats and mice have been tested extensively. In tests with colored objects, such as colored yarns, papers, etc., they exhibit, as most animals do, the ability to form habits which have been interpreted as showing color sensitivity. More careful experiments upon the dancing mouse, where ray filters were used as sources of light, failed to give any definite evidences of such sensitivity. Extensive tests upon albino rats, black and white rats, and rabbits with monochromatic light failed to give positive evidence of sensitivity to wave-length difference. The *red-green* and *yellow-blue* habits were formed after a large number of trials, but it was shown in the *red-green* habit that the green was the only effective stimulus, the animals probably being completely insensitive to the red rays. In the *yellow-blue* habit, while both stimuli were effective, it was shown that the yellow was low in stimulating value, and that when the blue was decreased greatly in intensity, the habit broke down. The habit likewise disintegrated when white light was substituted for either of the monochromatic stimuli (see p. 220). Tests upon the rabbit with colored papers show likewise that its responses were probably based upon intensity difference.

Of birds.—When hens are roughly tested by a method similar to the one used on human beings suspected of color defects but with colored grains instead of colored yarns, they pass the test with the ease of the human being normal in color vision. We quote the following test from Hess. It gives the methods and the results.

Upon a dead-black tablecloth 15 by 30 cm. in diameter he lightly fastened yellow-red grains and between these strewed the different grays and greens. On the second day the hen avoided not only the yellow-red grains, but also the red grains and the bluish-red, and pecked only at the grays and greens. This was also the case when he strewed red grains among the greens and the grays (although in this case the red grains were no longer fastened down). With astounding quickness and sureness the animal pecked all the green and gray grains lying between the red grains. If there were only a few of these at hand it hunted all over the entire cloth between the red grains so that after a short interval only the red grains remained untouched. If he brought a hen into the dark room to a row of white rice grains, strewed upon a black background, and colored the grains by means of the spectrum, she here likewise left the yellow-red grains untouched.

He now laid before a so-called red-green blind person (relatively yellow sighted, red-green blind) the differently colored yellow-red and blue-red grains and let him choose out of the pile the grains which for him had the same stimulating value. This subject put yellow-green with yellow-red, pale blue with bluish-red. The differently colored grains which the hen had differentiated with such sureness were similar or alike to the red-green blind subject. A hen which had been taught to avoid the red grains was fed on a black cloth upon which the green grains were fastened down while the red, orange, etc., were scattered loosely about. After a short time she refused to take the green grains when these were loosely strewn among the others, but did take the red ones. In the spectrum she picked the grains lying in the red end as far as they were visible to the normal human eye. He concludes that the possibility of a red-green blindness in the hens experimented upon is excluded, and that greater strength is given to his contention that their "visual qualities" in this respect are similar to or the same as a normal man's.

K. S. Lashley in an unpublished work finds that when the Indian game bantam is tested with spectral light by the double stimulus method there is good evidence of keen sensitivity to wave-length difference. There is a rather wide literature here also on the ability of birds to pick out differently colored papers, glass, foodstuff, etc. While these tests in the case of birds probably do indicate sensitivity to wave-length difference, we are never on safe ground in so interpreting them.

Demonstration of the Purkinje effect.—One of the most important facts yet demonstrated concerning the sensitivity of birds and other animals to wave-length difference is the presence of the Purkinje effect. Several investigators of animal vision agree, some of them without really proving the fact, that the region of greatest stimulating effect shifts with the state of adaptation of the animal and with the decrease or increase in the intensity of the spectrum. Hess finds that the phenomenon occurs in all of the higher vertebrates tested with the exception of the fish. Bauer and Frisch find it even in fish. While the demonstration of the Purkinje effect cannot be taken as the equivalent of a demonstration of sensitivity to wave-length, it certainly is to be considered as a very positive bit of evidence in that direction, if any parallel can be drawn between animal and human responses. We have in the case of human beings the apparently well supported fact that this effect is present in the case of individuals normal in color vision, but entirely absent in those who are defective in color vision.[8] On account of the theoretical importance attaching to this phenomenon, K. S. Lashley undertook to test for its presence in some Indian game bantams of pure breed. It will be recalled that on p. 339 the author has shown that the point of highest stimulating value on the threshold curve of the dark-adapted chick lies at $520\mu\mu$. Lashley, instead of trying to obtain a similar curve for the whole spectrum under conditions of light-adaptation, used only

[8] It is interesting to note that the presence of the Purkinje effect is apparently not dependent upon the presence of visual purple. The day birds are almost wholly lacking in rods, and hence in visual purple, and yet it can be shown that the point of highest stimulating effect in their spectrum is dependent upon adaptation.

the two bands, *red* and *green* (and later yellow and blue-green). The chicks were first trained to respond to the *more intense of two white lights.* In the preliminary training to white light it was shown that when the intensity of the white light contrast is great (ratio of 20 to 1) and the absolute intensity of both is low, the chick is positive to the more intense. When the intensity of both lights was raised proportionately the positive tendency disappeared. Training was instituted and continued until the animal would respond to the more intense light when the intensities stood in the ratio of about 3 to 1 (absolute intensity was varied from day to day between the limits of 5 to 18 candle meters). Red ($650\mu\mu$) and green ($518\mu\mu$) were then equated in energy and allowed to fall upon the stimulus plates. By a long series of preliminary trials upon thresholds under conditions of light- and dark-adaptation, Lashley finally found a certain intensity relation at which the shift could be obtained. When the green has an intensity of 1/45 the standard (p. 75) and the red 1/6, we obtain the following positive responses:

light-adapted: red 6 ...... green 0
dark-adapted: " 4 ...... " 5

On repetition several days later, but with energy relations slightly different, the following were obtained:

light-adapted: red 3 ...... green 2
dark-adapted: " 1 ...... " 5

Similar tests were made with yellow ($590\mu\mu$) and with blue-green ($490\mu\mu$). In a similar way it was found that when the yellow was cut to 1/22 of the standard energy and the bluish-green to 1/90, the dark-adapted chick went to the bluish-green 9 times and to the yellow twice; when light-adapted, to the yellow 9 times and to the bluish-green once. This evidence is not wholly conclusive. The number of tests made is small. Nevertheless the results seem to show clearly that the stimulating effect of the blue-green region is heightened by adaptation to darkness.[9]

[9] In order that there may be no misunderstanding about the possibility of getting the Purkinje shift with yellow and blue, we

Results from a physiological method of testing for color sensitivity.—Rouse made some tests several years ago upon the effect of colors upon the respiration and circulation of pigeons. He obtained different types of change in these processes depending upon the color which confronted the animal. His records so far are not to be depended upon, since the light was not in any sense monochromatic nor was its energy at all controlled. If it could be shown that a white light, within a wide range of intensity, produced no marked change in these physiological processes; i.e., if the experimenter could stimulate the animal first with a white light of 1 c.p and then with one of 2 c.p. without producing a marked disturbance in such processes (or if it varied in a fixed way with the increase in intensity), while on the other hand if he stimulated them with a red and then with a green light, and such disturbance did not ensue, then we should have to conclude, after proper control, that the wave-length of the light exerts characteristic stimulating effect. The presence of such changes would again be no demonstration of color sensitivity, but such evidence would certainly be supporting.[10] A similar set of tests should be made upon the pupil, both where the energy carried by the different bands is equal and again where the energy is proportional to its stimulating effect.

In fish.—Investigators do not agree as to the presence of sensitivity to wave-length difference in the fish. Hess give here the complete range of wave-lengths employed in the four stimuli:

red band... $645\mu\mu$-$655\mu\mu$	green band ...... $515\mu\mu$-$522\mu\mu$
yellow band $585\mu\mu$-$595\mu\mu$	greenish-blue band $485\mu\mu$-$495\mu\mu$

[10] Babák has recently made some tests on the sensitivity to colored lights (filters) of frogs from which the forebrain had been removed. The animal to be studied was placed in faint white light for a half hour. At the end of this time the normal breathing rate was determined. The frog was then subjected to lights of different colors and its rate of breathing determined under each condition. It was found that very intense green light had little stimulating effect, as was also the case with weak red light. A very weak violet had, on the contrary, a much greater stimulating effect than the most intense green. A beam of white light as a whole has less effect than the violet constituent of that beam.

finds that fish have a spectrum shortened at the red end; that they seek always, both in dark- and light-adapted states, the same part of the spectrum, viz., yellow-green to green; i.e., no shift of the point of greatest stimulation is produced by the process of adaptation or by changing the absolute intensity of the spectrum. They behave in this respect as do the totally color-blind human beings who have E to b as the brightest point in the spectrum regardless of its intensity. The view that fish are without sensitivity to wave-length is strengthened by the facts which Hess has brought out by other methods. When offered food on colored or colorless backgrounds of the same white value as the foodstuffs the fish do not respond to it because object and background have the same stimulating values. On the other hand, nearly every other investigator [11] finds " color " vision in fish. Bauer, e.g., comes to the astonishing conclusion that fish in the light-adapted state are " terrified " by red (*rotscheu*) and hence must have color vision when light-adapted. On the other hand, when dark-adapted they behave as though color blind. Hess repeated Bauer's work and was unable to find " red shyness." Hess had no sooner ended the controversy with Bauer than Frisch's work appeared. The latter investigator has recently stated that fish (*Phoxinus lœvis*) are able to " discriminate " red from all shades of gray and especially from dark gray and black.[12] Yellow, green, and blue are likewise " distinguished " from all shades of gray. Green and blue likewise can be distinguished from one another and from other colors as well. On the other hand, red is confused with yellow. Hess, after the appearance of Frisch's work, retested this species by methods of his own and got only negative results.

Mimicry or adaptation to background no test of color sensitivity.—Within recent years many experiments have been carried out upon mimicry in fish—the tendency for many species of fish to appear like the background upon which they rest. We have described these changes on

---

[11] Bentley and Washburn, Reighard, Bauer, Frisch, Goldsmith, etc.
[12] The honey bee, according to Frisch, is unable to pass this test.

p. 124 under the heading of special forms of instinctive response. Although Mast, Frisch, and others maintain that since the eyes are necessary for this reaction, the fish in which such reactions occur must necessarily have color vision, it appears to us that these responses do not necessarily have any bearing whatsoever upon the question of color vision as we ordinarily understand that term. Ordinarily we mean when we say that an animal is sensitive to difference in wave-length that such stimuli play a rôle in the adjustment of the animal to food, sexual objects, shelter, escape from enemies, etc. I.e., that *such stimuli initiate activity in arcs which end in the striped muscles.* It is highly probable that the changes in color involved in mimicry of this kind are controlled entirely by the sympathetic system (i.e., through a system of conductors running possibly from some special type of terminal in retina to nucleus of oculomotor and other motor nuclei, thence through white rami to sympathetic ganglia). The recent work of Frisch at least brings out the fact that when the sympathetic nerves are cut the changes in color fail to appear.[13] We may make our point concerning the lack of bearing of such changes upon sensitivity to wave-length clearer by saying that we can easily conceive of mimicry of this kind taking place in an animal whose retina does not contain the physico-chemical processes (photo-chemical substances?) necessary to initiate response to differences in wave-length. At any rate the burden of proof falls upon those investigators who hold that adaptation to the color of the background necessarily proves that fish are sensitive to wave-length difference.

In reptiles and in amphibia.—No very careful work has been undertaken to test the ability of reptiles to react differently to visual objects which differ only in wave-length. We have the assertion of Hess that the several species of turtles respond to monochromatic light as does the human

[13] Some experiments made a few years ago upon *Anolis*, the so-called Florida chameleon, by Charlton, show that the dark-brown state and the pea-green state of that animal are probably induced through the action of the sympathetic system. The receptors involved, however, in this case lie in the skin instead of in the retina.

being when the latter is tested with an orange glass in front of his eyes. This assertion is made upon the basis of experiments upon the limits of spectral sensitivity and the distribution of stimulating effect in the spectrum rather than upon any clean-cut control work upon the formation of sensory habits. Much the same may be said of the work which has been done upon amphibians. Hess tells us that the Purkinje effect exists in both reptiles and amphibia. But notwithstanding the enormous output from Hess' laboratory it must be evident even to the casual reader that his results are very superficial in character and leave the problems almost *in statu quo*. The important results obtained by Gotch upon *R. temporaria* several years ago have been taken as the equivalent of a demonstration of color vision. Gotch showed, by taking the time-relations of the photo-electric change in the retina, that there are three fundamentally different types of response to colored light: (1) the response to red light is characterized by a long latency of nearly 3/10 second and by its attaining to a considerable maximum, averaging about .0004 volt; (2) to green light by the same short latency as that found in the response to white light, i.e., less than 2/10 second; it is also characterized by its magnitude, the maximum reached averaging over .0005 volt; (3) the response to violet light is characterized by a latency longer than that of the green but shorter than that of the red (25/100 seconds); also by very low intensity, the maximum averaging .00024 volt. We do not see how these results can be interpreted at all until we can carry out the same experiment upon a form in which by other methods color sensitivity has been shown to be lacking. It lies well within the bounds of possibility that an excised human eye, from an individual lacking totally in color sensitivity, would yield the same three temporal relations in the photo-electric change and the same differences in potential. If we examine the direct or reflex-like responses of frogs to monochromatic light we find little which bears upon our problem. Such work deals almost altogether with the mechanics of orientation to light. We have learned from it that under certain conditions of experimentation the frog turns away from *red* light and moves towards *blue,* and that when *red* light is admitted at one end of the receptacle that contains the animal, and *green* light at the other, the frog moves from the *red* end to or towards the *green.* When *red* and *yellow* light are opposed in the same way, movement is from the *red* to the *yellow.* When *red* and *blue* are opposed, movement is immediately towards the *blue.* In such tests there has been little attempt to control intensity. Usually filters were employed which certainly did not yield monochromatic light. On the whole, it seems safe to say that no single crucial test has yet been made either upon reptiles or upon amphibia which gives positive evidence in support of the view that these forms are sensitive to wave-length difference.

Delicacy of the problems in color sensitivity.—As may be seen from the above survey, we are far from having a satisfactory phylogeny of the color sense. The ideals in color experimentation have not been very high. As one goes through the literature on color sensitivity one is struck by the lack of any critical attitude on the part of investigators. Almost any kind of a response to a colored light has been taken as the equivalent of a demonstration of color sensitivity. This lack of a critical spirit may be due in part possibly to the failure to scrutinize carefully the various possibilities of reaction in such stimuli—i.e., the number of factors in them which may afford a basis for reaction. A colored object, paper, light, etc., is a very complex stimulus. Whenever a sensory habit is established with respect to such stimuli the animal is certainly being stimulated by one factor or another, but by which one? How can we answer this question until we know a great deal more than we do now about the limits of spectral sensitivity and the relative stimulating value of the different regions of the spectrum? And by relative stimulating effect here we mean both at low (threshold) intensities and at ordinary intensities. In the case of the chick we have the relative stimulating effect at the threshold but we do not know it at any other intensity. The relative stimulating effect may be wholly different at high intensities (regardless of the question whether the animal is normal in its color reactions or abnormal). There is a method of ascertaining these relations which we pointed out some years ago. It would be possible to start with the threshold intensity of red ($660\mu\mu$, e.g.) and then gradually to increase the intensity of another red of exactly the same wave-length until the animal could just respond positively to the more intense, say 70 out of 100 times. We would take this intensity (in terms of energy) as a new standard and determine similarly the next reaction threshold (D.L.). In this way we could lay off ten reaction thresholds at $660\mu\mu$. The energy value or its reciprocal of the red at this point would give us our first point on our new curve. In a similar way we would lay off ten such points at each of the other wave-lengths (probably three wave-lengths, $660\mu\mu$, $520\mu\mu$, and $480\mu\mu$, would give us a good basis for control work). The curve obtained would give us the relative stimulating effect of different regions of a spectrum at intermediate intensity. What bearing have such facts upon our color work with animals? Those who have worked at all critically are willing to admit, when *red* and *green* have been used, that they have been ignorant in nearly all cases of the fundamental fact as to whether the red was actually stimulating the animal. The habit would arise just as well regardless of whether the (non-sensed) red were the positive color or the negative—i.e., an animal stimulated by green can learn to respond either negatively or positively to it. Similarly when yellow and blue were used as stimuli, the blue may have been outside the range of the animal's spectrum at the violet end. Again, after such habits have been established experimenters have tried to break them down by altering the intensity (also the form, the size, etc.) of one or both stimuli. Now such alterations in intensity cannot be made except in a very unsatisfactory way until we have some clear idea as to the change in the amount of energy which it is necessary to make in order to reverse the stimulating effect (assuming that the animal is color-blind). In order to make our point clearer let us take a supposititious case: Suppose we have made the sensitivity curve (spectrum of medium intensity) suggested above. The energy value at $660\,\mu\mu$ we will assume to be $400x$ and at $520\,\mu\mu$, $20x$. The relative stimulating effect is in the ratio of 20 to 1. Suppose, further, that we have established such a habit with the green at the energy $20x$ and the red at $200x$. We now introduce our "controls." We give the animal a red of greater intensity—a red the energy of which is $300x$, or one of less intensity, the energy of which is $100x$. Neither of these would affect the habit. Not until we have run the energy of the red up to $400x$ will we have offered the (color-blind) animal two stimuli of identical stimulating effect. Nor have we intentionally exaggerated the conditions which we suspect exist. To attempt to control the color responses of animals by substituting lighter or darker shades of one of the papers used as a stimulus where the possible range in intensity is so limited is to attempt the impossible. Furthermore, on account of the many possibilities for the entrance of secondary criteria where colored paper are employed, such, e.g., as differences in the texture of the paper and differences in the ironing of the paper, it would seem almost impossible to use such stimuli in the behavior laboratories for anything except preliminary work.

V. Responses to White Light

Mammals.—Very few of the mammals have been tested as regards sensitivity to differences in the intensity of white light. The results in our possession come from rough tests made with gray papers and from projected lights (Pawlow's method). Monkeys apparently respond readily to one of two gray cards when the difference in "brightness" between them is 9%. They show remarkable readiness in picking out foodstuffs on the basis of intensity difference. When tested in the dark room by standard methods the monkey (as is the case with all animals so far tested) shows a surprising lack of readiness to form sensory habits based upon intensity difference. Careful experiments by this method have never been carried very far. Raccoons apparently respond readily to intensity difference: one observer states that only 4% difference in the brightness of two grays is necessary to give a basis for the rise of a habit. When tested with white and black (positive) about 90 trials are necessary to eliminate errors. Field observers report that their sense of sight is very delicate and much depended upon when they are living in the wild. Porcupines have been similarly tested and the results of such tests show about the same sensitivity to intensity difference that we find in the raccoon. Interesting studies of a similar kind have been made upon the dog. Nearly all of the investigators using the Pawlow method report that the conditioned reflexes in the dog arising from optical stimulation are dependent upon the intensity of the light. Experiments upon the brightness vision of the dancing mouse show that it has a certain capacity for forming habits based upon intensity difference. In the first place, when confronted with black and white cardboards it exhibits an original and positive tendency to go to the black. By training, this tendency can be overcome and the animal can be forced to respond positively either to the black or to the white cardboard at the will of the experimenter. If it is tested with numbers 10 and 20 of the Nendel series of grays, it is found that the habit is formed with exceeding difficulty or not at all. Consequently this difference represents, under the conditions of such experimentation, the threshold (D.L.). The number of trials required to eliminate errors in such habits (175 to 42) has been shown to depend upon two factors—the intensity difference between the two grays, and the strength of the electric shock (see p. 204). More careful tests by the use of reflected light show that Weber's law probably holds. When 5, 30, and 80 hefners are chosen as the standard intensities the difference must be approximately $\frac{1}{10}$ (i.e., a dancer can "discriminate" between 5 and $4\frac{5}{10}$ hefners, between 20 and 18 hefners, and between 80 and 72 hefners). White, gray, black, and brown mice show a similar readiness to react upon the basis of intensity difference when tested with gray cards, yarns, etc. The white rat and the hooded black-

and-white rat require from 500 to 600 trials to perfect the habit of responding positively to the brighter of two stimulus plates when the plates are illuminated respectively by a 2 c.p. and a 16 c.p. tungsten (see p. 206). Some interesting experiments have been carried out upon the behavior of bats when forced to fly in a room thickly strung with wires; but since the blind animals miss the wires about as often as the normal ones, it seems evident that the reaction is effected through some cutaneous receptor (p. 424). The bat does respond positively (reflexly) to light at certain seasons; so that there is some evidence that vision plays a rôle in their general behavior.

Birds.—When chicks are tested with Bradley black and white cardboards with black as the positive stimulus they are found to require a larger number of trials to perfect the habit (310 trials) than where white is used as the positive stimulus (150 trials). This is to be explained on the grounds of the fact that the chick is positive to the more intense of two achromatic light stimuli where the absolute intensity of the lights is not great (Breed). Some recent tests have been made upon the effect on habit formation of varying the strength of the electric shock. The habit consisted of learning to respond positively to the darker of two stimulus plates. While these experiments deal only indirectly with the problem which concerns us here, certain facts come out which bear upon the chick's sensitivity to intensity difference. The three separate problems given the chick were to go towards the darker of two plates when their relative " brightness " stood respectively as follows:

$$(1) \quad 0: 8.9$$
$$(2) \quad 1:13.7$$
$$(3) \quad 1: 5.1$$

These tests were carefully made with an apparatus similar to the one described on p. 78. Neglecting here the effect of varying the intensity of the electric shock, we find that the average number of trials required to learn (1) varied from 44 to 16; to learn (2), 105 to 40; to learn (3), 171 to 53 (Cole).

Fish.—We know very little about the fishes' sensitivity to differences in the intensity of white light stimuli. Parker has shown that certain fresh water forms (*Ammocœtes, Aniblyopsis*, etc.) are usually negative to light. When their optic nerves are cut the animals still respond as do normal individuals; thus showing that the skin of the fish, like that of the frog, is sensitive to light. The tail is especially sensitive as contrasted with other bodily areas. Strangely enough the skin of marine forms is not sensitive. A number of forms (dogfish, killifish, tomcod), the optic nerves of which had been cut, were tested with very intense arc and sunlight, but no response to the light was forthcoming. If Hess is right about the lack of sensitivity to wavelength difference in the fish it follows that white light vision (intensity, form, size) plays a predominating rôle in its response to objects. It is probable that the behavior of the fish (in daylight), when placed in currents of water (so-called rheotropism), is in part controlled by optical reflexes. As is well known, the fish takes a direction of motion against that of the current. It apparently tends to keep the same visual field,—i.e., to swim towards a stationary visual object. Animals with only one eye react as do the normals (Lyon).

Amphibia and reptiles.—Several investigators have shown that both the eye and the skin of the frog is sensitive to light. These investigators have concerned themselves with the mechanics of orientation rather than with the range of sensitivity or with the delicacy of the functioning of the visual mechanism. Torrelle shows that the frogs (*Rana virescens virescens* and *R. clamata*) are positive to light at room temperature (21° C.) and that when the temperature is raised to 30° C., the rate of positive response is accelerated. On the other hand, when the temperature is lowered to 10° C. the response to light is negative. Riley shows that they (at least *Bufo Americanus Le Conte*) are negative even at room temperature when the light is very intense (from projection lantern, about 10,000 candle meter). When the eyes and cerebral hemispheres are removed from the frog (*R. pipiens Schrefer*) it is found that they are still sensitive to light. Such animals after a time turn towards the source of the light and finally jump towards it. The time of such reactions, though, is greatly increased. It has been shown that this behavior is due to the sensitivity of the skin to light (Parker). Direct stimulation of the neural tissue by light will not produce the response. It is interesting to note that frogs possessing only one eye orient to light as do normal frogs. It has further been shown that when definite objects are in the field of vision they are reacted to, whereas the ordinary photic responses are inhibited (L. J. Cole). We know very little about the delicacy with which amphibia and reptiles react to intensity difference. Some recent tests have shown that the turtle (*Chrysemys marginata*) is able to learn the black-white (cardboard) habit. Four animals gave positive results, but one animal showed no improvement in 220 trials (Casteel). Vision is very important in the daily adjustments of the tortoise.[14] When land and water species of the tortoise are forced to jump from a board into a net of black cloth it is found that the time spent on the board before jumping is shorter in water species than in land species. Total inhibition to jumping, i.e., failure to crawl from the board and fall off in the allotted time (60 minutes), appears at a much less height for the purely land species than for the water-land and water species. It is quite probable that there are tactual and kinæsthetic factors here in addition to the visual (Yerkes).

VI. Response to Form and Size

In mammals.—Response of monkeys to form and size has so far not been carefully tested. In the ordinary rough

[14] All observers agree that one finds the strongest support for the view that moving visual stimuli possess higher stimulating value than stationary ones in the responses of amphibia and reptiles. Animals belonging to these groups do not as a rule strike even at food objects unless such objects are moving. Certain of these animals would unquestionably perish from hunger in a cage filled with plenty unless precautions were taken to dangle the food in front of them until it is struck at.

tests the monkey shows the readiness we should expect in picking out a food vessel of given shape from others differing in form. Similar rough tests upon size differences yield the same results. In the size tests the monkey apparently seeks the larger vessels. When tested with designs drawn upon cards monkeys failed to show a high order of discrimination. The writer has made some form tests upon the rhesus (spring of 1911). The results were never published because the work could not be completed. The tests were made in the dark room with the standard method and apparatus. The two monkeys (*M. rhesus*) tested formed the habit of discriminating between a circle and a square (equal in area) very slowly; not much more rapidly than is found to be the case with some of the lower orders of mammals. In fact " J," the larger of the two monkeys, never became very steady in his response (84%). " B," on the other hand, after perfecting the habit, could be counted upon to run correctly every day (100% for several days). Substitution of a square which could be inscribed in the standard circle produced no breakdown; nor did marked changes in intensity. In the case of " B," after perfecting the circle-square habit, the hexagon-triangle habit arose very rapidly—in about 40 trials. Nor was the habit disintegrated by interchanging the apex and base of the triangle. Monkeys are able to learn readily to respond in a given way or to inhibit response to a given visual signal. Thorndike states that their behavior in this respect is truly remarkable. In the light of what we now know about Hans and other highly trained animals, it is just possible that we have here responses based upon a generalized type of behavior on the part of the experimenter. In rough tests it is found that the raccoon and porcupine easily react to the difference between a circular and a square pasteboard card, and between two cards differing in size. No careful tests with standard methods have been made upon their form and size vision. The dog has been extensively investigated by Orbelli, using Pawlow's method. These tests show apparently that the dog is sensitive to form and size, and to differences of shading and form in objects.

We cite certain of Orbelli's conclusions as given in the report of Yerkes and Morgulis.

(1) The intensity of a photic stimulus depends not only upon the degree of change in light intensity, but also upon the size of the illuminated or shaded area. These two factors may compensate for one another.

(2) Qualitative (it is to be noted that this does not refer to color) differences in photic stimuli are determined not only by the fluctuations of the intensity of the light, but also by the specific grouping of the illuminated and the dark retinal elements (i.e., by the form of objects).

(a) Early in the formation of a reflex the significance of form is indefinite and the reflex is determined wholly by the appearance of a light or a dark figure.

(b) Later the importance of the definite grouping of light and shadow (form) gradually becomes apparent. This specialization in the reflex is developed slowly.

(c) It is possible, in a short time, to produce a marked difference in the influence of two figures by systematically weakening the reflex to the unfamiliar figure and by reinforcing the influence of the familiar figure by the use of food.

(d) Rendering different the influences of a familiar and an unfamiliar figure produces conditions which greatly favor the improvement of discrimination of the familiar from the unfamiliar figure. Under these circumstances unfamiliar figures retain their independence to a certain extent.

(e) The different effects produced by various figures depend not upon quantitative differences (intensity of light), but upon qualitative differences, that is, upon the unequal or dissimilar grouping of simultaneously stimulated retinal elements.

(3) When a difference in the effects of a familiar and an unfamiliar figure has been established, intensification of light, increase in the area of the figure, and repetition of the stimulus do not increase the effect produced by the unfamiliar figure.

(4) When a difference in the effects of a familiar and an unfamiliar figure has been established, and the unfamiliar figure produces only a slight effect, its influence may be considerably increased by the introduction of irrelevant stimuli.

(5) Moving objects may act upon the eye of the dog as distinct stimuli. In this case the direction of movement may determine the qualitative difference of stimulation and modify the reaction of the dog.

(a) In the early stages, after a conditioned reflex to movement has been established, the direction of the movement is not important and a familiar direction will have the same effect as an unfamiliar direction of movement.

(b) A distinct difference in the influence of movements varying in direction may be produced in a short time (by the process of wearing out the reflex to one stimulus by repetitions, and of reinforcing the other by giving food in connection with the stimulus).

(c) The differences in the effects of different figures, and of movements of various direction, is apparently based upon the establishment of a conditioned inhibition. Stimulation of some regions of the retina establishes among the various groups of retinal elements the same sort of relation which obtains between the separate receptors of the entire organism.

A long series of tests upon albino rats to test sensitivity to difference in form and size has been made. In the first place, it was found that the introduction of a slowly moving sector in the pathway of one of the light stimuli produced no hastening of the habit. One animal formed the vertical-horizontal line habit and another the 30 mm.—50 mm. circle habit. In testing the threshold for form it was found that while two rectangles 20 x 30 mm. with their long axes respectively horizontal and vertical afforded sufficient difference in stimulating effect for the rise of a habit, forms more widely different (square and circle) did not. Form and size vision in the dancer seems to be not so well developed as in the rat. Tests on the ability of the dancer to form a habit when a star-like figure and a circle were used as stimuli failed to give positive results both at high intensity and at low intensity. They are attracted to some extent by moving objects. The mouse (gray, black, white, brown) has equally poorly developed size and form vision.

In birds.—We may summarize the results of the rough early experiments upon birds somewhat as follows: When tested with wooden boxes differing in form it is found that the English sparrow does not easily react to such differences. On the other hand, both the sparrow and the cowbird are able to learn different designs (markings on cards). The cowbird is able to distinguish the triangle from all the other forms, the sparrow failing in this test. The pigeon readily learns to discriminate, apparently by vision, the position of a feeding-box placed in a row with others (so-called counting experiments). They show ability to pick out a given form of box,—triangular, square, cylindrical, etc., when all are presented simultaneously

(Porter).   Chicks will readily learn to leave rice grains untouched and to take wheat grains when the former are glued down to the table.   After the chicks have perfected the habit, one can scatter the rice grains loosely among the wheat without their being eaten.   If one cuts squares and triangles from green peas and places the squares on the top of a glass plate and the triangles under the plate the chicks readily learn to pick at the squares.   When the habit is perfected the triangles and squares may be laid side by side but only the squares will be eaten (Katz and Révész).   The scientific results upon reaction to form in birds are not altogether harmonious.   Bingham, who has recently worked over this whole field with chicks as the subjects, comes to the conclusion that while the chick can apparently respond to the difference in form between the circle and the square, and the circle and the triangle, when they are equal in area, yet such responses, after all, are really nothing more than keen perception of size differences.   He draws this conclusion from the fact that after the chick has learned the circle-triangle habit with the base of the triangle down, the habit will disintegrate if the apex is placed down.[15]   All observers agree that the chick is sensitive to size difference even when tested by critical methods.   In a very carefully controlled

[15] Bingham has raised the whole question as to what is meant by form.   " Reactions to optical stimuli which have been interpreted by observers as indicating form discriminations are probably made on the basis of unequal stimulation of different parts of the retina.   If local inequality of excitations on the retina be the basis of these reactions, then the apparent discrimination of form by the chick is, in reality, a keen perception of size differences."   Hunter argues that we should not expect the child to discriminate forms in the abstract in the sense in which form is used by Bingham.   He states that form discrimination is always " pattern " discrimination.   The whole discussion is somewhat academic.   It marks an attempt to introduce structuralism into behavior.   What we desire to know is how the animal will react in the presence of known and reproducible stimuli when the experimental conditions as regards the control of the animal are standard.   Nevertheless it would be a distinct gain to test for " form " discrimination under the conditions which Hunter suggests.   His paper should certainly be consulted in planning experiments upon " pattern " and " form " discrimination.

experiment upon size it has been shown that a standard circle (6 cm.) and a circle lying between 4.5 and 5 cm. (slightly larger than 4.5 cm. and slightly smaller than 5 cm.) affords a basis for a differential reaction. After the chick has been trained to react positively to the larger of two circles it will continue to react positively to the larger when the absolute size of both has been made proportionately larger or smaller.[16] In regard to the chick's use of size, form, and brightness stimuli, Bingham states that difference in size is most potent in determining visual response, and next in order come brightness, general illumination, and then form.

In reptiles and in amphibia.—Experiments on the turtle (*Chrysemys marginata*) bring out the fact that the animals failed to discriminate between patterns. Two learned to discriminate vertical and horizontal lines and 2 between 2 series of parallel horizontal lines 8 mm. and 2 mm. in width respectively. One turtle learned to discriminate between 2 series of parallel vertical lines 8 mm. and 1 mm. wide, and then between lines 4 mm. and 2 mm. wide, and finally between lines 3 mm. and 2 mm. wide. The average number of trials necessary to form such habits was 183 (Casteel). Habits of avoiding certain food objects can apparently be established in the frog (as in the monkey) in a very few trials. Under the influence of punishment by the electric shock *R. clamata* learned to avoid earthworms treated with chemicals in two trials (Schaeffer). Just what such results as these really mean it is impossible to say.

BIBLIOGRAPHY

BABÁK, E., "Ueber den Farbensinn des Frosches, vermittels Atemreaktionen untersucht," *Zeit. f. Psychol. u. Physiol. d. Sinnesorgane. Abt. f. Sinnesphysiologie*, 1913, XLVII, 331.

BAUER, V., "Ueber das Farbenunterscheidungsvermögen der Fische," *Arch. f. d. ges. Physiol.*, 1910, CXXXIII, 7.

BINGHAM, H. C., "Size and Form Perception in *Gallus domesticus*," *Jour. Animal Beh.*, 1913, III, 65.

[16] From experiments now in progress at the Nela Physical Laboratory (Johnson) it would seem that this observation cannot be confirmed.

BREED, F. S., " Reactions of Chicks to Optical Stimuli," *Jour. Animal Beh.*, 1912, II, 280.

CASTEEL, D. B., " The Discriminative Ability of the Painted Turtle," *Jour. Animal Beh.*, 1911, I, 1.

CHARLTON, F. C., " The Color Changes in the Skin of the So-Called Florida Chameleon (Anolis Carolinensis Cuv.)," *Proc. Amer. Acad. Arts and Sciences*, 1903, XXXIX, 259.

COLE, L. J., " An Experimental Study of the Image-Forming Powers of Various Types of Eyes," *Proc. Amer. Acad. Arts and Sciences*, 1907, XLII, 335.

COLE, L. W., " Abstract," *Jour. Philos., Psychol., and Sci. Meth.*, 1914, XI, 90.

————————— " Concerning the Intelligence of Raccoons," *Jour. Comp. Neu. and Psych.*, 1907, XVII, 211.

COLE, L. W., and LONG, F. M., " Visual Discrimination in Raccoons," *Jour. Comp. Neu. and Psych.*, 1909, XIX, 657.

COLVIN, S. S., and BURFORD, C. C., " The Color Perception of Three Dogs, a Cat, and a Squirrel," *Psychological Monograph*, Ser. No. 44.

DAVIS, H. B., " The Raccoon: A Study in Animal Intelligence," *Am. Jour. Psych.*, 1907, XVIII, 447.

FRISCH, v., " Ueber den Farbensinn der Fische," *Verhandl. d. Deutsch. Zool. Ges.*, 1911, p. 220.

GOLDSMITH, M., " Contribution à l'étude de la mémoire chez les poissons," *Bull. Inst. gén. psych.*, 1912, XII, 161.

GOTCH, F., " The Time Relations of the Photo-Electric Changes in the Eye of the Frog," *Jour. Physiol.*, 1903, XXIX, 388.

HAHN, W. L., " Some Habits and Sensory Adaptations of Cave-Inhabiting Bats," *Biol. Bull.*, 1908, XV, 135.

HESS, C., " Untersuchungen zur Physiologie des Gesichtssinnes der Fische," *Zeit. f. Biol.*, 1913, LXIII, 245.

————————— [17] *Vergleichende Physiologie des Gesichtssinnes.* Jena, Gustav Fischer, 1912.

HIMSTEDT, F., and NAGEL, W. A., *Versuche über die Reizwirkung verschiedener Strahlenarten auf Menschen- und Tieraugen.* Freiburg, Festschr. d. Univ., 1902, 259.

HUNTER, W. S., " The Question of Form Perception," *Jour. Animal Beh.*, 1913, III, 329.

KATZ and RÉVÉSZ, " Experimentell-psychologische Untersuchungen mit Hühnern," *Zeit. f. Psychol.*, 1908, L, 93.

KINNAMAN, A. J., " Mental Life of Two *Macacus rhesus* Monkeys in Captivity," *Am. Jour. Psych.*, 1902, XIII, 98.

LASHLEY, K. S., " Visual Discrimination of Size and Form in the Albino Rat," *Jour. Animal Beh.*, 1912, II, 210.

LYON, E. P., " On Rheotropism in Fish," *Am. Jour. Physiol.*, 1904, XII, 149.

MAST, S. O., *Light and the Behavior Organisms.* New York, John Wiley & Sons, 1911.

————————— " Changes in Pattern and Color in Fishes, with Special Reference to Flounders," *Science*, N. S., 1913, XXXVIII, 699.

[17] In this volume, on p. 67 ff., will be found many references to the color vision of birds which are not to be found in the present list.

NICOLAI, G. F., "Die physiologische Methodik zur Erforschung der Tierpsyche," *Jour. f. Psychol. und Neurol.*, 1907, X, 1.

ORBELLI, L. A., "Réflexes conditionnels du côté de l'œil chez le chien," *Archives des Sciences Bib.*, T. XIV, 1 et 2.

PARKER, G. H., "The Skin and Eyes as Receptive Organs in the Reactions of Frogs to Light," *Am. Jour. Physiol.*, 1902, X, 28.

———————— "On the Stimulation of the Integumentary Nerves of Fishes to Light," *Am. Jour. Physiol.*, 1906, XIV, 413.

PORTER, J. P., "A Preliminary Study of the Psychology of the English Sparrow," *Am. Jour. Psych.*, 1904, XV, 331.

———————— "Further Study of the English Sparrow and Other Birds," *Am. Jour. Psych.*, 1906, XVII, 248.

REIGHARD, JACOB, "An Experimental Field Study of Warning Coloration in Coral-Reef Fishes," *Pap. Tortugas. Lab. Carnegie Inst.*, Washington, 1907, II, 257.

RILEY, C. F., "Responses of Young Toads to Light and Contact," *Jour. Animal Beh.*, 1913, III, 179.

ROUSE, J. E., "The Mental Life of the Domestic Pigeon," *Harv. Psych. Stud.*, 1906, II, 580.

———————— "Respiration and Emotion in Pigeons," *Jour. Comp. Neu. and Psych.*, 1905, XV, 494.

SACKETT, L. W., "The Canada Porcupine: A Study of the Learning Process," *Behavior Monograph*, Ser. No. 7.

SCHAEFFER, A. A., "Habit Formation in Frogs," *Jour. Animal Beh.*, 1911, I, 309.

SHEPHERD, W. T., "Some Mental Processes of the Rhesus Monkey," *Psychological Monograph*, Ser. No. 52.

SMITH, E. M., "Some Observations Concerning Color Vision in Dogs," *Brit. Jour. Psych.*, 1912, V, 119.

THORNDIKE, E. L., *Animal Intelligence.* New York, Macmillan, 1911.

TORRELLE, ELLEN, "The Response of the Frog to Light," *Am. Jour. Physiol.*, 1901, IX, 466.

WASHBURN, M. F., and ABBOTT, EDWINA, "Experiments on the Brightness Value of Red for the Light-Adapted Eye of the Rabbit," *Jour. Animal Beh.*, 1912, II, 145.

WASHBURN, M. F., and BENTLEY, MADISON, "The Establishment of an Association Involving Color Discrimination in the Creek Chub Semotilus atromaculatus," *Jour. Comp. Neu. and Psych.*, 1906, XVI, 113.

WATSON, J. B., "Some Experiments Bearing upon Color Vision in Monkeys," *Jour. Comp. Neu. and Psych.*, 1909, XIX, 1.

WATSON, J. B. and M. I., "A Study of the Responses of Rodents to Monochromatic Light," *Jour. Animal Beh.*, 1913, III, 1.

WAUGH, K. T., "The Rôle of Vision in the Mental Life of the Mouse," *Jour. Comp. Neu. and Psych.*, 1910, XX, 549.

YERKES, R. M., *The Dancing Mouse.* New York, Macmillan, 1907.

———————— "Space Perception of Tortoises," *Jour. Comp. Neu. and Psych.*, 1904, XIV, 17.

YERKES, R. M., and MORGULIS, SERGIUS, "The Method of Pawlow in Animal Psychology," *Psych. Bull.*, 1909, VI, 257.

CHAPTER XII

AUDITORY AND RELATED FUNCTIONS

Introduction.—In the preceding chapter we saw that
investigators were not wholly in accord as regards the
results obtained from testing the visual responses of animals. In view of the lack of any standardized method for
testing the responses of animals to auditory stimuli, we
shall find a still greater lack of harmony in the field of
audition. The auditory work has been largely done by
physiologists and zoölogists for the purpose of throwing
light either upon the localization of function or upon comparative anatomy. Little attention has been given to the
strictly behavior side of audition—i.e., to the influence of
audition upon habit formation, the instincts released by
auditory stimuli, etc. The experiments have been conducted in such a way that we can do little more than present
the results of the different investigators. In the discussion of audition we shall include some experiments which
have been conducted for the purpose of determining the
function of the lateral line organs. The functions of the
semicircular canals and vestibular portions of the ear

should naturally appear in this chapter, but since the physiologists have from time immemorial included these structures in their treatises, we shall not deal with them in this sketch.[1] On p. 36 we indicated some of the problems which belong in a study of audition in animals. The present summary shows how far from complete are our actual data.

Some structural differences in the auditory organs.— The mammalian ear is so well known that it is not necessary to enter into a description of its parts. Since Helmholtz we have come to look upon the organ of Corti as the structure in the inner ear which is essential at least to all of our finer reactions to sound. In more recent times there has appeared the tendency to regard the tectorial membrane as a part of the essential structure. Helmholtz at first supposed that the analyzing mechanism of the inner ear was the arches of Corti. When C. Haase called his attention to the fact that birds do not possess the arches of Corti, Helmholtz then assumed that the basilar membrane fibers were responsible for tonal analysis. Birds and all mammals possess a basilar membrane. In birds, however, this membrane is shorter than in mammals. And although there is no real factual justification it was assumed by the early zoölogists that the range of pitch sensitivity in birds was very limited. In the more highly developed fishes, although there is no external ear, there is a well marked internal ear consisting of an utriculus and its semicircular canals, and of a sacculus with its appended lagena. We are particularly interested in the lagena, since it is the forerunner of the cochlea of birds and mammals. In fish (*squeteague*) the lagena exists as a small triangular pocket. A branch of the eighth nerve is distributed to this region, ending in a sensory patch called the papilla acustica basilaris. This area contains a single otolith, the astericus. The sacculus, while communicating freely with the lagena, does not communicate (in most forms) with the utriculus and its appended semicircular canals (structures which are in some way necessary to the maintenance of equilibrium

[1] See the excellent summary of Wilson and Pike.

and muscular tonicity). The sacculus, like the lagena, contains a single sensory patch, the macula acustica sacculi, and a single large otolith, the sagitta. It is supposed by Parker and others that both the sacculus and the lagena function in the reception of sound stimuli, and that these organs play no part in the maintenance of equilibrium and muscular tonus. Parker further supposes that the sac-

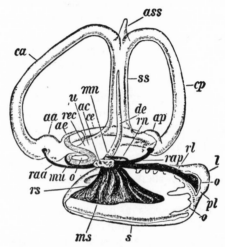

FIG. 62. MEMBRANOUS AUDITORY ORGAN OF FISH (*Perca fluviatilis*) SEEN FROM WITHIN *

l, Lagena cochleæ; pl, Papilla acustica lagenæ; o, o, o, Otoliths of the utriculus, sacculus, and lagena; s, Sacculus; u, Utriculus; ca, Canalis superior; ce, Canalis lateralis; cp, Canalis posterior.

culus is the most important organ in the reception of sound, since when the sagitta on each side is pinned down, the fish are only feebly sensitive to sound. How the sagittæ function " in the reception of sound is not known with certainty; but since in the squeteague they have a specific gravity of 2.84 and that of the whole head is about 1.8, it is quite probable that when sound vibrations influence the normal fish they induce the relatively lighter parts of the head, including the macula acustica sacculi, to vibrate

* Figs. 62, 63, and 64 are taken from Weidersheim, *Vergleichende Anatomie der Wirbeltiere* (Jena : Gustav Fischer, 1906). He in turn copies them from Retzius.

against the relatively heavier otolith; in other words, the otolith is a relatively stable body against which the auditory hairs of the macula acustica sacculi may strike.'' According to such a view the fish could react to sound only on the basis of difference in intensity—there is no differentiating or selecting mechanism. In amphibia there are both a middle ear and an internal ear. The tympanic membrane lies imbedded in the dermal surface. This membrane is connected with the opening in the inner ear

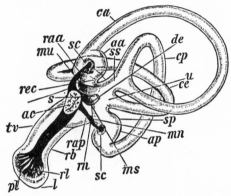

FIG. 63. MEMBRANOUS AUDITORY ORGAN OF A BIRD (*Turdus musicus*) SEEN FROM WITHIN, RIGHT SIDE

l, Lagena cochleæ; pl, Papilla acustica lagenæ; u, Utriculus; ca, Canalis superior; ce, Canalis lateralis; cp, Canalis posterior.

(*Fenestra vestibuli*) by a straight slender bone (there are really two bones—stapes and columella) called the *columella auris*. The sacculus, with its appended lagena, is far more highly developed in the frog than in the fish. We have in the amphibia, at least, rudimentary basilar and tectorial membranes. In birds and in reptiles there is still further development in these structures. We find here first a true cochlea—with a scala tympana and a scala vestibuli clearly marked. The basilar membrane is increased in length and has become more highly differentiated. Figs. 62, 63, and 64 show the progressive changes in the auditory portions of the ear as we pass from fish, through the birds, to mammals.

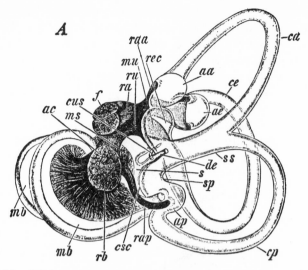

FIG. 64. MEMBRANOUS AUDITORY ORGAN OF A MAMMAL (RABBIT)
SEEN FROM WITHIN, RIGHT SIDE

mb, Membrana basilaris; aa, Ampulla superior; ac, N. acusticus;
ae, Ampulla lateralis; ca, Canalis superior; cp, Canalis posterior;
de, Ductus endolymphaticus; rb, Ramulus basilaris.

AUDITORY RESPONSES IN MAMMALS

(a) Dog: Kalischer's experiments.—Kalischer reported
in 1907 some experiments upon dogs made for the purpose
of testing the relation between the temporal cortex and the
reception of tone stimuli. He wished particularly to test
the validity of Munk's conclusion that the center of tone
lies in the temporal lobe and that the perception of high
tones is taken care of by the anterior portion of the center,
while that of the deeper tone depends upon the activity of
the posterior portion of the center. Kalischer trained his
dogs so that they would take food at one tone and refrain
from taking it upon the sounding of all other tones. The
food was held in the experimenter's hand or was laid on
a chair near by the experimenter. The tones were first
sounded upon an organ which contained nine pipes ranging
from C_1 to c^7. Later he substituted a piano and later

still a harmonium, finding the latter better suited to his purposes. In training the dogs he sounded at first only the food tone so that he might accustom the animals to being fed at the sound. "From about the third day on," says Kalischer, " I struck now and then another tone and closed my hand over the bit of food while this tone was sounding." Then he caused the food tone to sound again, this time allowing the animal to eat. In a short time Kalischer found that the desired habit arose. In his own words, he says: " From the fifth or sixth day on, even if I held the bit of meat in the open hand, many of the animals would no longer attempt to seize it when the confusion tone was sounded." Some of the animals were taught to take food at high tones (c-2048 d.v.) and others at low tones (C-64 d.v.). As may be seen, the confusion tones at first were made quite different from the food tone. After progress in association had resulted, the confusion tones were made to lie nearer and nearer the food tone. He says that it was not very difficult to train the animals to respond differently to two tones when they were only a semitone apart. In order to control his results, Kalischer made the following checks: Some of the dogs were temporarily blinded by sewing their eyelids together. He reports that the accuracy of response was not affected. This apparently would rule out the possibility that the dogs were reacting to visual clues. Besides this form of control, Kalischer destroyed one cochlea in other well-trained dogs. No disturbance ensued. But when the other cochlea was destroyed the habit broke down. This shows, he thinks, that the dog was not reacting to non-auditory stimuli. It is perfectly clear that if Kalischer's control tests were accurately made, they were adequate; but from experiments which Johnson has carried out (p. 379) the whole matter is left in doubt. It is very probable that Kalischer himself did not give the customary clues to the dogs after the cochlea had been destroyed, since he was not expecting them to react. Nevertheless, he himself was convinced that his dogs had been trained to react on the basis of the difference in pitch between the two tones. He then began his operative work. The first operation consisted of extirpation of one temporal lobe from an animal whose cochlea on the same side had previously been destroyed. According to Munk, the eighth nerve makes a perfect crossing and this operation should render the animal completely deaf. Kalischer reported that his animal reacted to tones as before, no matter whether extirpation was partial or complete. Before proceeding to extirpate the opposite temporal lobe, Kalischer allowed four or five weeks for recovery, during which time he continued training the animals. When the second temporal lobe was removed from some animals, the visual area was also injured. After this operation the dogs no longer reacted to *spoken commands,* nor did they show by pricking up the ears or by movements of the head any sensitivity to *loud noises.* Later they began to resume such movements at very loud noises and at very loud commands, but did not learn to react differently to them. Before the operation the least whistle or call had been enough to bring forth the appropriate responses. Even the movements of the head and ears at noises finally disappeared after the destruction of the posterior corpora quadrigemina with a needle. The animals' reactions to tone, however, were much less affected. Tests were resumed three days after the operation. Kalischer says that some disturbance of tonal habits followed, but he asserts that the animals undoubtedly reacted properly to the food tones and kept still on the sounding of the confusion tones. He ascribes the disturbance wholly to the shock of the operation. After two weeks the animals began to exhibit the old habits. They snapped in accustomed fashion at the food tone and shrank back at the confusion tones. They reacted also accurately to chords and discords. It was possible even in the most mutilated of these dogs to retrain them to react to a new food tone and to inhibit reaction to the former one. He concludes, accordingly, that the reception of noises and that of tones are mediated by different end organs and that different centers are involved for each. The center for noise he locates in the temporal lobe, the afferent pathway to which passes through the posterior corpora quadrigemina. The end organ for noise reception is indeterminate. On the other hand, he considers that the cochlea contains the end organ for tone and that the center for tone is infra-cortical and even below the posterior corpora quadrigemina, since the only known auditory pathway to the cortex passes through the quadrigeminal bodies. Kalischer concludes on the behavior side that we must attribute to the dog an exceedingly fine sensitivity to absolute pitch.

Rothman's experiments.—Later Rothman, not satisfied with Kalischer's behavior work, decided to make the same type of experiment. His method of training the dogs was similar to that of Kalischer except that he allowed an assistant to feed the dogs upon the sounding of the food tone. After some of the dogs had been trained he made the following operation. Both posterior corpora quadrigemina were removed on four dogs. Three had been previously trained. After the operation he tried to train two of the three dogs for about a month to react positively to c-1024 d.v. and negatively to the other c's on the organ, but without success. The fourth animal previously trained to react only to c-1024 d.v., and which had learned the problem faultlessly, was again subjected to the training process four weeks after the operation. Three weeks were spent in training to the same tone, without success. Then for twenty-three days he tried to teach this animal to react to the words " Mach schön," with the same outcome. From Rothman's brief account one gathers that the animals reacted when noises or tones were made, but did not react differently to them. Post-mortem showed total destruction of the posterior corpora quadrigemina in all animals. Extirpation of both temporal lobes in five animals produced lack of sensitiveness to both tone and noise when the entire area described by Munk was removed. If the removal was not complete some trace of the reactions remained. A sixth dog, however, not previously trained, having been deprived of both temporal lobes and of one convolution of the *gyrus sylviacus* was successfully trained in three weeks to respond to one of the tones. From these and other

results which we cannot enter into, Rothman concludes
that the dog's auditory center lies in the temporal region,
but extends over a wider area than that defined by Munk.
According to him the pathway from the end organ passes
through the posterior corpora quadrigemina and the interior geniculate bodies.[2]

Further experiments by Kalischer.—Kalischer in 1909
continued his report. A dog was first.trained to react in
one way to a high tone and in another way to a low tone.
After the habit was perfected one labyrinth was destroyed,
making the animal wholly deaf on that side. (Destruction
of both cochlea and vestibular apparatus was made complete.) Training was continued for two or three weeks
after the operation, which had not at all damaged the
dog's habit of responding to the low tones. The second
cochlea was then exposed, and the desired part of it destroyed. The part destroyed was removed with a needle.
The first animal operated upon, which had been trained
before the operation to respond to the two tones A_1 and c^3,
showed no loss of accuracy in the habit when one cochlea
was entirely destroyed and removed and the other destroyed as far down as the lowest turn. Only a small
portion of the (one) cochlea-vestibular apparatus was left
intact. The part of the organ of Corti and of the membrane of Reissner contained in this part of the cochlea,
and also the cells of the spiral ganglion, which belong to
this turn of the cochlea, were uninjured. Reaction to
spoken words, etc., was perfect. Kalischer made a number
of such cochlea extirpations. In general he concludes
that the theory of Helmholtz and others, that the different
parts of the cochlea and of the basilar membrane act selectively as receptors of long or short sound waves, is untenable. He assumes further that the vestibular apparatus
possesses an auditory function and that it is necessary for
pitch discrimination.[3]

---

[2] Since destruction of both internal geniculate bodies destroys
the possibility of training to both noise and tone.

[3] Swift has also made experiments similar to those of Kalischer.
He comes to the conclusion, from his experiments, that while the

Johnson's experiments.—After the experiments of Kalischer and Rothman had appeared Johnson undertook in the Hopkins laboratory to repeat their work upon blind dogs. The forks used in the first test were standard forks mounted upon resonators. Two were used as stimuli, middle c-256 d.v., and g-384 d.v. To the c the dog had to respond by going to the right and climbing up in a chair, and to the g by going to the left and climbing up on a box. In the early tests, in which two dogs were used, the experimenter was in the room. Between the tests the dogs usually crouched between the experimenter's legs or else sat upon their haunches near by. In a remarkably short time the habit arose. After the response to simple tones had been perfected clangs were tried. Again the dogs soon learned to climb up on the chair when the clang contained the c and to climb up on the box when it contained the g. Their responses soon became so machine-like that Johnson became suspicious of the stimulus to which the animals reacted. It became absolutely necessary to test the dogs in the absence of the experimenter. Several different methods were tried. The one proving most satisfactory is the one described on p. 85 ff. After several months of experimentation by this improved method both upon normal and upon blind dogs Johnson having failed to confirm both his own earlier work and that of Kalischer reached the conclusion that if the dog is sensitive to differences in pitch it does not appear in tests of such a character. Since Johnson in his preliminary work was able to repeat both Kalischer's and Rothman's findings in every detail, it would appear that their dogs were reacting to the same types of accidental stimuli as were Johnson's dogs in the early tests. Johnson did not determine the nature of the secondary criteria in any detailed way. He supposes that his own dogs in the tests where positive results were obtained were using a variety of cues such as (1) breathing of experimenter, and (2) involuntary movements of the body, etc.

center for pitch cannot lie in the temporal lobe, it does lie in the cortex, but in some other region.

Since we know that the dog does respond to auditory stimuli, such as calls, whistles, etc., Johnson next designed a simple experiment. Two electric buzzers, differing in pitch and in their overtones, were employed. One buzzer was placed directly over the right-hand food box and the other over the left-hand food box. Here we have not only differences in pitch and timbre, intensity, etc., but difference in localization as well. The problem assigned the dogs was to go to the right when the buzzer over the right compartment sounded and to go to the left when the left buzzer sounded. The dogs quickly learned this problem. When the buzzers were interchanged, however, the habit broke down. They had been reacting apparently on the basis of difference in localization. While these experiments of Johnson completely discredit the work of Kalischer, Rothman, and Swift, it would not be safe to conclude until further experimentation has been undertaken that the dog is insensitive to pitch difference.

Experiments made by the Pawlow method.—The results of tests made with the Pawlow method are fully as positive as those described by Kalischer; e.g., Selionyi states that tones which differ from each other by not more than a quarter of a tone can be reacted to differently by the dog; furthermore, that those which differ from one another only slightly in timbre are received as distinct stimuli. A single tone of a familiar chord of three tones of the same timbre and intensity produces a less intense response than do two tones of the same chord. Furthermore, positive results were obtained with respect to the analysis of chords, etc. It is extremely improbable, in the light of Johnson's work, that these responses are really responses to tone. From reading the description of this work we cannot gather that the results were controlled in Selionyi's work any better than in Kalischer's.

Experiments of Syzmanski on localization.—In connection with the above experiments of Johnson on the localization of sound stimuli (electric bells) it is extremely interesting to note that Syzmanski failed both with cats and dogs to establish such a habit. His experiments were quite

similar. Three fairly large boxes were placed in the form
of an isosceles triangle. The two boxes on the ends of
the base of the triangle were made large enough to contain
food boxes. The food boxes were so constructed that only
one could be entered. The other contained an equal amount
of food which could not be reached (to equalize smell).
A small electric bell was placed first on one box and then
on the other. (The two food boxes could be interchanged.)
The animal was released from the box at the apex of the
triangle. Upon release the animal could go to the box
from behind which the bell sounded and get food. The
trials, as is usual in such cases, were given irregularly.
Apparently only one trial per day was given each animal.
Only about 21 days were used in the regular test and then,
since a position habit developed, Syzmanski gave up the
attempt to establish the habit. While from casual observation he states that the animals can localize sounds, he
thinks that the reason they failed to do so in the above
test was due to the narrowness of the room (this being
unfavorable to localization).

(*b*) **Cat: the response of cats to tones, noises, and to
articulate sounds.**—Numerous incidental observations at-
test the fact that the cat is apparently keen-eared. Such
observations, however, cannot be relied upon until tests
experimentally controlled have been undertaken. We are
lacking totally in exact information concerning auditory
sensitivity. Rough tests, such as are about to be described,
have been made. The absence of even such a simple control as being out of sight of the animal when the stimulus
was given robs them of much of the value they might otherwise have. Shepherd tested two cats, P and M, with two
tones on a harmonica. To the note A-3 (food tone) cat P
had to rear up on the cage with the fore-feet and look up
at the top of the cage, M, being an inactive cat, merely had
to look up at the top of the cage. To the note A-1 (non-
food tone) both cats were to inhibit reaction. Forty-five
trials were necessary to perfect the habit in one animal
—P. The other cat, M, never learned entirely to inhibit
reaction to the non-food tone, although there were signs

of definite improvement. The stimuli were then changed to A-2 (food tone) and to A-1 (non-food tone). P perfected this habit in about 20 trials. The stimulus was then changed to piano tones—F-1 (food tone) and F-2 (non-food tone). Forty trials in all were necessary to perfect the habit. Selionyi states that the cat can be taught to come from another room to be fed on the sounding of the C of a set of tuning pipes and to inhibit response to the other c's in the same set.

A rough test has also been made on the sensitivity of the cat to the difference in intensity between two noises. The noise-producing apparatus consisted of a wooden box 18 x 11 x 10 inches and a slat 13 x 4 x 5/12 inches, fastened to the top of the box by a leather hinge. By raising the free end of the slat and letting it go a noise could be made, the intensity of which varied with the height of the fall. To give sounds of different degrees of intensity, two sticks, one $2\frac{1}{2}$ inches in length, and the other $4\frac{1}{2}$ inches, were separately used and placed perpendicular to the box under the free end of the slat. By pressing on the slat near the hinge and suddenly removing the stick two sounds could be produced which varied in intensity. Shepherd states that one cat learned in 40 trials to respond to the louder noise and to inhibit response to the fainter.

The same observer states that the cat readily learns to respond to articulate sounds. A 7-months-old animal not hitherto called by any name was placed in a cage. The experimenter stood at a distance of 1 meter from the front of the cage and called the name given to the animal— "Pet." Ten seconds were allowed the animal, if necessary, in which to give a proper motor response. Whether or not a response was obtained the animal was fed. In conjunction with the name given, other words were called, viz., "no feed," and when these latter words were called the cat was not fed. The response on the animal's part was to rear up on its legs at the front of the cage. On the third day this animal began to show indications of forming the habit. The animal continued to improve and on the ninth day, or after 150 trials in all had been given, it responded to the name 19 times in 20 trials. But it had not learned wholly to inhibit on the no feed call. On the thirteenth day, or after 250 trials, the cat had perfected the association. The words were called in varying tones of voice,—quite loud tones and very low ones. As a third test the words were called by different persons. Another and much older animal showed no clear indication of forming the habit until the tenth day of experimentation. On that day it responded to " Mary " 10 times and to " no feed " 6 times. After this, progress was slow; so slow that Shepherd attributed its slowness to the marked inactivity of the older animal. He noticed, however, that when the cat's name was called it would look up to the top of the box or at the food lying at a distance of about 1 meter from the front of the cage. The type of response required of this animal was then changed. It was counted sufficient indication of a habit if the animal looked up towards the food when its name was called. Improvement was rapid. On the second day thereafter there were definite signs of the appearance of the desired habit. On the twenty-fifth day it responded to the name " Mary " 19 times and to " no feed " 4 times. The animal never succeeded entirely in inhibiting the tendency to respond to the " no feed " call. Shepherd, in summarizing, says that the younger cat formed the habit in 250 trials and the older in 490.

(c) **Raccoons: reactions of raccoons to tones and articulate sounds.**—Cole tested the ability of raccoons to react positively to a high tone and to inhibit response at a low tone. The response expected was that of mounting a high box on hearing the high tone. Pure tones were not available, so the highest possible note, A1, on an ordinary A French harp, and the lowest, A″, were used as stimuli. For the first few trials the hand was extended towards the high box when the food signal was given and the animal fed when it mounted the box. When this aid was withdrawn it was found that No. 1 was practically perfect in its response to the high tone, refusing to move at the low tone. No. 2 did not form the habit. There seems to have been no effort to control the experiments. It is possible that the observer's movements might have been the cue to the reaction.

Shepherd states that raccoons can learn to respond to articulate sounds. Each raccoon was placed in a separate cage. Four cages were arranged in different parts of the room. The observer sat from 4 to 8 feet from the cages. The names of the raccoons were called in irregular order and the observer noted whether each animal responded to its own name or to all the names. Each animal was fed when it responded to its own name and was not fed when the other names were called. The names of the animals were Jack, Jim, Tom, and Dolly. The experiments were continued for 18 days, at the end of which time all the animals appeared to know their names perfectly. After the names had been learned, the observer called such words as " box," " floor " after the name, i.e., he called " Jack, box, floor " in succession and not alternately. No substantial difference in the percentage of proper responses was noted. Again, the sound of the voice was varied. The number of trials required to perfect the association varied with the different animals: Jack, 270 trials; Tom, 375; Jim, 425; Dolly, 500.

Tests upon mice and rats.—Yerkes has made some interesting observations upon the dancing mouse. His results are in agreement with those of Zoth. Both deny auditory sensitivity of any kind in the adult dancer. This animal is insensitive to such noises as are made by clapping the hands, shouting, whistling, exploding pistol caps, striking on steel bars, and even the squealing of other mice. They are likewise insensitive to tones, such as the Galton whistle throughout its entire range, the Appunn whistle, and to the König forks, giving tones from 1024 to 16,382 d.v. Indirect methods were attempted, as with the frog. Yerkes first tested to see if sounds interfered with their whirling. It had no effect. He then tested by the discrimination method, using punishment and food as motives. The animal had to enter one of two boxes which could be interchanged in position. If it attempted to enter the wrong box, it was warned by a bell. The mouse should then have sought the other box. Punishment ensued if it persisted in entering the box before which it was warned. No positive results came from these experiments. A different condition obtained in the case of young mice. When they are tested at or before the age of three weeks, evidence of auditory sensitivity is found; it appears in the form of starts, or trembling of the entire body. When the young are tested with the König forks, steel bars, etc., the results are as follows: During the first two weeks of life there is no evidence of hearing; during the third week, certain individuals respond vigorously to sudden high tones and loud noises. Not all of the young are sensitive even at this period. After the third week, no reaction is obtained. No careful experiments have been made upon the white rat, but all agree that from about the twelfth day after birth they respond by starts, cessation of activity, etc., to sounds. Some experiments made in the Hopkins laboratory in a control cage similar to that described on p. 87 show that the rats can learn to go to the right when a shrill rattling noise is made the instant before the animal is released and to go to the left when no sound is made before the animal is released. Sensitiveness to ordinary environmental sounds, such as feeding of companions, voice of mates, danger calls, etc., has been observed in a number of mammals, such as the guinea pig, porcupine, etc.

Incidental tests upon other mammals: (*a*) **monkeys.—** Although observations apparently show that the monkeys are extremely sensitive to noises in their environment, to calls and cries of companions, etc., there is little reliable experimental data on the subject. Shepherd, with the noise-producing device described on p. 382, finds that the two rhesus monkeys tested required respectively 80 and 110 trials to perfect a habit of responding to the louder of two noises. Their sensitivity to pitch was tested with the German mouth organ. When A-3 was sounded the monkey under observation had to climb to a platform. To other tones the animal had to inhibit action. One of the animals formed the habit in 60 trials, the other in 80 trials.

(*b*) **Horses.**—Tests made by Pfungst on cavalry horses do not confirm the view that they have the ability to respond appropriately to the various bugle calls when not directed (involuntarily by the rider). At the bugle call the horses, if standing, would start to walk. If the commands were given while the horses were trotting or walking no effect of the order was noted. Likewise tests on ability to respond unequivocally to their own names failed: any similar word spoken with the same inflection produced the same effect. Pfungst finds that few habits are developed around auditory stimuli.

(*c*) **Bats.**—Hahn finds that bats are very sensitive to vibrations of high frequency. A sharp whistle, sucking noise with the lips, tearing a sheet of paper, etc., caused them to start violently, but lower pitched noises had no effect. It has been stated that the sound of the hairy-armed bat's voice has a frequency of 17,000 d.v. The pitch of the voice of American species has not been determined. It is not known whether bats hunt prey (insects, etc., usually at twilight) on the basis of sound.

Auditory Response in Birds

In pigeons and parrots.—It has been shown by Rouse that mechanical jars and sounds have marked effect upon the breathing rate of pigeons. It has also been shown that pigeons, chickens, etc., hurry through a labyrinth when they can hear other birds pecking at food. The sensitivity of parrots to sound has often been remarked. On p. 295 we described the experiments made by Lashley on the imitation of sounds by parrots.

Auditory Response in Amphibia

Frogs.—It is an interesting fact that the frog does not respond visibly to sound when tested under experimental conditions. In nature the animal seems to utilize sound

stimuli as warning data. We quote Yerkes' observations
on the behavior of frogs in their natural habitat.

" In order to learn how far fear and artificial conditions were
causes of the inhibition of responses to sounds in the laboratory, and
how far the phenomenon was indicative of the animal's inability to
perceive sounds, I observed frogs in their native haunts.

" By approaching a pond quietly it is easy to get within a few
yards of the frogs sitting on the banks. In most cases they will not
jump until they have evidence of being noticed. Repeatedly I have
noted that it is never possible to get near to any frogs in the same
region after one has jumped in. In this we have additional proof that
they hear the splash-sound. To make sure that sight was not responsible for this on-guard condition in which one finds the frogs
after one of their number has jumped into the water, I made observations on animals that were hidden from one another. The
results were the same. I therefore conclude that the splash of a frog
jumping into the water is not only perceived by other frogs in the
vicinity, but that it is a peculiarly significant sound for them, since it
is indicative of danger, and serves to put them ' on watch.'

" A great variety of sounds, ranging in pitch from a low tone in
imitation of the bull frog's croak to a shrill whistle, and in loudness
from the fall of a pebble to the report of a pistol, was tried for
the purpose of testing their effects upon the animals in their natural
environment. To no sound have I ever seen a motor response given.
One can approach to within a few feet of a green frog or bull frog
and make all sorts of noises without causing it to give any signs
of uneasiness. Just as soon, however, as a quick movement is made
by the observer the animal jumps. I have repeatedly crept up very
close to frogs, keeping myself screened from them by bushes or trees,
and made various sounds, but have never succeeded in scaring an
animal into a motor response so long as I was invisible. Apparently
they depend almost entirely upon vision for the avoidance of dangers.
Sounds like the splash of a plunging frog or the croak or pain-
scream of another member of the species serve as warnings, but the
animals do not jump into the water until they see some signs of an
unusual or dangerous object. On one occasion I was able to walk
to a spot where a large bull frog was sitting by the edge of the water,
after the frogs about it had plunged in. This individual, although it
seemed to be on the alert, let me approach close to it. I then saw
that the eye turned towards me was injured. The animal sat still,
despite the noise I made, simply because it was unable to see me;
as soon as I brought myself within the field of vision of the functional eye the frog was off like a flash.

" Many observers have told me that frogs could hear the human
voice and that slight sounds made by a passer-by would cause them
to stop croaking. In no case, however, have such observers been able
to assert that the animals were unaffected by visual stimuli at the
same time. I have myself many times noticed the croaking stop
as I approached a pond, but could never be certain that none of
the frogs had seen me. It is a noteworthy fact that when one frog
in a pond begins to croak the others soon join in. Likewise, when

one member of such a chorus is frightened and stops the others become silent. This indicates that the cessation of croaking is a sign of danger and is imitated just as is the croaking. There is in this fact conclusive evidence that the animals hear one another, and the probability is very great that they hear a wide range of sounds to which they give no motor reactions, since they do not depend upon sound for escaping their enemies.

" The phenomenon of inhibition of movement in response to sounds which we have good reason to think the frogs hear, and to which such an animal as a turtle or bird would react by trying to escape, is thus shown to be common for frogs in nature as well as in the laboratory. This inhibition is in itself not surprising, since many animals habitually escape certain of their enemies by remaining motionless, but it is an interesting phenomenon for the physiologist. We have to inquire, for instance, what effects sounds which stimulate the auditory organs and cause the animal to become alert, watchful, yet make it remain rigidly motionless, have on the primary organic rhythms of the organism, such as the heart-beat, respiration, and peristalsis. It is also directly in the line of our investigation to inquire how they affect reflex movements, or the reaction of time for any other stimulus—what happens to the reaction time for an electrical stimulus, for example, if a loud noise precede or accompany the electrical stimulus." (*Harvard Psychological Studies*, I, p. 629.)

When certain physiological processes are being recorded, e.g., breathing, it can be shown that auditory stimulation is effective. If the animal is being stimulated while breathing is being observed, marked changes in the rate and form of the curve are noticeable. The easiest way to observe the indirect effect of auditory stimulation is to mount the frog in a saddle in such a way that its legs hang free (p. 89). When the frog has ceased to struggle it is possible to stimulate it tactually and to measure the distance to which the leg is jerked up. It is found that sounds given shortly before the tactual stimulus influence the height of the leg movement. If the sound (an electric bell) precedes the tactual stimulus by 1″ it has no effect. If the interval is not longer than .35″ it usually causes reinforcement. When the interval is .4″ to .9″ there is partial inhibition of the leg reaction. The green frog was tested under three conditions: (1) When the tympanum was exposed fully to the air, although the body was submerged up to the level of the ear drum; (2) when the tympanum was half under water, the head and nares being in the air; and (3) when the head of the frog was submerged to a depth of 4 cm. A bell electro-magnetically driven hung in the air and excluded from vision was used as the auditory stimulus. The effect of the sound on the leg reaction noted above was obtained under these several conditions. The range to which the frog's ear is responsive is from 50 to 10,000 vibrations per second. The response to sound may still be obtained after the tympana and columellæ are removed. Sectioning of the eighth nerve, however, causes complete loss of sensitivity. Attention is called to the fact that the influence of sounds is more marked in the spring months than in the winter months.

Auditory Response in Fishes

Some investigators who report lack of auditory sensitivity in fishes.—Bateson's early observations on the effect of blasting on fish are interesting. It caused the congers to draw back a few inches, flat fish to bury themselves, and pouting to scatter momentarily in all directions. Certain other fish are not affected by the sound. Similar results were obtained by striking with a heavy stick upon an aquarium containing soles. Bateson concludes that the fish are sensitive to the sound of sudden shocks when severe but not to the sound of bodies moving in the water when the latter are unseen by them. E.g., striking a glass with a stone under water and out of sight of the fish does not produce a response.

Kreidl reached similar conclusions with goldfish. These fish never responded to sound produced either in the water or outside in the air, but they did respond to heavy mechanical jars. Fish made sensitive by strychnine would respond to jars produced by tapping the aquarium and even to clapping the hands in the air, but not to tuning forks or vibrating rods, even when these were in contact with the water. Kreidl removed the auditory nerves and the attached ear sacs and then gave the animals strychnine. In all cases they responded as did the strychnized animals whose ears were intact. His conclusion was that the cutaneous receptors are stimulated by the sound waves (those produced by jars, etc.).

Lee obtained no evidence that fish hear. He used the clapping of the hands, striking stones together in the air and in the water, the human voice, etc. He, with Kreidl, found that they are extremely sensitive to jars.

Bernoulli, who has recently repeated the experiments of Zenneck cited below, fails to find any response to sound. A bell with c_3 for its fundamental, with a basal diameter of 94 mm. and a height of 62 mm., was fastened to a firm support with the dome immersed. The bell was electro-magnetically driven. The key for closing the circuit was placed on land several meters away, behind a stone wall. The fish (" Forellen," also eels and individuals belonging to " Zander," *Lucio perca Sandra Cuv.*) were tested in an open stream. He was never able to get the slightest response. Further tests showed that certain species of fish (*Salmo fario L.*, and *Thymallus vulgaris Nilos*) were insensitive to shrill pipes, the sound waves from which were conducted to the water by the aid of a metal tube 4 m. long and 30 mm. in diameter. Other observations showed that fish (" Zander ") were totally insensitive to pistol shots fired at a distance of 2 km. He believes that when the fish respond at all they do so because they are either tactually or *visually* stimulated.[4]

While the above summaries do not exhaust the literature on the negative side, they are the most important ones.

Investigators reporting sensitivity to auditory stimulation.—Parker [5] has been the champion of hearing in fish for many years. His experiments, though, are not conducive to complete trust. He argues that most of the work upon fish has failed to note that the auditory reflexes may be very inconspicuous and that a closer scrutiny of their behavior might reveal changes in them due to the effect of sound stimuli. He began his experiments upon

[4] Parker and his students seem never to have considered the fact that the fish might be stimulated by the wave motion in the water.

[5] It will be recalled, however, that Parker himself was unable to get any response to auditory stimuli in the dogfish *(Mustelus canis)* by the method about to be described.

killifish, *Fundulus hetereroclitus*. There are three possibilities of obtaining response to such vibrations: (1) Stimulation through the skin; (2) stimulation through the lateral
line organs; and (3) stimulation through the eighth nerve
(auditory response?). In response to the vibrations made
by the string (see p. 393 for method) he noted in normal fish
four kinds of movement: (1) Vibratory movements of the
pectoral fins; (2) change in the rate of respiratory movement, usually increased; (3) if the sound was at all intense
there was a slight movement of the caudal fin; (4) finally,
the fish under strong stimulation would make a quick
spurt or spring forward. In fish whose auditory nerves
had been cut, he failed to obtain the movements of the
pectoral fins, which was the most characteristic response
and the one easiest to observe. Ten fish were observed and
10 observations were made upon each animal. In 82 observations he obtained no response from the pectoral fin.
In 18 there was a slight movement. He next made the skin
insensitive by cutting the sensory nerve supply innervating
the skin area—viz., the fifth, seventh, and part of the
tenth cranial nerves and transecting the cord between the
fourth and fifth vertebræ. The auditory organs, after
such an operation, were presumably still completely functional. Parker states that the auditory responses in such
animals were normal.

Recently, Bigelow, under the guidance of Parker, retested goldfish (*Carassius auratus L.*). His results are
wholly different from those obtained by Kreidl (p. 389).
His method of testing the fish was as follows: An
aquarium was made with one end of wood. An electric
tuning fork of 100 vibrations per second was used as the
stimulus. The fork rested upon a table separate from the
one which supported the tank. After the fork was started
it was moved until its base came in contact with the
wooden end of the aquarium. " This could easily be accomplished without observable jar to the water in the
aquarium, and certainly in itself had no effect on the
fishes. For when I made the fork, not in vibration, touch
the aquarium in the usual way, the fishes gave no reaction,

although to the vibrating fork they were very responsive; I tried this many times.'' When tested under these conditions normal fish respond to the stimulus usually in one of several different ways, such as tail jerks followed by forward swimming movement; tail jerks without locomotion; tail jerks and trunk jerks followed by a turn to one side, etc. Of 193 observations 150 gave positive results. Of the 43 failures 12 were observations on albino fish. The other 31 were due, Bigelow states, to the difficulty of observing certain individuals which were in continual rapid motion. The skin was next made insensitive by cutting the cord just posterior to the pectoral fins, and the lateral branches of the tenth, fifth, and seventh nerves on both sides of the body. When such fish are tested (they lie quietly on their sides on the bottom of the tank unless stimulated) they are normal essentially in their reactions to the fork. When, however, the eighth nerves were cut, reaction to the fork disappeared. Similarly, Zenneck has obtained evidence of response to sound in three fresh-water fish *(Leuciscus rutilus, L. dobula,* and *Alburnus lucidus).* He used a bell electro-magnetically driven. Occasionally he put a piece of leather over the place where the clapper struck. The fish responded by swimming away when the stroke of the bell was given, but did not respond when the leather damped the sound. In exact contradiction to this work stands that of Bernoulli (cited above, p. 390). The work of Bernoulli is more recent and seems to have been carried out much more carefully.

Intensity of sound stimuli in water.—Parker criticizes all work earlier than his own on account of the fact that the sound fish were supposed to respond to was always generated, not in the water where the fish reside, but in the air. He cites an experiment where a dinner bell was rung in the air by a person standing breast deep in the water. The listener remained a few feet away with head under water. The sound seemed to cease when the diver got his head under water. In like manner a bell rung or hit with a stone under water is heard at best faintly by a person standing in the water unless his head is also im-

mersed. In a recent paper he states that the noise even of
a motor boat is extremely faint under water. The author,
with the coöperation of Dr. Alfred G. Mayer and Dr. A. J.
Goldfarb, at the Marine Biological Laboratory of the Carnegie Institution, Tortugas, Florida, has made several tests
upon sounds heard under water. The experimenter tapped
two small pieces of coral together under water. The observers would swim farther and farther away, diving at
intervals to listen for the sound. It was found that this
faint noise was heard clearly for a distance of at least
200 feet. The same sound made in the air and heard by
the observer with his head in the air was audible for a
much greater distance than in the test just described.
Parker is unquestionably right in his statement that
sounds made in the air are all but inaudible to an observer
whose head is under water. In one experiment carried out
by the author at Tortugas with Dr. Goldfarb, it was found
that the noise of a 38-caliber revolver when fired in the air
directly over the surface of the water could not be heard
by an observer who had dived to a depth of 4 feet. The
fact that sounds made in the air offer very faint stimulation to the ear under water has led Parker to adopt a very
crude apparatus to increase the sound intensity, viz., to
insert a wooden board in place of one of the glass sides of
one of his tanks, and to attach to it a string, vibrating at
40 d.v. per second.

Summary.—It seems very difficult to reach any conclusion in the face of such contradictory evidence. The failure
to obtain response to sound vibration in earless fish would
seem to offer crucial evidence, and yet the cutting of the
eighth nerve must produce profound changes in the motor
apparatus of the fish. It must be remembered that the reaction of the fish to auditory stimuli (at least those which
can be surely observed, such as the movements of the
pectoral fins, starts, etc.) are not very marked at best and
even those movements may be dependent upon the impulses
which normally come from the semicircular canals, vesti-
bules, etc. Elimination of these impulses, which occur
when the eighth nerve is cut, might easily account for the

facts observed in earless fishes. It seems strange, since Parker so clearly recognizes the fact that sounds made under water are reasonably intense, that he did not repeat Bateson's experiment of tapping objects together under water outside the range of vision of the fish. Such an experiment upon one of the forms which gave positive results would have been far more conclusive than all of the evidence he gathered through cutting the eighth nerve. Certainly the forms of apparatus used by Parker and by Bigelow to produce intense sounds are open to the severest kind of criticism. It would indeed have been hard to devise apparatus which would have offered more secondary criteria.

The lateral line organs.—Examination of the external markings of the fish shows a line which extends along the side from the head to the tail. The line is pierced at intervals by small pores, which lead into an underlying canal, the lateral line canal. This canal branches at the head into three divisions: one passes forward and above the eye; a second forward and below the eye; and the third downward and over the lower jaw. The system as a whole is known as the lateral line system. The system in one or another form appears in amphibia in the water inhabiting stage as well as in fishes. The lateral line system is richly supplied with sensory structures, which look not unlike the ordinary taste buds. Microscopic examination shows that these sensory structures as a whole are made up of supporting cells and sensory cells, which are pear-shaped and supplied with cuticular hairs. It is around the base of these cells that the medullated nerve fibers end. The sensory innervation comes largely from the seventh and tenth cranial nerves. Various opinions have been held as to the function of these organs. As long ago as 1870 Schulze developed the view that the stimulus was to be found in mass movements of the water and in sound waves of too great length to affect the ear. Other views have been advanced as to their probable function. Certain observers who have made operative experiments have held the view that they were organs for the production of gas in the swim-bladder; that they were organs for secreting slime; that they were necessary to orientation, equilibration, etc. Recent experiments by Parker tend to support Schulze's (theoretical) view that they are intermediate in character between the skin and the ear and that the stimulus to which the lateral line organs respond is a water vibration of low frequency. By a very simple operation (sectioning the sensory nerves which run to these organs) the whole system can be thrown out of gear. When these nerves are sectioned the fish almost invariably recover. They are then hardly distinguishable from normal fish. This difference, however, appears: If normal fish are observed in an aquarium it will be found that any slight jar or oscillation of the tank will cause them to dart at once to the bottom. The fish whose lateral line organs have been thrown out of gear will not respond to such a stimulus. They swim about even when the tank is violently agitated.

Hofer, however, does not accept this conclusion of Parker. He carried out an extensive series of investigations upon the lateral line organs. He asserts that the stimuli cited by Parker as affecting the lateral line system—such as slow vibrations obtained by jarring the aquarium, blowing waves across the water, dropping in stones, etc.—affect really only the cutaneous receptors. Hofer was enabled to get reactions to these stimuli when the lateral line system had been destroyed in certain fish *(Cyprinus carpio, Cottus gobio, Esox lucius)*. They are more prompt and pronounced when the fish are left for some time in a weak solution of strychnine. The reason why Parker failed to get such responses in fish whose lateral line organs were destroyed is due to the choice of a poor method of operation—one which destroyed along with the lateral line system certain of the cutaneous nerves supplying the skin of the head region (according to Hofer the skin of the body of the fish is not supplied with touch spots, i.e., with organs for the reception of such stimuli as fixed bodies, etc. In the head region the skin is supplied with such spots, also with warm spots, but it is lacking in cold spots). The loss of the very sensitive cutaneous areas of the head thus apparently accounts for the results obtained by Parker. From numerous experiments Hofer concludes that the lateral line organs are stimulated only by the streaming movements of the water. Such streams exert continuous pressure which differs in direction and in force. Their function in guiding the fish in migration is apparent. The stream or current of water need only possess slight intensity—a stream too slight to influence the labyrinths will arouse the lateral line system. Hofer states that the organs are not directly involved in reactions to fixed objects. On the other hand, as the fish approaches fixed objects currents are generated which, when reflected towards the animal, stimulate the lateral line organs. In this way these organs act like distance receptors. Increasing or decreasing the depth of the water (hydrostatic pressure) does not arouse the receptors in the lateral line organ.

BIBLIOGRAPHY

ALLEN, JESSIE, "The Associative Processes of the Guinea Pig," *Jour. Comp. Neu. and Psych.*, 1904, XIV, 293.

BATESON, W., "The Sense Organs and Perceptions of Fishes, with Remarks on the Supply of Bait," *Jour. Mar. Biol. Assoc., United Kingdom*, N.S., 1890, I, 225.

BERNOULLI, A. L., "Zur Frage des Hörvermögens der Fische," *Pflüger's Archiv für Physiol.*, CXXXIV, 633.

BIGELOW, H. B.. "The Sense of Hearing in the Goldfish, Carassius Auratus L.," *Amer. Nat.*, 1904, XXXVIII, 275.

COLE, L. W., "Concerning the Intelligence of Raccoons," *Jour. Comp. Neu. and Psych.*, 1907, XVII, 211.

CRAIG, WALLACE, "The Voices of Pigeons Regarded as a Means of Social Control," *Am. Jour. Sociol.*, 1908, XIV, 86.

FRANZ, S. I., "Über die sogenannte Dressurmethode f. Zentralnervensystemuntersuchungen," *Zentbl. f. Physiol.*, 1907, CXXI, p. 583.

HAHN, W. L., "Some Habits and Sensory Adaptations of the Cave-Inhabiting Bats," *Biol. Bull.*, 1908, XV, 135 and 193.

HELMHOLTZ, H. L. F. von, *On the Sensations of Tone as a Physiological Basis for the Theory of Music*. New York, Longmans, 1912.

HOFER, BRUNO, "Studien über die Hautsinnesorgane der Fische," *Berichte aus der Kgl. Bayerischen Biologischen Versuchsstation in München*, 1908, I, 115.

JOHNSON, H. M., "Audition and Habit Formation in the Dog," *Behavior Monographs*, Ser. No. 8.

KALISCHER, O., "Weitere Mitteilung über die Ergebnisse der Dressur als physiologischer Untersuchungsmethode auf den Gebieten des Gehör-, Geruchs- und Farbensinns," *Arch. f. Physiol.*, 1909.

—————— "Zur Function der Schläfenlappens des Grosshirns," *Sitz. der K. Preuss. Akad. d. Wisschftn.*, 1907, p. 204.

KREIDL, A., "Ein Weiterer Versuch über das angebliche Hören eines Glockenzeichens durch die Fische," *ibid.*, 1896, LXIII, 581.

—————— "Ueber die Perception der Schallwellen bei den Fischen," *Arch. ges. Physiol.*, 1895, LXI, 450.

LASHLEY, K. S., "Reproduction of Inarticulate Sounds in the Parrot," *Jour. Animal Beh.*, 1913, III, 361.

LEE, F. S., "The Function of the Ear and the Lateral-Line in Fishes," *Am. Jour. Physiol.*, 1898, I, 128.

MUNK, H., *Ueber die Functionen der Grosshirnrinde.* Berlin, 1890.

PARKER, G. H., "The Effects of Explosive Sounds Such as Those Produced by Motor Boats and Guns upon Fishes," Bureau of Fisheries, Document 752.

—————— "The Function of the Lateral-Line Organs in Fishes," *Bull. Bureau Fisheries*, 1904, XXIV, 183.

—————— "Hearing and Allied Senses in Fishes," *Bull. U. S. Fish Comm.*, 1902, p. 45.

—————— "The Sense of Hearing in Fishes," *Amer. Nat.*, 1903, XXXVII, 185.

—————— "The Structure and Function of the Ear of the Squeteague," *Bull. U. S. Bureau Fisheries*, 1908, XXVIII, 1211.

PFUNGST, O., *Clever Hans.* New York, Holt, 1911.

RETZIUS, G., *Das Gehörorgan der Wirbeltiere.* Morphologische-Histologische Studien. I. "Das Gehörorgan der Fische und Amphibien." Stockholm, 1881.

ROTHMAN, MAX. "Ueber die Ergebnisse der Hörprüfung an dressierten Hunden," *Arch. f. Physiol.*, 1908, p. 103.

ROUSE, J. E., "The Mental Life of the Domestic Pigeon," *Harv. Psych. Stud.*, 1906, II, 580.

—————— "Respiration and Emotion in Pigeons," *Jour. Comp. Neu. and Psych.*, 1905, XV, 494.

SACKETT, L. W., "The Canada Porcupine: A Study of the Learning Process," *Behavior Monographs*, Ser. No. 7.

SELIONYI, G. P., *Contribution to the Study of the Reactions of the Dog to Auditory Stimuli.* St. Petersburg, 1907. (In Russian.)

SHEPHERD, W. T., "The Discrimination of Articulate Sounds by Cats," *Am. Jour. Psych.*, 1912, XXIII, 461.

—————— "The Discrimination of Articulate Sounds by Raccoons," *Am. Jour. Psych.*, 1911, XXII, 116.

—————— "On Sound Discrimination by Cats," *Jour. Animal Beh.*, 1914, IV, 70.

—————— "Some Mental Processes of the Rhesus Monkey," *Psychological Monographs*, Ser. No. 52.

SWIFT, W. B., "Demonstration eines Hundes dem beide Schläfenlappen extirpiert worden sind," *Neurol. Centbl.*, XXIX, 686.

—————— "Psychological Results in Reaction to Tone Before and After Extirpation of the Temporal Lobes," *Jour. Animal Beh.*, 1912, II, 225.

SZYMANSKI, J. S., "Lernversuche bei Hunden und Katzen," *Archiv f. d. ges. Physiol.*, 1913, CLII, 307.

WIEDERSHEIM, R., *Vergleichende Anatomie der Wirbeltiere.* Jena, Gustav Fischer, 1906.

WILSON, G. J., and PIKE, F. H., "The Effects of Stimulation and Extirpation of the Labyrinth of the Ear and Their Relation to the Motor System." I, Experimental. *Phil. Transactions of the Royal Society of London*, Series B, CCIII, 127.

YERKES, R. M., *The Dancing Mouse.* New York, Macmillan, 1907.

————————— "Inhibition and Reinforcement of Reactions in the Frog," *Jour. Comp. Neu. and Psych.*, 1904, XIV, 124.

————————— "The Instincts, Habits, and Reactions of the Frog," III, Auditory Reactions of Frogs, *Harv. Psych. Stud.*, 1903, I, 627.

————————— "The Sense of Hearing in Frogs," *Jour. Comp. Neu. and Psych.*, 1905, XV, 279.

YERKES, R. M., and MORGULIS, S., "The Method of Pawlow in Comparative Psychology," *Psych. Bull.*, 1909, VI, 257.

ZELIONY, G. S., "Ueber die Reaktion der Katze auf Tonreize," *Zeit. f. Physiol.*, 1910, XXIII, 762.

ZENNECK, J., "Reagiren die Fische auf Töne," *Arch. f. ges. Physiol.*, 1903, XCV, 346.

ZOTH, O., "Ein Beitrag zur den Beobachtungen und Versuchen an japanischen Tanzmaüsen," *Archiv. f. d. ges. Physiol.*, 1901, LXXXVI, 147.

CHAPTER XIII

SMELL, TASTE, AND THE " COMMON CHEMICAL SENSE "

I. Smell

Olfactory reactions in mammals.[1]—Behavior can contribute but little at the present time towards the solution of the many problems which arise in the field of smell in mammals. In the course of a number of years of work upon the other senses several incidental observations have been made upon mammals which show that olfactory stimuli influence behavior, but few specific studies have so far been instituted. The technical difficulties in the way of making careful experiments are very great. Smell sensitivity in the white rat has been tested incidentally several times in connection with experiments upon learning: It has been shown that this animal, when given the opportunity of going to two food boxes, the one of which contains a bottle filled with bread, the other of which contains a similar bottle without food and a piece

---

[1] We know from Read's recent work that the olfactory nerves are large and numerous in the dog and in the cat, and that they are larger and more numerous in the former than in the latter. In both dog and cat nearly one-half of the ethmoturbinal folds bear olfactory structures, which is a much larger distribution than we find in man.

of buried cheese, runs quickly to the food box containing the empty bottle and the buried cheese. Certain experiments have been made to test whether rats track one another through entrances, etc. The following apparatus was used: Four rectangular boxes with wooden sides and wire netting at the two ends were constructed. Through one of the wire ends of each box a pasteboard mailing tube three inches in diameter was admitted. Strips of paper were rolled and used to line the tubes. Two of the tubes whose positions could be varied were kept smelling of the odor of a rat and two were kept free from such odor (the lining was changed after each test). The animal could obtain food in any one of the four boxes after passing through the tube attached to it. The animals were admitted to the restraining cage first on the West side, then in order, East, North, and South. The young rats failed to show any tendency to track one another. On the other hand, when adult males and females not living in the same cage were tested, the results were positive. In 24 trials the total number of tubes entered smelling of the opposite sex was 19, whereas the total number entered free from odor of opposite sex was 5. When white rats were tested on the problem given the ring dove (see p. 406) they learned after a short time to run towards the source of the odor (oil of bergamot). In a total of 59 trials where there were 3 chances of error on each test the male rat's responses were right in 62% of the trials, the females, 71%. Considering the small number of trials given this high percentage of correct responses is remarkable. Incidental tests upon raccoons, porcupines, and monkeys fail to show any great use of the sense of smell. Cole states that the raccoon will find a piece of sugar lying upon the floor of the cage more quickly .than a piece of meat. Monkeys occasionally discard an object after smelling it before putting it into the mouth (but rarely). The Cebus will occasionally smell an object, discard it, and then wipe the hands upon the body.

Romanes' test of the hunting dog.—The dog's sense of smell is probably very highly developed. In a well-known experiment Romanes tested the ability of a setter to track her master's scent.

He used twelve men, forcing them to walk Indian file, each man taking care to step in the tracks of the leader. " I took the lead while the game-keeper brought up the rear. When we had walked two hundred yards, 1 turned to the right, followed by five of the men; and at the point where I had turned to the right, the seventh man turned to the left, followed by all the remainder. The two parties . . . having walked in opposite directions for a consider- able distance, concealed themselves, and the bitch was put upon the common track of the whole party before the point of divergence. Following this common track with rapidity, she at first overshot the point of divergence, but quickly recovered it and without hesi- tation chose the track which turned to the right." [2]

Difficulties in the way of explaining the hunting be- havior of dogs.—It is believed by hunters that the com- mon hounds used for hunting rabbits in the South can follow a trail 10 to 12 hours old without back-tracking! It has been stated that the bloodhound has an even more highly developed sense of smell. Some writers have gone so far as to say that the animals will follow a trail at least 24 hours old and in the direction taken by the quarry. In trying to explain how the dog follows a trail always in the forward direction we meet with a number of difficulties. It is generally supposed that the dog is able to do this on the basis of the difference in the intensity between the tracks earlier made and those made later. Johnson finds on theoretical grounds that this explanation is not satisfactory. He presents the difficulties in the way of such a view so clearly that we quote his statements at length:

" Suppose that in each of a series of tracks, *a, b, c,* etc., a like quantity of the same single smell-substance had been deposited by the rabbit; that the tracks had been made one second apart, and that *a* was made three hours ago. It is evident *(changes of chemical composition being excluded)* that the smell-substance is greatest in quantity when first deposited. It becomes dissipated in time so that in this case there is hardly enough left in the track *a* to affect the dog.
" If the smell-substance is deposited in a gaseous state its diffusion could be represented by one of the well-known ' curves of decay.' The absolute intensity of the stimulus (i.e., the amount of odorous

substance present in the track at a given moment of time) may, within limits, be formulized:

$$\text{Log } S_t = \text{Log } S_0 - kt,$$

wherein S_0 equals the amount of the substance first deposited, t the time which had elapsed since the deposit was made, and k a constant function dependent on conditions of temperature, pressure, etc.

"In the case under consideration the stimulus-intensity at the track a is nearly zero when it is presented to the dog. The absolute difference of stimulus-intensity at a, b, and c would have to be extremely small, since the difference in the respective values of t is of the order of one part in nearly 11,000. Further: even this difference between a and b would exist only if they were simultaneously presented. Since the dog is supposed to be following the trail of the rabbit, for him to be affected by even a part of the difference between a and b it is necessary that he travel faster than did the rabbit in making the tracks. If the dog travels at the same rate as did the rabbit, when he reaches b its intensity will be just equal to that of a when a was passed. Moreover, in actual practice other difficulties arise. Suppose the rabbit has run from moist ground to dry ground. The smell-substances are diffused more rapidly under conditions of relatively small humidity than under conditions of greater humidity. The stimulus-intensity of the recently made tracks on dry ground could thus be less than those made earlier on the wet ground. In such case our assumption fails to explain the dog's failure to show confusion.

"But the dissipation of the smell-substance may be a complex process. For instance, it may be deposited, not in a gaseous state, but as a liquid or solid. In such case vaporization must precede diffusion. Vaporization, conditions being constant, proceeds at nearly a uniform rate in the open air. The amount of substance present in a gaseous state might thus be as great at a very advanced stage of dissipation as at an earlier stage. Since the substance to be odorous must be gaseous, we are not warranted in assuming that the stimulus-intensity is greater at a recently made track than at one made earlier, unless we know that all the smell-substance in the later track has been vaporized.

"There may be other factors such as chemical changes by which the deposited substance becomes odorous, etc., but consideration of them only increases the presumption against the intensity-difference theory.

"It has been suggested also that the dog may have an acute olfactory sensitivity to the *form* of the tracks made by his quarry and follow the trail from heel to toe. Certain features of the dog's behavior certainly indicate that he is *very* sensitive to differences of spatial position of olfactory stimuli. Another suggestion is that the smell-substances deposited by the different parts of the foot or body may differ specifically in stimulating quality, and that the dog is affected by this difference. Assuming either of these suggestions as a complete explanation of the dog's hunting behavior would require us to expect a bloodhound striking a man's trail at right angles, to back-track if the man had walked backward instead of forward across the field.

"Dr. P. W. Cobb has suggested a simple hypothesis; that the dog's sense of direction may be due to the trailing of *ground* smell-substances. For instance: the smell-substances affecting a dog trailing a man who had crossed a mint-bed might be (1) ground + man; (2) ground + man + mint, the mint being intense; (3) ground + man + mint, the mint-smell-substances diminishing rapidly in the direction the man had taken. The hypothesis impresses the writer as being valuable, although it does not afford a complete explanation of the facts as variously alleged.

"The value of careful field-tests should be apparent. The question may well be raised whether the hunting-behavior of the dog is really an olfactory response. A comparison of the field-behavior of anosmic dogs and normal dogs of the same litter and of a hunting breed, such as the beagle-hound, should prove highly interesting. It would be well worth while to ascertain as a beginning what responses a good hunting dog actually makes when introduced to trails the time and direction of which had previously been ascertained. The effect of numerous disturbing factors which could be introduced, some of which have been suggested above, ought to be quite interesting. It is to be hoped that some one with proper facilities and ample training may become interested enough to make an experimental investigation in this field."

Of the " field of smell " in mammals; of their " positiveness " or " negativeness " (preferences) to certain smells and of the groups or classes of smells to which they are sensitive, we know almost nothing.

Experiments on the olfactory sensitivity of birds.— The question of the influence of smell stimuli on the behavior of birds has always been an interesting one. Some birds possess both well-developed central and peripheral apparatus. Below (Fig. 65) are shown the dissections of the brain of the fulmar—a bird allied to the petrel and albatross—which has a well-developed olfactory system, and that (Fig. 66) of the raven, which has a poorly developed olfactory organ.

No incontestable positive evidence has ever been obtained to show that birds are sensitive to olfactory stimuli. The anecdotal literature is lengthy and interesting, but inconclusive. As an example we cite the following observation, which appears in the literature: An observer states that while digging sweet potatoes in a field he noticed a luxuriant growth of vines over a small mound and that the potatoes dug at this place were unusually large. On inquiry he learned that a horse and a cow had been buried there during the previous winter. In the afternoon and all during the next day vultures came in scores, swooping to the

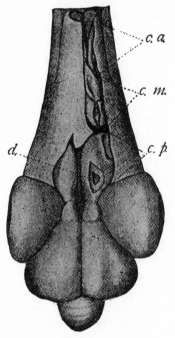

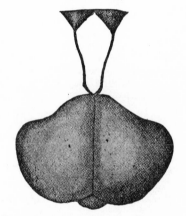

Fig. 65. Fulmarus Glacialis (Fulmar)

Dorsal view of portion of dissected head with the brain case material, which separates the eyes from the brain, removed. The right nasal chamber and a posterior portion of the left nasal chamber are exposed. The posterior turbinal of the right side has been opened at *d* to show the turns or rolls of its structure. The middle and anterior turbinals have been mutilated slightly in the dissection. *c.a.*, anterior turbinal; *c.m.*, middle turbinal; *c.p.*, posterior turbinal.

Fig. 66. Corvus Corax (Raven)

Dorsal view showing the minute olfactory lobes and the slender olfactory nerves. The posterior ends of the nasal chamber are included. (Both cuts from R. M. Strong, *Journal Morphol.*, XXII, 1911.)

ground about the mound. These birds continued to come for several days but in lessening numbers. No taint could be detected in the air. The experiments of Audubon are well known. The ones cited below were conducted with some care. The first four experiments were made by Audubon himself; the remaining ones are cited by Audubon from other sources.

1. An entire deer skin, including the hoofs, and provided with artificial eyes, was stuffed with dried grass, the whole being allowed to become "perfectly dry." The stuffed skin was exposed in a large field, and the observer concealed himself not far away. In a few minutes a vulture, soaring about, saw the deer skin and sailed down to it. The hide was torn open, and much grass was pulled out.

2. A large dead hog was hauled to a ravine and concealed by a covering of cane. As the weather was warm, the body became "extremely fetid" in a couple of days. Dogs found the carcass and fed heartily upon it, but vultures sailing over from time to time did not find it.

3. A young pig was killed, and its blood was scattered about on the ground. The body was concealed by a covering of leaves. Vultures found the blood and followed it down the ravine to the body, which was then discovered and devoured.

4. Two young vultures were kept for some weeks in a cage where they became accustomed to receiving food. The birds were in the habit of hissing and gesticulating when they saw food approaching. However, when food, either fresh or putrid, was brought up to the immediate rear of the cage where the vultures could not see it, no excitement was shown.

5. A dead hare, two dead birds, and a wheelbarrow full of offal from a slaughter house were deposited on the ground at the foot of Bachman's garden in South Carolina. A frame was raised above the pile at a distance of twelve inches from the ground, and this was covered with brush, allowing air to pass under freely. Though hundreds of vultures passed over in the next twenty-five days, none noticed the meat.

6. A coarse painting on canvas of a sheep skinned and cut open was placed on the ground, where it was noticed by vultures. They walked over the painting and tugged at it with their beaks. The painting was then placed within fifteen feet of the offal mentioned above, but the offal was not touched.

7. The most offensive portions of the offal were next placed on the ground, and these were covered by a thin canvas cloth on which were strewn several pieces of fresh beef. Vultures came and ate the beef, but they did not discover the offal beneath the canvas. A rent was then made in the canvas, whereupon the offal below was seen and eaten. (Taken largely from Strong.)

The following experiment of Darwin on condors likewise gave negative results:

"The condors were tied, each by a rope, in a long row at the bottom of a wall and having folded up a piece of meat in a white paper, I walked backwards and forwards, carrying it in my hand at the distance of about three yards from them, but no notice was taken. I then threw it on the ground, within one yard of an old bird; he looked at it for a moment with attention but then regarded it no more. With a stick I pushed it closer and closer, until at last he touched it with his beak; the paper was then instantly torn off with fury, and at the same moment, every bird in the long row began struggling and flapping its wings."

Rouse has made experiments in the laboratory of the respiratory changes in pigeons when subjected to smell stimuli. To such odors as oil of bergamot and lily of the valley no appreciable change in the respiratory curve could be noted. Only slight change was noted when asafœtida was used as the stimulus. On the other hand, " marked reaction " was produced by turpentine and ammonia. Such substances affect the fifth nerve rather than the olfactory, as Rouse clearly recognized. Beebe, on the other hand, feels that he has obtained slight positive evidence that birds use the olfactory organs:

Three boxes were placed some distance apart in the floor of a cage containing turkey and black vultures. After several days of fasting a piece of tainted meat was placed under the central box. Care was taken to raise the other boxes and to go through the farce of placing something under them. The vultures were very hungry, yet they did not leave their perches and come to the ground, although they had watched his movements. He next reëntered and threw two or three bits of meat to the ground.

Within a second or two, almost as the meat left the hand of the keeper, every vulture swooped to the ground and was hissing and struggling for a portion of the food. Twice the black vultures walked close about the meat box without appearing to notice the odor which was clearly perceptible, even to persons outside the cage. A turkey vulture walked to leeward, instantly turned and made his way to the box, which he examined on all sides. He was soon joined by two others of the same species, and all three took up their stations close to the source of the odor. Soon two black vultures came up, apparently impelled more by imitation than by actual discovery of the smell. All five birds remained for a long time grouped close to the box, going to it now and then, and examining it carefully. Thus even in the turkey vulture the sense of smell is certainly not highly developed, and compared with the sense of sight, is defective indeed.

R. M. Strong in this country has paid most attention to the olfactory responses in birds. His observational material is mainly inconclusive or negative. In one observation he states that a turkey vulture was flushed from the entrance of a gopher-turtle hole:

"The bird showed a great disinclination to leave the spot, although other individuals which were seen by the writer outside of cities were disposed to be wild. A dead gopher-turtle was found inside the burrow. It was impossible to view the turtle except when in a position to look down the oblique burrow, and it did not seem probable that a bird when flying overhead could see the body. A very strong odor of carrion prevailed for some distance on the lee side of the burrow.

"The writer could not rule out the possibility that the vulture had found the turtle outside of the hole through its sense of vision and had later pushed the body inside, but it seemed unlikely that this had happened. The circumstances all appeared to favor the conclusion that the carrion had been smelled, even though the evidence was far from conclusive."

In a long series of laboratory experiments where ring doves were used as subjects Strong obtained some evidence that these birds were stimulated by oil of bergamot. The apparatus was somewhat elaborate. The animal under test was put down in such a position that it could be stimulated by a gentle air current passing over oil of bergamot. If the animal followed up this odor it could obtain food (seeds). The apparatus was so arranged that the food could be placed in any one of four food compartments. The birds, while showing definite improvement in forming such a habit, never became perfect in their responses. Unfortunately Strong did not control his work by sectioning the olfactory bulbs. It is of course possible that the birds were reacting to cutaneous stimulation (fifth nerve).

The sense of smell in fishes.—Until within recent times there has been little scientific evidence that fish react to foods at a distance. It has been the general practice of fishermen, however, to bait a locality preparatory to fishing in it. This has worked well in the case of the shark and certain other fish, but in such cases it is difficult to say whether the shark senses the food at a distance and then follows the trace or whether chance swimming in the neighborhood leads him to the place where the food can be seen (or, if at night, tasted). We know from anatomical studies that the olfactory bulb and its central connections are well developed, and that the peripheral organs are also well developed. Furthermore, we know that the fish has well-developed gustatory structures. The neural systems involved in the gustatory organs are different from those which care for the olfactory mechanism. Notwithstanding these well-marked morphological differences certain authors have maintained that the so-called olfactory organ is only a finely developed taste organ. The difficulty the human being has in smelling a substance contained in a fluid when the fluid is actually in contact with the olfactory membrane has led him to say that he smells only gaseous and vaporous materials, while, on the other hand, he tastes fluids and solids. No one can say positively that gaseous particles have to be dissolved by the mucus present on the surface of the *regio olfactoria* before activity is initiated in that receptor, yet it is generally so admitted. We know positively, on the other hand, that no substance which cannot be dissolved by the fluids of the mouth can be tasted. The only difference between smell and taste on this view would be in the concentration of the fluids in the two cases. The olfactory mechanism is sensitive to fluids of slight concentration. On such an hypothesis we can conceive of a very small particle of meat being carried out by currents and stimulating the olfactory receptors, e.g., of sharks, even at great distances. If such is the case the olfactory mechanism becomes a distance receptor ranking with the ear and with the eye. To Baglioni, apparently, belongs the credit of advancing the first scientific experimental evidence that food substances dissolved in a fluid medium can act upon the olfactory organs of marine forms in the way we have just described, and yet the distinction between animals which " scent " their food and those which see it was made by Bateson many years ago. Baglioni's experiments were carried out in 1908 upon the octopus and fish *(Balistes capriscus)*. He first blinded the animals in order to make observation more sure. He states that the effect of this operation was to be seen mainly in the limitation of their spontaneous movements. The blind fish especially remained quietly resting behind some object in the aquarium.

This limitation of movements favors the observation of their response to olfactory substances. Baglioni describes his experiments mainly with the octopus and states that the behavior of the fish is the same. We describe one of his experiments upon the octopus:

An octopus which had been blinded for more than a month was placed in a tank, the water of which was constantly being renewed from a faucet placed near the middle of the aquarium. The tank was 1.75 meters in length, 40 mm. in breadth, and 25 mm. in height. When the octopus was quietly resting at one end a small dead fish was thrown into the opposite end which came to rest on the bottom. In 1.25 minutes the octopus became agitated. Movements of the arm began and then of the whole body. In 3.5 minutes the animal had reached the middle of the basin. At the end of 5 more seconds one arm touched the fish. The fish was seized and carried to the mouth.

Experiments by Parker and Sheldon.—Parker and Sheldon have obtained still more striking evidence of the essentially olfactory nature of such responses. They have worked mainly with the smooth dogfish *(Mustelus canis)*, the killifish *(Fundulus heteroclitus)*, and the fresh-water catfish *(Ameiurus nebulosus)*. All three forms, while differing in the details of their responses, show ability to respond to stimuli which affect the olfactory apparatus. We present Parker's excellent summary of his experiments upon the catfish:

"*Ameiurus nebulosus* is a bottom-feeding fish possessing fair powers of sight and unusual gustatory organs located not only in the mouth and on the general outer surface of the body, but especially on the eight barblets about the mouth (Herrick, 1903). It is a hardy fish, living well in confinement and undergoing operations with success. It possesses near its anterior end a pair of nasal chambers, each of which is provided with two apertures, one anterior, the other posterior. The anterior aperture is nearly circular in outline and is located on a slight conical elevation somewhat anterior to the root of the dorsal barblet. The posterior aperture is slit-like in form and lies immediately posterior to the same barblet. The anterior aperture is apparently always open; the posterior one seems capable of slight closure, but is usually freely open.

" By keeping catfishes a few days without food they can be made most eager for it, and if into an assemblage of such individuals a few fragments of fresh earthworms are dropped, the excitement that ensues will last some time after the final piece of worm has been swallowed. During this period the fishes swim about actively in the lower part of the aquarium, now in this direction, now in that, and frequently sweep the bottom with their barblets. As can be noticed when feeding actually occurs, the fishes seldom seize a fragment of worm until their barblets have come in contact with it. Yet before they have thus touched any food they show a marked degree of excitement and it is this initial nervous state that would lead an observer to suspect that they scented their food. This phase of their activity was, therefore, taken as the one to be tested in connection with their olfactory organs.

"The nasal chambers of the catfish contain ciliated epithelium, the action of which is to draw water in at the anterior olfactory opening and discharge it at the posterior one. As can be demonstrated with carmine suspended in water, the passage through the chamber is accomplished in 8 to 10 seconds.

"As a preliminary step in testing the catfishes, five normal fishes were placed in a large aquarium over night that they might become accustomed to their surroundings. In this aquarium were then hung two wads of cheesecloth, in one of which was concealed some minced earthworm. The fishes, which were swimming about near these wads, were then watched for an hour and their reactions in reference to the wads were recorded. The wad without worms was passed by the fishes many times and did not excite any noticeable reaction. The wad containing the worms was seized and tugged at eleven times in the course of the hour, notwithstanding the fact that from time to time this and the other wad were interchanged in position. Not only did the fishes thus openly seize this wad, but when in its neighborhood they would often turn sharply as though seeking something without success, a form of reaction seldom observed near the wad which contained no worms. Two other sets, of five normal fishes each, were tested in this manner and with similar results. It was perfectly clear to any one watching these reactions that the fishes sensed the difference between the wad of cloth with worms and that without worms.

"To ascertain what receptive organs were concerned in the reactions just described, two sets of 5 fishes each were taken from among the 15 normal fishes already tested, and each set was prepared differently by subjecting its members to a special operation. One set was etherized, and, through a small incision between the eyes, their olfactory tracts were cut, thus rendering their olfactory apparatus functionless. From fishes of the other set all the barblets were removed, whereby their external gustatory organs were partly, though not wholly, eliminated. After these operations both sets of fishes were liberated in the large aquarium, where they remained for over two days At the expiration of this time, they were carefully inspected and tested. They swam about in an essentially normal way and members of both sets snapped bits of worm from the end of a hooked wire much as a normal fish does. Presumably they were in a satisfactory condition for experimentation.

"The tests were begun by introducing into the large aquarium containing the 10 fishes a wad of cheesecloth within which were hidden some minced earthworms and recording the kind of fish that visited it and the nature of their reactions. During the first hour the wad was seized 34 times by fishes without barblets but with normal olfactory organs and, though often passed by fishes with cut olfactory tracts, it was 'nosed' only once by one of these. A wad of cheesecloth without worms was next substituted for that with worms and the reactions of the fishes were recorded for a second hour. Though members of both sets frequently swam by this wad, none at any time during the hour seized it or even nosed it. These tests were repeated on the same fishes for two succeeding days and with essentially similar results. On the second day the wad with worms was seized 16 times during the test hour by fishes with normal olfactory organs and on the third day 54 times. On both these days the fishes with their olfactory tracts cut made no attempts on the wad with worms nor did any fish at any time nose the wormless wad. The movements of the two sets of fishes when in the neighborhood of the wad containing minced worms were characteristically different. The fishes with their olfactory tracts cut swam by the wads without noticeable change; those without barblets, but with their olfactory apparatus intact almost always made several sharp turns when near the wad as though seeking something, and then either moved slowly away or swam more or less directly to the wad and began to nose and nibble it. These reactions were so clear and so characteristic that when taken in connection with the conditions of the fishes, they lead inevitably to the conclusion that the olfactory apparatus of the catfish is service-able in sensing food at a distance much beyond that at which the organs of taste are capable of acting; in other words, catfish truly scent their food."

The reactions of the killifish under such conditions offer enough points of difference to require noting. It, in con-trast both to the catfish and the dogfish, uses its eyes as well as its nose in seeking food. If a small piece of dogfish is dropped into a pool containing the killifish they imme-diately spring toward it—too suddenly to suppose that diffusion could have taken place to such an extent that the olfactory system could be stimulated. Even if a ball of filter paper is thrown into the tank they dart forward and seize it, but soon discard it. It is the eye likewise which makes them dart forward and seize a packet of plain cheese-cloth. On account of their use of vision it is hard to make conclusive experiments upon their olfactory sensitivity un-less they are blinded at the same time that they are made anosmic. On account of the fact that in normal fish plain cheesecloth packets are soon discarded, it is possible to test the effect of cutting the olfactory nerves. Anosmic animals, when tested with two packets, the one containing hidden meat and the other without food, nibble at both packets in such a way that an uninformed observer could not tell which contains food. When these same two packets are placed before normal animals the food packet becomes immediately surrounded by a vigorous assemblage of contesting individuals.[3]

II. TASTE

Location of gustatory organs.—The gustatory organs in certain fishes have a widespread distribution. In addition to the taste buds, which are found in the mouths of fishes, we find them frequently upon the lips, the outer skin of the head and on the trunk. In *Ameiurus* it has been shown that the terminal buds occur in the skin of practically the whole body surface but especially on the barblets. These terminal buds must be sharply distinguished from the sensory structures in the lateral line system, which they resemble rather closely (p. 394). The sensory nerve supply to the terminal buds of the mouth is shared in by X, IX, and VII pairs of cranial nerves; those of the bodily surface *(Ameiurus)* largely by the lateral accessory branch of the VII cranial nerve.

Herrick's experiments upon the functional significance of the taste buds.—In the discussion of the functional significance of the taste buds we shall consider mainly the experiments which have been made upon the catfish *(Ameiurus)*. As has been stated, this animal rarely uses its eyes in the search for food. If, in the course of random and aimless movements, the fish pass near the sides and bottom of the aquarium which contains food, they touch the food with the lips or barblets, and instantly seize and swallow it. They are easily frightened and experimentation is difficult. If one arranges the aquarium so that the fish may partially conceal themselves, leaving certain of the fins and other parts uncovered, it is possible to make experiments which show the functions of these

[3] More recently still Copeland has found that the puffer (*Spheroides maculatus*) shows the same ability to respond to concealed food. His method of determining this fact was essentially like that of Parker.

taste buds. If, under these conditions, a piece of meat is lowered so that it touches the barblet, the meat is instantly seized and swallowed. Touching any part of the body, head or tail, produces the same reaction. Vision is not necessary to set off the reflex of seizing and swallowing. From the above experiments we are not able to decide whether touch or taste is the functional sense. When they are touched with cotton wool on any part of the body under similar conditions, they will likewise turn and seize the wool, but soon drop it. If, now, one continues stimulating them with cotton wool, they cease to respond. When they have become habituated to the contact with the wool, one again tries them with meat. Invariably the response is called out. It is evident that both senses participate. The response is both a tactual and a gustatory reflex. The gustatory reflex is obtained (after tactual accommodation) if the cotton wool is soaked with meat juice. In order to produce typical gustatory reflexes, the stimulus must be strong and localized. Diffusion of juices called forth only seeking movements.[4] While the olfactory receptors may have participated in these reactions, it is quite probable that they would have occurred in anosmic animals. While Herrick did not section the olfactory nerves in the catfish, he did perform such an operation on several tomcods (*Microgadus tomcod*). From the second day after the operation the animals fed normally. Furthermore,

" After the third or fourth day the fishes took their food in all respects like uninjured fishes, so far as could be observed. They gave all of the characteristic reflexes that have been mentioned above, including the discrimination between cotton wool and cotton dipped in clam juice, and between sea water and clam juice applied with a pipette, etc. The operated fish would locate a concealed bait by means of pelvic fins exactly as the normal fish does, and he would similarly root it out and eat it. In short, the gustatory reflexes, so far as I have observed them, were absolutely unmodified by the

[4] Similar tests upon the pollack (*Pollackhius vires*), hake (*Urophycis tenuis*), and the tomcod (*Microgadus tomcod*) have yielded similar results. The pollack has very well developed eyes and darts for the food when he sees it. Sight plays a large part in its daily life. It is not well suited to experiments upon taste. The fins are very sensitive to meat.

operation. That the olfactory apparatus was totally destroyed was verified by autopsy dissections made after the close of the observations." [5]

Parker's experiments upon the gustatory responses of fishes.—Parker's own experiments confirm the work of Herrick and afford some additional facts. He investigated the sense of taste in the common hornpout. The taste buds in this form occur not only in the mouth and in the barbules but also over most of the external surface. Those on the exterior of the fish are innervated by the branches of the seventh nerve. Hornpouts will snap at a bait when it is presented to the flank of the body as well as when it is close to the mouth. The exterior of the body is sensitive to sour, saline, and alkaline solutions, the head being more sensitive than the trunk. In hornpouts, if the branches of the seventh nerve distributed to the skin have been cut, thus destroying the sensitivity of the skin, there is no longer a response to bait brought near to the trunk though the same bait is eagerly taken when brought near to the mouth. Such animals, however, retain their full sensitiveness to sour, saline, and alkaline solutions when applied to the skin of the trunk. The loss of sensitivity to bait is not due to shock. They still snap at the bait if the lateral branch of the tenth nerve has been cut. After cutting the lateral branches of the seventh and tenth nerves the only sensory nerves left intact on the flanks of the body are the branches of the spinal nerves. Fish in this condition still respond to sour, saline, and alkaline solutions. It follows that these solutions must stimulate the terminals of the spinal nerves and that these

[5] While there is a seeming contradiction between these experiments and those cited from Parker and Sheldon on p. 409, it may partially be removed by supposing that the tomcod has an extraordinarily finely developed sense of taste in its pelvic fins—so highly developed, indeed, that it functions like a distance receptor. Neither Parker nor Sheldon worked with this form. Parker worked with the catfish, having its olfactory mechanism as the chief point of interest, while Herrick was interested mainly in the gustatory mechanism. Their results are not strictly in harmony. It is unfortunate that Herrick did not work with anosmic catfish. Even allowing for the apparent contradiction it would seem that both investigators have made their respective points, viz., that the terminal buds distributed over the bodily surface are true taste structures (Herrick) and that the olfactory mechanism serves as a distance receptor (Parker).

nerves must be regarded as chemical in function, though they are not primarily concerned in the response to bait. In hornpouts, the posterior half of whose spinal cord has been destroyed but whose seventh nerve is intact, there is no response when sour, saline, and alkaline solutions and bait are applied to the flanks and near the tail. The absence of response to *bait* in this experiment Parker believes to be due to the loss of the motor mechanism of the cord whereby the fish turns to snap at the bait and not to the loss of the spinal sensory fibers. The loss of these fibers would account for the absence of response to sour, saline, and alkaline solutions. Parker believes that the sense of taste is complex and involves not only the seventh nerve but also the spinal nerves; i.e., that there is both a sense of taste and a " common chemical sense." This conception, which does some violence to the common notion of the function of cutaneous receptors, should be carefully considered.

III. THE " COMMON CHEMICAL SENSE " IN FISHES

Introduction.—There is a growing tendency to use the term " chemical sense " generically and to make it include smell, taste, and a sense which may be described as the " common chemical sense." While this usage seems undesirable it is impossible to discuss certain experimental results without using at least the term " common chemical sense." This is especially true when we come to treat of the responses of fish, amphibia, and the invertebrates to chemical substances. It is asserted (Sheldon) that the " common chemical sense " is entirely different from the ordinary cutaneous system, and that all vertebrates from the lancelet to man possess it (as well as all invertebrates). In man the receptors for this organ lie especially on the exposed mucous surfaces such as those of the nasal chambers, the mouth cavity, and the moist surfaces of the eyelids. Parker states that " the receptors on these surfaces are normally stimulated by the chemical action of the material in direct contact with them and they represent collectively a sense as distinct and well defined as smell or taste." The work on human sensory physiology within recent years has tended to show that there are four distinct kinds of cutaneous receptors—stimulated respectively by (1) pressure, (2) cold, (3) warm, and (4) noxious substances. These may be stimulated separately or simultaneously. Furthermore, there is some positive evidence (von Frey and others) that the hairs and Meissner corpuscles mediate pressure responses, while the end bulb type of corpuscle mediates cold, and the Ruffini cylinder and related types mediate warm stimuli. The free nerve endings are supposed to be stimulated by noxious substances, acids, cuts, burns, bruises, etc. This whole system is collectively called the " cutaneous sense." It would seem that our present concept of this sense is adequate and that the use of the term " common chemical sense " is confusing. There has been no distinction made between the external skin and the skin bathed by mucus. The experimental work of Head and Sherren (and of Rivers), however clearly it may show that our former ideas of localization of impulses in the cord were in error and that motor nerve trunks carry sensory fibers, does not seriously modify our ideas of the nature of the external cutaneous system. That the cutaneous system, as we understand that term in man, exists unchanged through the vertebrate series, we do not for a moment claim (especially in view of the fact that highly organized sensory terminals like those found in man apparently do not exist in the skin of the fish). The experiments of Parker and of Sheldon on fish tend to establish the view that differences do exist between man and certain of the lower vertebrates.

Sheldon's experiments upon the smooth dogfish.—The older experiments upon the " common chemical sense " in fish (e.g., Nagel's) are unsatisfactory because they failed to make any distinction between those forms which possess taste buds only in the mouth cavities, and those which possess such terminals on the bodily surfaces. Sheldon worked only upon the smooth dogfish (*Mustelus canis*), which possesses taste buds only in the mouth cavities. The sensitivity of the whole bodily surface to chemical stimuli was tested as well as the mouth and nasal capsules, and the nerves mediating the reactions were determined. The chemicals used were hydrochloric, nitric, and sulphuric acids for acid stimuli; sodium, ammonium, and lithium chlorides for saline stimuli; sodium hydroxide for alkaline; cane sugar, dextrose, saccharine, and its carbonates for sweet; and quinine hydrochloride, picric acid, ammonium and sodium picrates for bitter.[6] The solutions were applied by means of a pipette. They were ejected slowly with the tip of the pipette 2 mm. from the skin of the fish. Stimulation of the mouth or spiracles is followed (when the stimulus is effective) by one or more violent gulps accompanied by a quick ejection of water through the bronchial openings and more rapid respiration. When the nostrils were stimulated there followed a quick jerk of the head. Stimulation of the different fins likewise produced characteristic reactions. Stimulation of the dorsal, lateral, and ventral surfaces results in a movement which is a part of the general swimming movement. In general it may be stated that all parts of the body are very sensitive to acids and alkalis in very dilute solutions, less sensitive to salt and bitter substances, and *not sensitive at all to sugars*. Certain parts of the bodily surface are more sensitive to salts and alkalis than is the mouth. The outer skin and the mouth are equally sensitive to acids, while the mouth is more sensitive to bitter substances. In regard to the nerves mediating the response to chemical stimuli it may be stated that when the cord is *destroyed* the caudal part of the body becomes insensitive. This shows that the lateral line organs do not participate in these reactions (since destruction of the cord does not affect them). When the cord is merely severed from the brain the response to chemical stimuli is more

[6] These were made up in distilled water on the basis of the grammolecular solution. The inorganic acids were prepared as normal solutions, titrated against an alkali of known strength for accuracy. The other solutions were made up by weight, the concentration first used as a test depending partly on the solubility of the chemical used. The chlorides were prepared as 5n solutions, the sugar, 3n, sodium hydroxide as n, saccharine n/6, quinine hydrochloride n/10, picric and its salts n/15. These solutions were gradually diluted until the limit of reaction was reached.

marked than before. Sectioning of that part of the fifth
nerve which supplies the nasal passages (*ramus maxillaris
trigemini*) produces insensitivity to chemical stimuli in
that region, thus showing that the olfactory nerves do not
participate in the reactions. Sheldon finds evidence that
the " common chemical sense " is likewise distinct from the
tactual sense. This evidence may be summarized as follows:
Parts of the body may be fatigued for tactual stimuli and
remain sensitive to chemical stimuli, but when any region
is fatigued for a given chemical stimulus it no longer or
rarely is sensitive to tactual stimuli. It usually remains
sensitive to other forms of chemical stimuli, however.
When cocaine is applied response to tactile stimuli disappears before response to chemical. Among chemical
stimuli, sensitivity to bitter disappears first. These results
are supposed to furnish evidence that the cutaneous mechanism is separate from that of the " common chemical
sense." Similar experiments have been carried out upon
the catfish (*Ameiurus*) and upon *Ammocœtes* by Parker,
with results which confirm those of Sheldon.

" Common chemical sense " in amphibia.—The common leopard frog (*Rana pipiens Schreber*) reacts to chemicals much as does the fish. Cole, who made the tests, prepared brainless frogs and dipped them to the ankle in a
given solution. After a few seconds the leg would be
withdrawn in case the stimulus was effective. A frog
dipped into distilled water does not so withdraw the leg.
Solutions of the chlorides of ammonium, potassium, sodium,
and lithium were found to be effective stimuli. Since these
same solutions produce gustatory reactions in man, the
question arises here, as in the case of the fish, does the frog's
skin possess a general chemical sense comparable with the
special sense of taste? Cole is inclined to answer this
question in the affirmative, since he was able to show that
frogs which had been cocainized until pain reactions were
abolished still responded at least once to the chemical
stimulus (a 3 m. solution of ammonium chloride).

Summary.—While it has been shown beyond question
that both the fish and the frog (spinal) are sensitive to

acids on bodily surfaces, the experiments of Sheldon and Cole do not conclusively militate against the view that these reactions are mediated by the pressure-cold-warm-pain terminals (and apparently there are such specificities even though the sensory endings are not highly differentiated. See work of Hofer, p. 428). Their results can possibly be harmonized with the view that these receptors do mediate the response to acids by supposing that any or all of such terminals may be " inadequately " stimulated by the solutions; that their threshold of sensitivity is markedly altered by the chemicals; and that when superficial terminals are destroyed or otherwise made insensitive (fatigued?) the deep-lying cutaneous structures together with the kinæsthetic (muscle spindles or their homologs, etc.) begin to function. However, Herrick supposes that the " common chemical sense " is the primitive one from which the olfactory and gustatory have been differentiated.[7]

BIBLIOGRAPHY

Audubon, J. J., *Ornothological Bibliography*, 1835, II, 33.

Baglioni, S., " Contributions expérimentales à la physiologie du sens olfactif et du sens tactile des animaux marins (*Octopus et quelques poissons*),"*Arch. Ital. de Biol.*, 1909, LII, 225.

——————— " Zur Kenntnis der Leistung einiger Sinnesorgane (Gesichtssinn, Tastsinn, und Geruchssinn) und des Zentralnervensystems der Cephalopden und Fische," *Zeitsch. f. Biol.*, LIII, 255.

——————— " Zur Physiologie des Geruchsinnes und des Tastsinnes der Seetiere," *Zentralblatt für Physiologie*, XXII, 719.

Bateson, W., " The Sense Organs and Perceptions of Fishes, with Remarks on the Supply of Bait," *Jour. Mar. Biol. Assoc., United Kingdom*, N.S., 1890, I, 225.

Beebe, C. W., " New World Vultures," Part II, *Zool. Soc. Bull.*, No. 32, 465.

Cole, L. J., " Reactions of Frogs to Chlorides of Ammonium, Potassium, Sodium, and Lithicum," *Jour. Comp. Neu. and Psych.*, 1910, XX, 601.

Copeland, M., " The Olfactory Reactions of the Puffer or Swellfish, Spheroides maculatus " (Bloch and Schneider), *Jour. Exp. Zool.*, XII, 363.

———————

[7] Parker differs from Herrick and Sheldon in holding that the olfactory sense presents the primitive form from which the others have been derived. He is led to this view chiefly by the similarity of the olfactory neurone to sensory cells found in invertebrates.

HERRICK, C. J., " On the Morphological and Physiological Classification of the Cutaneous Sense Organs of Fishes," *Amer. Nat.*,
1903, XXXVII, 313.
————————— " The Organ and Sense of Taste in Fishes," *Bull.
U. S. Fish Comm.*, 1902, XXII, 237; also *Bull. of Scientific Lab.
of Denison Univ.*, 1903, XII, 39.

JOHNSON, H. M., " A Note on the Supposed Olfactory Hunting Responses of the Dog," *Jour. Animal Beh.*, 1914, IV, 76.

PARKER, G. H., " The Olfactory Reactions of the Common Killifish,
Fundulus heteroclitus (Linn.)," *Jour. Exp.' Zool*, II, 1.
————————— " Olfactory Reactions in Fishes," *Jour. Exp. Zool.*,
VIII, 535.
————————— " The Relation of Smell, Taste, and the Common
Chemical Sense in Vertebrates," *Jour. Acad. Nat. Sciences of
Phil.*, 1912, XV, 22.
————————— " The Sense of Taste in Fishes," *Science*, N.S., 1908,
XXVII, 453.

PARKER, G. H., and SHELDON, R. E., " The Sense of Smell in Fishes,"
Bull. Bureau Fisheries, 1912, XXXII, 35.

READ, E. A., " A Contribution to the Knowledge of the Olfactory
Apparatus in Dog, Cat, and Man," *Amer. Jour. of Anatomy*,
1908, VIII, 17.

ROMANES, G. J., " Experiments on the Sense of Smell in Dogs,"
Nature, 1887, XXXVI, 273.

ROUSE, J. E., " Respiration and Emotion in Pigeons," *Jour. Comp.
Neu. and Psych.*, 1905, XV, 494.

SHELDON, R. E., " The Reactions of the Dogfish to Chemical Stimuli,"
Jour. Comp. Neu. and Psych., XIX, 273.
————————— " The Sense of Smell in Selachians," *Jour. Exp. Zool.*,
II, 51.

STRONG, R. M., " On the Olfactory Organs and the Sense of Smell
in Birds," *Jour. Morph.*, 1911, XXII, 619.
————————— " On the Habits and Behavior of the Herring Gull,"
Larus argentatus pont, The Auk, 1914, XXXI, 21 and 178.

WATSON, J. B., *Animal Education*. Chicago, Univ. of Chicago Press,
1903.

CHAPTER XIV

CUTANEOUS, ORGANIC, AND KINÆSTHETIC SENSES

I. CUTANEOUS

Cutaneous sensitivity in mammals.—Many mammals are well supplied with highly developed tactual mechanisms, such as hairy coats, vibrissæ, etc. No mammal seems to be lacking completely in hairs. The vibrissæ seem to be highly specialized tactual organs which play a considerable rôle in the daily life of many animals. It has been supposed that such specialized tactile organs are to be found mainly upon nocturnal animals. This position, however, cannot seriously be maintained. Vincent has made a careful histological study of the vibrissæ of the rat. Fig. 67 shows the structure of such a hair. Its rich sensory innervation and large arterial supply are apparent.

In addition to the tactile hairs, mammals are well supplied with highly specialized sensory endings in the dermal and muscular tissues. Vincent's investigation of the function of the vibrissæ in the daily life of the rat, and especially in learning problems, the solution of which is dependent upon the functioning of the vibrissæ, is the only comprehensive study we have upon the contact sense of animals. She constructed a simple maze, the runways to which were without sidepieces (restraining walls). The runways (4″ boards lying horizontally) were placed far enough apart to keep the animal from jumping from

one to the other. The maze was then raised 2 feet from
the floor. The normal animals behave characteristically
in this maze. In moving off after being put on the
runway they go at first along the very edge of the board

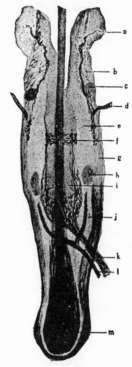

FIG. 67.—LONGITUDINAL SECTION OF FOLLICLE

This follicle was drawn from a Cajal silver preparation, but some
features of the nerves and arteries have been added from other prepa-
rations. It shows: *a*, nerve from dermal plexus running down to
form the nerve ring; *b*, conical body; *c*, sebaceous gland; *d*, artery
entering ring sinus; *e*, ring sinus; *f*, nerve ring; *g*, dermal sheath;
h, ringwulst; *i*, root sheath; *j*, cavernous sinus with trabeculæ;
k, main sensory nerve from below; *l*, large artery entering with
nerve; *m*, papilla. (From S. B. Vincent, *Jour. Comp. Neurol.*, Vol.
XXII, 1913.)

with vibrissæ dragging. They curl their toes over the edge
and run with noses against the floor. The animals moved
slowly at first, so there were few falls. Shortly bursts of

speed occurred and then falls became numerous at the turns. Finally, as in the Hampton Court maze (p. 103), the animals became automatic. The three photographs from Vincent's monograph show respectively a normal animal, a blind rat without vibrissæ, and a blind rat with vibrissæ. The influence of the vibrissæ can be thrown into relief by cutting them from one side. Strange to say when the vibrissæ are absent on the *right* side the animals keep close to the left

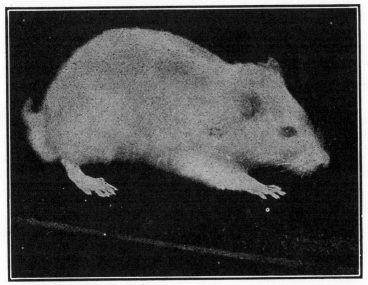

FIG. 68.—NORMAL ANIMAL WITH VIBRISSÆ ON MAZE WITHOUT SIDES

Note the position in the center of the track, the way the feet are placed, the lifted head and body.

side of the path, and *vice versa*. When running they pass to the edge, turn the remaining vibrissæ down, and follow the edges closely. Vincent has shown further that white rats can form the habit of entering an alley with corrugated sides when two smooth alleys are offered at the same time. Tactile hairs are much utilized in the learning of this problem. When robbed of them the animal makes use of the bare snout. When the snout is made insensitive by cutting the infra-orbital nerve it can no longer form such habits.

It is evident from this work that the vibrissæ are functional structures and that they serve as (short) distance receptors. The so-called " stereotropism " which such animals exhibit is probably no more a case of stereotropism than is the action of a blind man in keeping near a wall or the edge of the sidewalk. Experiments of Nicolai, where the salivary reflex was used as the indicator, show apparently

FIG. 69.—BLIND RAT WITHOUT VIBRISSÆ

Note the flattened body and the use of the toes and nose on the edge of the maze.

that the dog is sensitive to mechanical stimuli and that the localization of such stimuli is accurate.

Hahn's experiments on bats.—For a long time it has been known that blind, anosmic, and deaf bats were able to avoid objects in their way and even to avoid silken threads stretched closely together. Hahn, in his more recent work, states that the older experiments are lacking in scientific accuracy since none of his bats, even *with sense organs intact*, was able to do what has been claimed by the earlier experimenters for maimed animals. To test the mechanism by means of which they avoid obstacles, Hahn made the following tests: Bats were liberated in an un-ceiled room 15' wide, 18' long, 9' from floor to eaves, 12' from apex to ceiling. Pieces of black annealed iron wire 1 mm. in diameter were suspended from the rafters. These were spaced so that there was one wire to each 11" of space. The animals were tested under four conditions: (1) With eyes covered with glue and lamp-black; (2) with external ears and tragi excised; (3) with external auditory meatus stopped with plaster of Paris; and (4) with hairs of

FIG. 70.—BLIND RAT WITH VIBRISSÆ
Note the use of toes and vibrissæ on edge of maze.

body and membranes pasted down with vaseline. On *Myotis lucifugus* we get the following percentage of hits in the various controls:

Normal	Eyes covered	Ex. ears and tragi removed	Meatus stopped	Hairs covered
24%	15.3%	31.4%	66%	36.4%

It is evident that vision does not play a large part. It is stated by Hahn that the " *perception* " of a stationary ob-ject is probably due to the condensation of the air between the flying bat and the solid object that it is approaching—

the drum membrane functioning chiefly as a contact organ. He states also that the fine bodily hairs have a function in the avoidance of objects.

The " sense of support " in mammals.—In experiments upon rats, chicks, turtles, and many other vertebrates the influence of the contact sense is apparent in their behavior when placed on the edge of table-tops, etc. In trying to get blind rats to jump from one platform to another, Richardson found that " up to a certain distance the rat was able to step across with little difficulty; and the contact of the snout or vibrissæ with platform II. seemed to be the essential stimulus in the majority of cases." " . . . This (blind) rat would not allow his forefeet to leave the platform unless his vibrissæ reported contact with some object. When the platform was beyond the reach of his vibrissæ, the experimenter touched their tips with a pencil, whereupon he put out his forefeet to step over." Small finds the tendency to withdraw from the edge of the table strong in very young rats. The guinea pig seems to be lacking in such reflexes. Chicks and reptiles seemed to be influenced in such situations more by visual than by contact stimuli. (See p. 362 for Yerkes' experiment on tortoise.)

Yoakum's experiments upon the temperature sense in mammals.—Yoakum has tested the temperature sense of gray squirrels and white rats by forcing them to form the habit of entering the warmer of two boxes. The apparatus used is shown on p. 92. The warmer box (Standard) was kept at 40°±2°C., the other (Variable) at 15°±2°C. When the habit was perfected the temperature of the Variable was raised to 25°±2°C. The habit was again perfected. The temperature of the Variable was then changed to 30°±2°C. The experiment had to be interrupted at this point, but it was carried far enough to show that the difference limen had not been reached. A similar series of experiments was carried out upon white rats with the temperatures S=40°±2° C. and V=24°±2° C. The rats readily learned to enter the warmer of the two boxes under such conditions. The D.L. to temperature was not obtained. Both these animals will pile up cotton, straws, etc., to form a nest when the room temperature is lowered considerably. While stimuli other than temperature will call out this burrowing response, it probably is often called out by changes of temperature in the room. Yoakum describes the behavior of the squirrel as follows:

" The animal's method of covering itself is interesting. The squirrel will draw the shavings, or cotton, up in a pile in one corner of the cage, and will then burrow into it. When finally hidden in the pile, all that is visible is a portion of the tail; if this is drawn aside the tip of the nose and finally the entire head becomes visible. The little animal thus lies curled up in its nest with the tail as the final addition to its covering."

Nicolai states that when cold is applied to a particular spot on the skin of the dog a conditioned reflex is called forth. If the cold is applied to any other spot, the reflex again follows, showing that localization is not very exact. By the same method it has been shown that the dog is sensitive to warmth and that cold may be reacted to differently from warmth.

Contact sensitivity in fish.—Of contact sensitivity in fish in the narrower sense (pressure-temperature-pain) we know very little. Running through the experiments of Bateson, Baglioni, Herrick, Parker, and Sheldon we find abundant proof of the sensitivity to contact—to solid objects and to cotton wool, etc., but the observations have been more or less incidental. Herrick has brought out the fact that fish, which at first always respond to cotton wool, will eventually learn to inhibit response to this and to react only when stimulated with food objects. Baglioni finds in the trigger fish, *Balistes capriscus,* that the skin of the fins and of the upper anterior surface of the spine, stimulation of which causes erection of the spine, are quite sensitive to contacts. In the dog fish, *Scyllium,* the following regions are quite sensitive: the immediate neighborhood of the outer gill slits, stimulation of which causes respiratory reflexes; the neighborhood of the spiracles; the regions around the eyes, and the skin of the lids, stimulation of which produces closure of the lids. The external surface of the skin as a whole was found to be insensitive. Hofer, however, has shown experimentally that the fish has tactile spots and warm spots upon the skin of the head but not in the skin of other regions. Lyon has made experiments on the fish's ability to orient to currents in the water when in darkness. He had previously shown that the fish swims against the current (head up stream) through visual reflexes (p. 361). When tested in darkness the same reaction was observed, due to the contacts between the body of the fish and stationary objects. In the light of Hofer's work on the function of the lateral line organs it is probable that Lyon's conclusions will need confirmation.

Contact and temperature sensitivity in amphibia.—The contact and temperature sensitivity of the frog is somewhat better known. It has even been stated (Steinach) that the frog possesses " touch spots " but the evidence is far from being conclusive. Babák has recently studied the temperature sense of the frog by a new and very sensitive method which promises to be very useful in behavior. He has found that the breathing rhythm of a frog with the fore-brain removed proceeds with machine-like regularity, interrupted only when the animal is stimulated and resumed shortly after the stimulating agent is removed. In the maimed frog lung ventilation also occurs only after stimulation. In his first paper upon the sensitivity of the frog, the second of a series of studies upon the breathing rhythm, the author takes up the sensitivity of the animal to temperature as determined by changes in the breathing rate. The animals used had completely recovered from the shock resulting from operation upon the brain. The temperature stimuli were applied by means of the thermæsthesiometer held at a distance of 1 mm. from the animal's skin. The actual temperature changes in the skin could be judged only approximately. During experimentation great care was required to avoid auditory and tactile stimuli, etc. The specimens studied were found to be sensitive to slight changes in either direction from the physiological zero point. For comparison Babák obtained the threshold in human beings by applying the temperature stimulus 1 mm. from the skin surface. The frogs, if the above reaction may be taken as an indicator, are fully as sensitive as man. The head region is most sensitive. It is possible by this method to work out a complete topography of dermal temperature sensitivity. The experiments of Yerkes on the auditory-tactual reactions of the frog have already been noted on p. 388.

II. The Organic System

There seems to be no way at present whereby we can deal with organic responses in isolation. In one way organic stimuli and the responses to such are fundamental and basal—behavior to visual, auditory, and other sense stimuli is conditioned by the organic situation in which the animal finds itself. Physiology has claimed this province particularly. In recent years this science has shown itself amply competent to work out the many delicate problems which are inherent in this field. The work of Cannon and his students and of Carlson upon the nature of the muscular contractions of the stomach in the absence of food; of Cannon on the effect of fear and rage on the secretion of glycogen; and finally of Osborne and Mendel on the factors influencing growth are producing results which certainly bear as directly upon behavior problems as they do upon more strictly physiological problems. On p. 25 we touched upon the possibility of carrying out experimental work upon the influence of the " sexual state " upon the general reactions of the animal. There seems to be no good reason why we should not study habit formation in animals robbed of the efferent nerve supply to these regions (and hence robbed of " return " or sensory impulses). Already there is a certain amount of work upon the structural changes which occur in a developing organism when ovariotomy is resorted to and upon ovarian transplantations. The interest in such experiments, however, has been morphological. It is probable that the whole instinctive repertoire shifts in such cases and that the mechanism of habit formation is profoundly modified. When we look for a moment at the behavior complexes present in migration, mating, hibernation, etc., we can see that there must be rhythmical intra-organic factors which must be taken account of even by one who is primarily engaged in observing the behavior of animals to extra-organic stimuli. Jennings has well brought out the necessity of the study of such processes in investigating the behavior of lower organisms. The necessity of study in these fields is not less when we deal with the vertebrates. It is here primarily that the behaviorist and the physiologist meet. The behaviorist has not the equipment and the technique to engage in such studies and he must await the needed results at the hands of the physiologist.

III. The Kinæsthetic System

If we made the statement that all of the work upon habit formation in all of the behavior laboratories (excepting the studies upon birds) points to the fact that the kinæsthetic sense is the most important system of receptors, and yet that there was not one single thing that we could say about this sense in isolation, paradoxical as it might seem, it would not be far from the truth. When the author's experiments upon blind, anosmic, and deaf rats were made some twelve years ago, where it was shown that the daily lives of such animals were little affected by the loss of these distance receptors, it seemed to be a very special case. Since that time the view that the kinæsthetic sense is the one most depended upon by animals where possible (i.e., that kinæsthetic data are substituted for auditory, visual, and olfactory) has been confirmed by similar experiments upon many other forms. We need only to call attention to the fact that " place " or position habits develop rapidly in nearly all tests upon vision, audition, olfaction, etc. We have even found it necessary to handicap or penalize this sense by the introduction of punishment in order to give the distance sense stimuli a chance to influence the organism. The kinæsthetic system is peculiar with respect to the fact that we must work with it by the method of exclusion. We can eliminate by several methods the influence of vision, audition, and the other senses, but in view of the fact that the muscle is both the effector and the receptor we cannot isolate the receptor features without eliminating the possibility of obtaining diversified response. For this reason we cannot now view the functions of the various parts of this complex system in isolation (i.e., determine the relative importance in habit formation of muscular receptors, tendonous receptors, etc.). The tremendous importance of kinæsthesis in adjustment is not limited to the lower organisms. There is a growing tendency to make it responsible for man's so-called reactions to objects which are not (*at the moment of reaction extra-organically*) present. We mean here merely to reiterate the view already several times expressed that there are no centrally aroused sensations and that even in " thought " there is always a movement of a muscular mass somewhere, presumably usually in the laryngeal and related mechanisms.

BIBLIOGRAPHY

Babák, Edward, " Ueber die Temperaturempfindlichkeit der Amphibien," *Zeit. f. Sinnesphysiol.*, 1912, XLVII, 34.

Cannon, W. B., " Recent Studies of Bodily Effects of Fear, Rage, and Pain," *Jour. Phil., Psych., and Sci. Meth.*, 1914, XI, 162 (summary of several articles by Cannon and his students).

Carlson, A. J., " The Hunger Contractions of the Empty Stomach During Prolonged Starvation " (Man, Dog), *Am. Jour. Physiol.*, 1914, XXXIII, 95.

Carlson, A. J., and Luckhardt, A. B., " The Condition of the Œsophagus During the Period of Gastric Hunger Contractions," *Am. Jour. Physiol.*, 1914, XXXIII, 126. (Several other articles by Carlson and by Cannon and their students on the secretions and movements of the stomach tissue have appeared in recent numbers of the *Am. Jour. of Physiol.*)

Hahn, W. L., " Some Habits and Sensory Adaptations of the Cave-Inhabiting Bats," *Biol. Bull.*, 1908, XV, 135 and 193.

Hofer, Bruno, " Studien über die Hautsinnesorgane der Fische," *Berichte aus der Kgl. Bayerischen Biologischen Versuchsstation in München*, 1908, I, 115.

Jennings, H. S., *Behavior of the Lower Organisms*. New York, Columbia Univ. Press, 1906.

NICOLAI. (For summary, see YERKES and MORGULIS, "The Method of Pawlow in Comparative Psychology," *Psych. Bull.*, 1909, VI, 257.)

RICHARDSON, FLORENCE, "A Study of Sensory Control in the Rat," *Psych. Monographs*, Ser. No. 48.

SMALL, W. S., "Notes on the Psychic Development of the Young White Rat," *Am. Jour. Psych.*, 1899, XI, 80.

VINCENT, STELLA B., "The Function of the Vibrissæ in the Behavior of the White Rat," *Behavior Monographs*, Ser. No. 5.

———————— "Tactile Vibrissæ of the White Rat," *Jour. Comp. Neu. and Psych.*, 1913, XXIII.

WATSON, JOHN B., "Kinæsthetic Sensations," etc., *Psych. Monographs*, Ser. No. 33.

YERKES, R. M., "Space Perception of Tortoises," *Jour. Comp. Neu. and Psych.*, 1904, XIV, 17.

YOAKUM, C. S., "Some Experiments upon the Behavior of Squirrels," *Jour. Comp. Neu. and Psych.*, 1909, XIX, 541.

INDEX